SCIENCE FROM THE BEGINNING

Teacher's Book 4

SCIENCE
FROM THE BEGINNING

by

B. L. HAMPSON
and K. C. EVANS

illustrated by

MARTIN F. DONOGHUE

TEACHER'S BOOK 4

OLIVER AND BOYD
TWEEDDALE COURT, EDINBURGH
39A WELBECK STREET, LONDON, W.1

FIRST PUBLISHED 1964

PRINTED IN GREAT BRITAIN BY
ROBERT CUNNINGHAM AND SONS LTD., ALVA
FOR OLIVER AND BOYD LTD., EDINBURGH

CONTENTS

CONTENTS

INTRODUCTION

Science is a systematic way of examining things and occurrences. Very simply, it is a study of:

1 the different kinds of things which exist,
2 what happens to them.

The aim of this series of books is to provide:

1 a logical starting point for a general science training,
2 the establishment, by progressive stages, of a comprehensive foundation of general scientific knowledge from which any secondary phase of science education may be developed.

CONTENTS OF TEACHER'S BOOK 4

This consists of thirty-six lessons, each one corresponding to a double-page section in Pupils' Book 4. Each of these lessons is divided into five parts:

1 Demonstration material
2 Sample link questions
3 Relevant information
4 CODE (Collection, Observation, Demonstration, Experiment)
5 Notebook work

DEMONSTRATION MATERIAL

Under this heading will be found suggestions for apparatus or specimens suitable for illustrating the particular lesson.

Apparatus

Where this is listed, it is in most cases simple and of a kind familiar to children in their own homes, *e.g.* plastic ball-pen, jam jar, balloon.

I

Specimens

Alive. The value of keeping living specimens in the classroom is obvious. Where these are required to illustrate a lesson, suggestions are given for suitable ones, and also information on maintenance.

Dead. For many lessons, dead specimens are useful. Some animal and plant parts—for example, feathers and wood—do not deteriorate rapidly and therefore can be easily kept. Others —for example, a sea anemone—decompose quite quickly, and preserved specimens of these have been found invaluable. They are of even more interest when the children themselves have helped with the preserving. Included in this Introduction is a section dealing with simple methods of preserving animal and plant material, which may thus be kept indefinitely and used year after year, if required.

Never Alive. Various solids and liquids are not only useful as material for illustrating many lessons, but, together with preserved dead specimens, form a useful nucleus for any class or school science museum. It is better, of course, if they are simply, but meaningly, labelled.

SAMPLE LINK QUESTIONS

Although most teachers will undoubtedly apply their own methods of establishing lesson-continuity, based on their personal knowledge of the individual class, certain revisionary questions are included at the beginning of each lesson. These provide a link with previous lessons on the same subject, or on interrelated subjects, and are based on questions which have been found useful in actual practice. They are not exhaustive, but merely serve as a basis throughout the book for a systematic and constant revision of the most important points outlined during the successive stages which the course pursues. When an answer to a question has been discovered during a previous lesson, it is printed for convenience, beside the question.

In addition to these sample link questions, three lists of questions have been included at certain stages through the book. Between them, they cover the most important points and are phrased in such a way that in most cases they require an answer of only one or two words. This permits, where desired, of their being answered in writing.

RELEVANT INFORMATION

This is intended to serve two purposes:

1 to act as a source of material for that particular lesson,
2 to provide information and facts useful to the teacher as background knowledge.

CODE

Under this heading will be found suggestions for:

Collection of material which would suitably illustrate that particular lesson. On page 13 under the title of *Keeping Specimens for Demonstration Purposes*, will be found information on suitable methods of retaining material for indefinite use.

Observations which children may be encouraged to make—not necessarily at school, *e.g.* observing on a particular kind of flower whether or not the four main flower parts are present.

Demonstrations to emphasise a particular point. This is what is sometimes loosely termed 'experimenting'. There are two main ways in which this may be undertaken according to the discretion of the teacher:

1 by the teacher alone, where the demonstration material is such that it may be inexpedient for the children to handle it;
2 by the teacher with children assisting.

Experiments which may be undertaken by the class as a whole, or by children working individually or in groups. It is recommended that from the start the principle of controlled experiment should be emphasised, if the enquiring mind of a child is to be trained to pursue its enquiries scientifically. For example, in the experiment to show how some dead parts are preserved by being dried, if a prune is soaked in water and left to see if it will be attacked by a fungus, a second prune in a dry state should be left alongside, so that a comparison can be made.

3

NOTEBOOK WORK

This is in effect the 'Answer section', and assists in easy marking of the written work set in the Pupils' Book.

PUPILS' BOOK 4

This book consists of thirty-six double-page lessons. It follows the assumption that, even to young children, science will be an affair of observing and finding out first, and reading for confirmation last. Each section is divided into four parts:

1 A page of illustrations in full colour
2 A simple summary of the main points of the lesson
3 A part entitled 'Collect: Observe: Experiment' in which are suggestions on what the class can collect, observe and experiment with, relative to that particular lesson and subsequent lessons
4 A part entitled 'For Your Notebook'. In this, suggestions are given for:

(*a*) Drawings. Sometimes it is best for children to draw an actual specimen which is in front of them, *i.e.* from their own observation. In addition, there are obvious advantages in children being encouraged to make their own 'field drawings' of things which they experience outside school.

(*b*) Written work. In each case, the required answers will serve to emphasise the most significant points of the lesson.

The number of the lesson is shown on a blue spot at the top of the left-hand page.

THE SCHEME

The scheme for each year is divided into three sections:

1 The science table
2 Classification section
3 General subjects

4

THE SCIENCE TABLE

It is with this that the introduction to scientific study begins. It begins, not so much by assembling a haphazard collection of items and attributing to them names, but by classifying those items from the start according to whether they are *alive, dead* or *never alive*. Thus the question which a child needs to learn to ask first, when encountering something entirely new to his experience, is not 'What is it called?', but 'What kind of a thing is this?'. A separate section on the use of the science table will be found on pages 23-27.

By this method of classifying objects into groups first, and naming the known individuals last, the science table also provides an introduction to the classifications which follow.

CLASSIFICATION SECTION

The narrower interpretations of nature study may stress the study of certain selected objects—say, a bluebell or a jelly-fish. Learning numbers of facts about these particular things does not, however, enable a child to acquire an elementary knowledge of flowers in general or of simple mouth-and-stomach animals in general.

The answer to the question 'What is it called?' can only be supplied by someone who happens to have learnt what it is called. The question 'What kind of thing is it?' can be answered simply by a child mind equipped with a knowledge of the characteristics of groups of things. This is not intended to imply that a junior should be expected to examine with an analytical mind from the start. But he can be encouraged to examine in a logical way, and be systematically provided with the knowledge of how to do so. For example: A child encounters a living object. It is observed to move from one place to another, therefore it is established as a living animal, and not a living plant. The next observation is that it moves on six legs, therefore it is further established as an insect. One of the aims of this scheme has been to teach the observable characteristics of groups of things, so that any plant, any animal, or any never-alive thing may be examined with reasoning.

The number of classifications to be learnt has increased

with each successive year, so that during each year, established classifications have been consolidated, and further sub-classifications introduced.

GENERAL SUBJECTS

Lessons under this heading are of three main kinds:

1 Lessons to illustrate classifications. These are based on factual generalisations
2 Lessons on interesting topics
3 Lessons on observable phenomena or 'happenings'

The fundamental aim of any living species is the propagation of its own kind. It will be found that where topic lessons are about individual living organisms, they generally centre round their four basic needs—oxygen, food, to grow, to have young.

GENERAL SCHEME OF WORK IN BOOK 4

Subject	Topic	Collection of Material by Children, and Local Observation	Demonstration and Experiment
(A) *The Science Table* Collected items to be separated into six distinctly named groups	ALIVE (*a*) Animal (*b*) Plant DEAD (*a*) Animal (*b*) Plant NEVER ALIVE (*a*) Solid (*b*) Liquid	For suggested examples, see pages 6 and 7 in Teacher's Book 2	
(B) *Classification Section* 1 Herbs which store food	(*a*) Swollen parts above ground	Observe swollen leaves and swollen stems, *e.g.* leaf succulents and stem succulents	Grow plants from swollen parts
	(*b*) Swollen parts below ground	Observe swollen roots, stems and leaves, *e.g.* tubers, corms, bulbs	

Subject	Topic	Collection of Material by Children, and Local Observation	Demonstration and Experiment
The four main flower parts	(a) Sepals, petals, stamens, pistils	Collect different shapes and colours of each Observe (a) relative positions (b) colour (c) number (d) whether parts are free or joined (e) some flowers do not have all four parts	
	(b) The essential parts	Observe (a) colour of pollen on anthers of stamens (b) swelling of pistils into fruits, e.g. bluebell, daffodil, tulip (c) developing seeds in cross-sections of pistils	
Simple plants	(a) Algae and mosses	Collect specimens from land and freshwater habitats Observe (a) wide variety of marine algae (seaweeds) (b) spore cases on mosses (c) any spore receptacles and holdfasts on aquatic algae	Retain living specimens in suitable containers
	(b) Fungi and bacteria	Collect species of moulds, mildews, and other fungi that feed on various tissues Observe (a) spore cases, e.g. on bracket fungi, toadstools and mushrooms (b) obnoxious smell caused by active bacteria	Retain living specimens in separate jars
Insects	(a) With a three-stage life—dragonflies (b) With a four-stage life—caddis flies	Observe development to adult stage Observe larval cases	Keep larvae in suitable containers

7

Subject	Topic	Collection of Material by Children, and Local Observation	Demonstration an Experiment
5 The British reptiles	Three species of lizards, and three species of snakes	Observe differences in colour, markings, etc	
6 Simple animals	(a) Mouth-and-stomach animals	Observe on sea anemone, or hydra, the tentacles and general appearance, e.g. open and closed	
	(b) Animals with spiny skins	Observe on starfish, or sea urchin, spines, mouth, number of rays, and general appearance	
(C) General Subjects 1 Molecules	(a) A molecule of a substance is its tiniest possible part	Observe that molecules can be sensed by means of taste and smell	Demonstrate that m cules are very t e.g. by filtering
	(b) A molecule consists of one or more atoms		Make plasticine mo of molecules
2 Atoms	The main parts of atoms		Demonstrate rela size
3 The solar system	Asteroids, comets and meteors	Observe falling meteors (shooting stars)	Demonstrate posi of asteroid between Mars Jupiter
4 Stars	A galaxy is a collection of stars; a constellation is a pattern	Observe how direction may be found from Plough and Pole Star	Demonstrate (a) why Pole Star ways appears ab the earth's n pole (b) appearance of c stellations, us pierced card
5 Light	(a) Things which give out light and things which reflect light	Observe difference between luminous, transparent, translucent and opaque	Experiment to illusions

8

Subject	Topic	Collection of Material by Children, and Local Observation	Demonstration and Experiment
Light (*Cont.*)	(*b*) Shadows and reflections	Observe (*a*) the smoother the surface the better the reflection (*b*) that an image in a mirror is reversed	Experiment to show cause of shadows Experiment with simple periscope and kaleidoscope
	(*c*) Images and altered images	Observe magnified, diminished and distorted images (*a*) in different mirrors (*b*) through transparent substances	Experiment to show how rays of light can be made to change direction (*a*) when reflected (*b*) when passing through transparent surfaces
	(*d*) Colour rays		Demonstrate that colours are seen owing to (*a*) splitting of light into different colour rays (*b*) transmission of different colour rays (*c*) reflection of different colour rays
Sound	(*a*) Sounds are caused by vibrations	Observe examples of any objects which can be felt or seen to be vibrating	Experiment to show (*a*) big vibrations cause loud sounds and little vibrations cause soft sounds (*b*) quick vibrations cause high notes, and slow vibrations cause low notes
	(*b*) Transmitting vibrations and reflecting vibrations		Experiment to show (*a*) vibrations are transmitted better through some things than through others (*b*) reflected vibrations may cause additional sounds
Temperature and ever-alive things	(*a*) Gases expand when heated and contract when cooled		Experiment to show that air expands when heated and contracts when cooled

Subject	Topic	Collection of Material by Children, and Local Observation	Demonstration an Experiment
7 Temperature and never-alive things (*Cont.*)	(*b*) Most liquids expand when heated and contract when cooled (*c*) Many solids expand when heated and contract when cooled	Observe expansion and contraction of mercury or alcohol in a thermometer	Demonstrate the pansion and cont tion of a liquid Experiment to s the expansion contraction of metal
8 Air	(*a*) Air presses against things (*b*) Compressed air		Experiment to s that (*a*) air presses aga things (*b*) it presses in directions (*c*) removing the from one par something all it to push on ot Demonstrate that c pressed air pre with more force t the air about you (*a*) by forcing n air into an encle space (*b*) by squeezing already enclose
9 Friction	An increase in friction makes it more difficult for things to slip	Observe examples of sliding being made more difficult by (*a*) providing a rougher surface, *e.g.* ridged screw caps, tyre treads (*b*) pressing two solid surfaces more tightly together, *e.g.* with an elastic band	Experiment to s that friction betw two solid surf may be increase (*a*) making at l one of the surf rougher (*b*) pressing the surfaces m tightly togethe
10 Machines	Three ways of using a sloping surface as a simple machine	Observe examples of sloping surfaces in use (*a*) as ramps (*b*) on wedges (*c*) on screws	Experiment to s principle of (*a*) a ramp (*b*) a wedge Demonstrate that screw is a sp ramp

10

Subject	Topic	Collection of Material by Children, and Local Observation	Demonstration and Experiment
Forcing vehicles through air and through water	Pushing and screwing	Observe how pushing against something can force a vehicle to move, *e.g.* in paddling, poling and rowing Observe how a screw propeller can force a vehicle to move, *e.g.* on helicopters, toy boats	Demonstrate (*a*) how a turning screw can force something to move (*b*) how wings help to keep an aeroplane up
Power from moving gases Expanding steam	Pushing against (*a*) the blades of a turbine wheel (*b*) a piston		Make a simple steam turbine Demonstrate how a piston can turn a wheel
Expanding gases from burning fuel	Pushing against (*a*) a piston (*b*) the inside of a jet or rocket engine		Demonstrate the principle of a jet or rocket with a balloon Make a simple steam jet engine
Electricity	(*a*) Electric charges and currents		Demonstrate how electric charges can be (*a*) caused (*b*) detected Make a simple electric charge detector
	(*b*) Electric currents and circuits	Observe uses of (*a*) good conductors, *e.g.* in electric wires (*b*) poor conductors, *e.g.* as insulators	Experiment to show (*a*) the need for a complete circuit (*b*) some things conduct better than others (*c*) how weak currents can be caused Make (*a*) a weak current detector (*b*) model traffic signals (*c*) model question-and-answer game

Subject	Topic	Collection of Material by Children, and Local Observation	Demonstration an_ Experiment
13 Electricity (*Cont.*)	(*c*) Three main uses of electric currents	Observe uses to obtain heat, light and power	Make (*a*) model elec_ radiator (*b*) model elect_ magnet (*c*) model elec_ motor
14 Cells	Every living thing consists of one or more cells	Observe cells through a microscope or micro-projector, if possible	Demonstrate, by bu_ ing dead materi_ that cells consist_ never-alive pa_ *e.g.* carbon
15 Care of living things	Humans protect themselves from bacteria and fungi	Collect hygiene charts (particularly concerning care of teeth) Observe need for personal hygiene, *e.g.* washing before meals, disinfecting cuts, brushing teeth	
16 Care of dead things	Humans protect dead parts from bacteria and fungi	Observe examples of dead parts preserved by (*a*) drying (*b*) heating and canning (*c*) freezing (*d*) treating with chemicals, *e.g.* sugar, salt, vinegar	Experiment with a c_ trol to show h_ drying preser_ dead parts Demonstrate use_ liquid preservativ_ *e.g.* for plant_ animal parts_ tained for less_ purposes
17 Rocks	(*a*) The changing layers of the earth's surface	Observe collected specimens of sandstone, conglomerate rock or shale	Demonstrate h_ layers of rock_ posited below_ level are raised ab_ sea level Make models to sh_ how surface lay_ may be (*a*) folded (*b*) broken
	(*b*) Fossils	Observe specimens of fossils	Demonstrate how i_ pressions of fos_ may be obtained

Keeping Specimens for Demonstration Purposes

Dead and never-alive specimens for illustrating lessons fall into three general categories.

(A) Some specimens, *e.g.* rocks and shells, can be kept indefinitely as they are. All they may require is mounting.

METHOD FOR MOUNTING SELECTED SPECIMENS OF ROCKS, ORES, MOLLUSC SHELLS, ETC, IN GLASS-TOPPED BOXES

1 Cut coloured ground card to fit the inside of the box, and at one end of the card print information in Indian ink.

2 Fasten specimen to the other end of the card with a strong adhesive (*e.g.* Bostik).

3 Place in box.

1 Information
2 Green card
3 Specimen glued to card

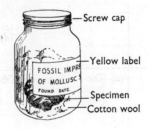

Screw cap

Yellow label

Specimen

Cotton wool

(B) Some more delicate specimens may need protection against careless handling or loss. Such specimens can be placed on cotton wool in a labelled specimen tube or screw-topped jar, as shown in the illustrations.

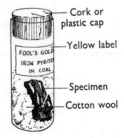

Cork or plastic cap

Yellow label

Specimen

Cotton wool

METHOD FOR RETAINING SELECTED SPECIMENS SUCH AS FEATHERS OR SECTION OF REPTILE SKIN

Use the following materials as shown in the diagram below.

1 Piece of hardboard, thin wood or stiff cardboard
2 Thin coloured card—red, green, or yellow according to whether specimen is animal, plant, or never alive
3 Specimen
4 Strip of acetate sheet or transparent polythene
5 Adhesive tape

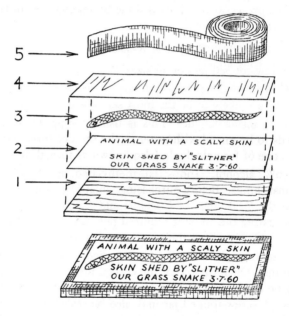

Notes

1 The inclusion of a few crystals of para-diChlorbenzene will serve as protection against possible invasion by mites.

2 Acetate sheeting, transparent polythene and adhesive tape may be obtained from suppliers of plastic materials.

(C) Some specimens, *e.g.* most parts of animals and plants, need protection against deterioration or decomposition. The preservation of dead specimens for illustrating various lessons provides an answer to many problems. The methods of preserving and mounting outlined briefly below have been employed by children themselves in the top half of a junior school.

METHOD USING LIQUID PRESERVATIVE

The purpose of a preservative is to prevent deterioration of specimens due to the attack by microscopic forms of plant or animal life. If specimens are to be kept for an indefinite period, then it is necessary to take precautions to prevent the evaporation of the preservative. This is done by sealing the container in some way.

Equipment Required

1 Screw-topped jars of all sizes

2 Corked specimen tubes of various sizes. $6'' \times 1''$, $5'' \times 1''$ and $4'' \times 1''$ are likely to be the most serviceable.

3 10% formaldehyde. This is usually supplied as 40%, and needs to be mixed with water in the ratio of three parts of water to one of formaldehyde (also known as formalin).

4 70% alcohol. Industrial methylated spirit will preserve most things. Before purchasing, an application should be made to the local office of Customs and Excise for a book of permits, stating the amount required per annum. To dilute to 70%, mix seven parts of this alcohol with three parts of water.

5 Capping solution. This is supplied as a white viscous solution into which the top of the corked tube or screw-topped jar may be dipped. The solution begins to set hard after a few minutes. A screw-topped jar may also be sealed with vaseline smeared on the inside edge of the cap. The purpose of the capping is, of course, to reduce evaporation of the preservative to a minimum, and is not essential.

6 Labels and Indian ink

7 Cellulose tape

Preserving Procedure

The following procedure has been found very successful for preserving general terrestrial animal and plant specimens.

1 Place specimen in clean specimen tube.
2 Add sufficient 30% alcohol to cover specimen. Leave for 24 hours.
3 Rinse out gently in running cold water for a minute or so.
4 Empty out the water.
5 Replace with alcohol diluted to 50%, and leave for 24 hours.
6 Rinse this out.
7 Refill with 70% alcohol
  (*a*) to the brim in the case of a screw-topped jar;
  (*b*) to just below the brim in the case of a corked tube.
8 Screw on cap or push home cork with slight twisting motion so as to leave as small an air space as possible at the top.
9 Make sure outer surface of container is dry, and then invert the whole of the top in capping solution.

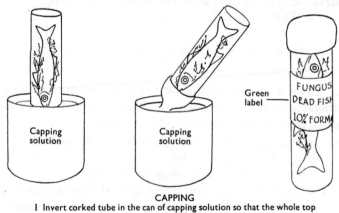

Green label

FUNGUS
DEAD FISH
10% FORM

Capping solution

Capping solution

CAPPING
1 Invert corked tube in the can of capping solution so that the whole top is covered. Twist tube slightly and remove.
2 Hold tube inverted and at a slight angle for a few moments to allow surplus solution to drain off.
3 Leave for a few hours to set.

10 Remove, and hold in an inverted position for a few moments to allow surplus solution to drain off, and until the remainder begins to harden. Leave for a few hours.

11 Print information in Indian ink on a strip of coloured card (red for animal, green for plant).

12 Fix this label near the top of the tube with cellulose tape.

Notes

1 The changes of alcohol mentioned are recommended only because direct immersion in 70% alcohol may lead to slight shrinkage. In most cases it will be found that quite satisfactory results can be obtained by placing in 70% alcohol to begin with, rinsing out once, and then proceeding with stage 7.

2 For marine and freshwater specimens, the same steps should be followed using 10% formaldehyde, but changing the solution only once.

3 Delicate soft-bodied aquatic specimens should be preserved in 5% or even 4% formaldehyde.

4 It is better to err on the side of a weak solution of preservative than on the side of one which is too strong.

5 When in doubt, use alcohol.

METHOD FOR OBTAINING A DRY MOUNT OF A SPECIMEN ON A SHEET OF GLASS OR PERSPEX

This method is suitable for large flat specimens where it is desirable to have both sides on view, *e.g.* a fern leaf showing spore cases on the undersides of the leaflets.

1 Place in position on a length of glass or perspex
   (*a*) the specimen to be mounted
   (*b*) coloured card bearing information

2 Fix these in position with lengths of wide cellulose tape. The cellulose tape not only fixes the specimen in position but provides at the same time a transparent airtight seal.

17

Notes

(*a*) Each length of tape should extend the full width of the glass or perspex and be turned over both edges.

(*b*) Each strip of cellulose tape should overlap the previous one.

3 Finally run a strip of adhesive binding tape round all four edges of the glass or perspex.

Perspex is of course a safer material for children to handle than glass; it is also more expensive. A clean planed board, unvarnished and unpainted, is a good working surface when using cellulose tape.

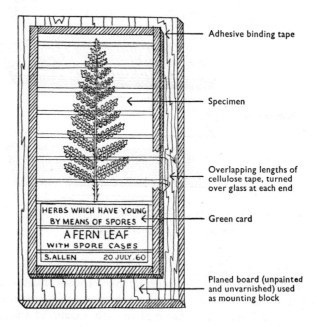

Adhesive binding tape

Specimen

Overlapping lengths of cellulose tape, turned over glass at each end

Green card

HERBS WHICH HAVE YOUNG
BY MEANS OF SPORES
A FERN LEAF
WITH SPORE CASES
S. ALLEN   20 JULY. 60

Planed board (unpainted and unvarnished) used as mounting block

METHOD FOR OBTAINING DRY MOUNTS OF SEAWEED

1 Float specimen in water.
2 Slide a sheet of card underneath, and lift.
3 After the water has drained off, tease out any fronds.
4 Cover with a layer of butter muslin.
5 Cover this with blotting paper.
6 Cover this with several layers of newspaper.
7 Leave under pressure for several days.
8 Remove gently from the card, and mount in the same way as the reptile skin on page 14 or the fern leaf on page 18.

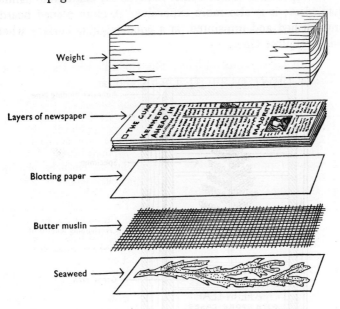

Weight ⟶

Layers of newspaper ⟶

Blotting paper ⟶

Butter muslin ⟶

Seaweed ⟶

KILLING SPECIMENS FOR PRESERVATION PURPOSES

In the living world in general, there are two main reasons for killing—for food and for self-protection against enemies.

Probably the only other motive with a claim to validity is that of killing for the purpose of scientific study, in order that

19

something of value to human beings may be learnt. Even so, it is obvious that every effort should be made to avoid indiscriminate killing.

When any living plant or animal is immersed in preservative, *e.g.* formaldehyde or alcohol, the preservative itself acts as a killing agent. However, if it is desired to kill a specimen before preserving, then the following equipment is simple and satisfactory.

1 Jam jar and tin lid
2 Ink bottle containing cotton wool
3 Chloroform

Method

1 Pour chloroform into the ink bottle containing cotton wool.
2 Invert jam jar containing specimen over ink bottle, and leave until killing is complete. The tin lid provides a smooth surface on which to place bottle and jar.

Useful Materials to have in Stock

1 Jam jars (various)
2 Dried-milk tins and lids
3 Screw-topped jars (clear glass)
4 Plasticine (various colours)
5 Drinking straws
6 Elastic bands (various sizes and thicknesses)
7 Medicine bottles
8 Circular cheese boxes
9 Plastic liquid-soap containers
10 Ridged caps for bottles
11 Drawing pins
12 Small tins with press-in lids
13 Small and large matchboxes
14 Tobacco tins
15 Cotton reels
16 Shoe (or similar) cardboard boxes
17 Toffee, Horlicks, or other large jars
18 Alka Seltzer tubes
19 Fine string and thread (linen or cotton)
20 Blotting paper
21 Corks
22 Thimbles
23 Various cloths, *e.g.* cotton, wool, silk, linen
24 Coloured water (tinted with red or black ink)
25 Clean bricks
26 Pieces of sandstone, puddingstone (conglomerate rock), and shale
27 Large empty bottle, *e.g.* wine bottle (clear glass)

28 Small sheet of clear glass
29 Plastic materials of various kinds, *e.g.* old ball-pens, perspex, sheet polythene, polythene bags, acetate sheeting
30 Any coloured transparent material, *e.g.* coloured glass, toffee wrappings
31 Old roller-skate
32 Old knife, fork, spoon
33 Old hacksaw blades
34 Old goldfish globe
35 Length of board
36 Nuts, bolts and various screws
37 4″ nails and other nails (roundheaded)
38 Copper wire
39 Large ball-bearing
40 Wood bit
41 Meccano parts
42 Short lengths of dowel rod
43 Coarse sandpaper
44 Balloons
45 Strong scissors
46 Cellulose tape (various widths and colours)
47 Large sheets of black and white card
48 Coloured card, including red, green, blue, yellow
49 Large sheets of coloured paper, including red, green, yellow, blue, black
50 Candles
51 Sealing wax
52 Nylon hair ribbons
53 Sewing or darning needles
54 Paper clips (large and small)
55 Brass paper fasteners
56 Cotton wool
57 Gummed labels

58 Impact glue
59 Vaseline, or similar greasy substance
60 Common sand
61 Common salt
62 Aquarium gravel
63 Sugar
64 Sawdust
65 Machine oil
66 Methylated spirit
67 Vinegar
68 Iodine
69 Dettol
70 Potassium permanganate
71 Mothballs, or camphor, or para-diChlorbenzene
72 Sodium bicarbonate
73 Aluminium wrapping foil
74 Magnesium ribbon
75 Perforated zinc
76 Objects in various metals, *e.g.* iron, steel, copper, brass
77 Carbon rods
78 Filter funnels (plastic)
79 Filter paper or paper handkerchiefs
80 Polythene buckets
81 Polythene bowls
82 Table-tennis balls
83 Steel knitting needles
84 Bunsen tubing (plastic or rubber)
85 Tuning fork
86 Pocket mirrors
87 Concave mirrors
88 Convex mirrors
89 Magnifying glasses (convex lenses)
90 Diminishing glasses (concave lenses)
91 Glass prism
92 Square jar or glass tank
93 Eye droppers
94 Rubber 'suckers' (various)

95 'Domes of silence' castors ($\frac{5}{8}''$ to $\frac{7}{8}''$ diam.)

96 Small pocket compasses (magnetic)

97 Torch bulbs (2.5 and 3.5 volts)

98 Torch bulb holders

99 1-amp. bell wire, plastic covered, in red, green, yellow and blue

100 Batteries (3, $4\frac{1}{2}$, and 6 volt)

101 Insulating tape

102 Electric-iron heating element

103 Strong bar magnet

104 Plaster of paris, or Keen's cement, or Alabastine

105 Cycle pump

106 Electric torch

107 Any fossils

Useful Extras

1 Toy periscope
2 Toy kaleidoscope
3 Large mirror
4 Dental charts and booklets
5 Small glass aquaria and covers
6 Glass aquarium and cover (*e.g.* $2' \times 1' \times 1'$)
7 Retort stand, boss head and clamp
8 Butane burner (see page 27)

9 Glass flask with one-holed rubber stopper to fit, and glass tubing to fit through the hole
10 Commercially manufactured model of a steam engine
11 Microscope or micro-projector
12 Pocket magnifiers ($\times 10$)
13 Spring balance (reading up to 8 lbs)

Some Useful Specimens in Preservative
In 70% Alcohol

1 Toadstools, bracket fungi, etc

2 Any British lizard
3 Any British snake

In 10% Formaldehyde

1 Great water moss (willow moss), with holdfast if possible
2 Any small complete specimens of marine algae, (with or without holdfasts)

3 Sphagnum moss
4 Dragonfly larva
5 Fish killed by fungus
6 Sea anemone
7 Sea urchin
8 Small starfish with a regenerating limb

Some Useful Mounted Specimens

1 Adult dragonfly
2 Different caddis fly cases
3 Bracket fungi on tree bark

4 Discarded skins of lizard and snake

Note: Mounted and preserved specimens can be bought from Biological Suppliers. When ordering, it is wise to state exactly which points are to show clearly, and to ask for English terminology.

General Materials for Mounting and Preserving

1 Corked specimen tubes of various sizes, *e.g.* $3'' \times 1''$, $4'' \times 1''$, $5'' \times 1''$, $6'' \times 1''$
2 Screw-topped jars and Alka Seltzer tubes
3 30% alcohol ⎫ Diluted from full-strength industrial methyl-
4 50% alcohol ⎬ lated spirit, for which a Customs and Excise
5 70% alcohol ⎭ permit is required
6 10% formaldehyde. Diluted from 40% formaldehyde
7 Capping solution
8 Indian ink
9 Coloured card (red, green, yellow)
10 Cellulose tape
11 Glass-topped specimen boxes
12 Bostik or strong glue
13 Para-diChlorbenzene
14 Hardboard or thin box-wood
15 Acetate sheeting (thickness ·02″)
16 Adhesive tape
17 Lengths of perspex or glass
18 Butter muslin

THE USE OF THE SCIENCE TABLE

The science table helps children to look at things systematically. In its layout it should reflect the fact that science, very simply, is concerned with

1 Things in general
   (*a*) Living things
   (*b*) Dead things
   (*c*) Never-alive things

2 What happens to them, or 'Happenings'

Children who have worked through Pupils' Books 1, 2 and 3 of this series will be familiar with the division of their science table into sections marked *alive, dead* and *never-alive*. They will also be aware of the colour system used throughout the series—

Red for animal (whether living or dead)
Green for plant (whether living or dead)
Yellow for never-alive things (whether solid, liquid or gas)
Their science table will have had a covering of coloured papers, like this:

ALIVE	DEAD	NEVER ALIVE
Red (*i.e.* living animal)	Red (*i.e.* dead animal)	Yellow (*i.e.* solid)
Green (*i.e.* living plant)	Green (*i.e.* dead plant)	Yellow (*i.e.* liquid)

or the names of exhibits will at least have been written on card of the appropriate colour.

During this fourth year the divisions of the science table should remain as shown above. The word 'table' is used, of course, only as a convenient description; several shelves and the top of a cupboard and a window ledge might together act as the science table.

Alive Section

Anything is alive so long as it continues to respire, but respiration is not always noticeable. Fresh fruits, flowers and greens are living plant parts, as are uncooked potatoes and peas. Potatoes are swollen stem parts, and will put out shoots if stored for long enough, as children may have observed in their own homes. Dried peas, being seeds, will retain life for years if stored in a container which allows them sufficient fresh air for their oxygen requirements. Dating the container in which pea seeds are kept will enable children to appreciate when the time comes to germinate some, just how long seeds are able to retain life.

The observable difference between non-microscopic forms of animal and plant life is that living animals are capable of movement from one place to another of their own choosing, whereas plants are not. This voluntary movement is quite distinct from the movement of plants in the wind or towards the light. It is also different from the movement of never-alive things activated by some independent force—for example, an aeroplane or motor car, or wind and sea and rivers, or a dislodged rock rolling down a hill.

Typical specimens for the *living animal* section would include pet hamster, fish, frogspawn, tadpoles, and terrestrial or aquatic insects in appropriate containers.

Typical specimens for the *living plant* section would include bulbs, carrot tops, twigs, beans, peas, acorns, and various other living samples of roots, stems, leaves, flowers, fruits, seeds; and specimens of simple plants, which of course have none of these parts.

Dead Section

Things to be included in the dead section should consist entirely of dead material (*i.e.* cellular in structure). These would include not only whole animals and plants, but parts of animals and plants which are dead. (For mounting and preserving see Introduction.) Because an object is only part of an animal or plant, it is not necessarily dead. Fresh fruits and flowers are only parts of plants, but they are alive, although, of course, they may be slowly dying. The top of a carrot, a section of potato with an 'eye' in it, and a cutting from a plant stem may all be capable of developing into complete new plants if given suitable conditions. Boiling, of course, kills most living things, although microscopic forms such as the amoeba may withstand temperatures of 100°C or more. Nevertheless the parts of animals and plants which have been cooked may be considered dead.

Some manufactured articles are made entirely of dead material, *e.g.* wool, fur, leather, or wood. In fact the human mammal relies a great deal on the dead parts of other animals and plants to furnish the material for food, clothing and even shelter.

Typical specimens for the *dead animal* section could

include any mounted or preserved specimens of whole animals, as well as parts of animals such as hair, fur, feathers, leather, snakeskin, teeth and bones.

Typical specimens for the *dead plant* section could include any mounted or preserved specimens of whole plants, or whole plant parts, together with such plant material as wood, cork, bark, autumn leaves, peat, coal.

Never-Alive Section

Never-alive things may occur in various ways.

1 Some occur naturally, such as air, water, rock. These are our chief concern.

2 Some are excreted by, or extracted from, living or dead things, *e.g.* sugar, milk, fat, oil, and resin (which is the basis of turpentine). Perspiration and tears are obvious never-alive excretions.

3 Some are manufactured by living animals. For example, glass, jewellery and metal goods are made by humans; a spider's web, a silken cocoon, and the shell of a bird's egg are manufactured by other animals. A mollusc, such as the whelk, cockle or snail, may be alive, but the limestone shell which it builds on the outside of its body, is as never alive as the bricks and mortar of a human home.

Pedantically speaking, every article manufactured by an animal is never alive, in the sense that it has been made in that shape and size and has not grown from a smaller version. However, where an object consists entirely of dead material, then logically it is dead material. A wooden peg, for example, has not lived, respired, fed and grown *as a peg*, but it consists entirely of material which has lived, respired, fed, grown and died. On the other hand, a metal shovel with a wooden handle is an object which has been manufactured from a combination of never-alive and dead material.

Typical specimens for the *never-alive solid* section could include various metals, salt, glass, plastic, collections of rock including clay and sand, and various articles manufactured from never-alive substances.

Typical specimens for the *never-alive liquid* section could include various liquids such as water, ink, oil, paraffin, methylated spirit, mercury, turpentine. Ink bottles are useful containers for these, the contents being safer if the bottles are tightly corked or capped.

OBTAINING HEAT

Rapid heat is not essential for any of the lessons in this book. However, if it is considered desirable, for example, to boil water in the classroom, a butane gas camping stove or a methylated spirit bunsen burner will be useful—failing gas or electric facilities.

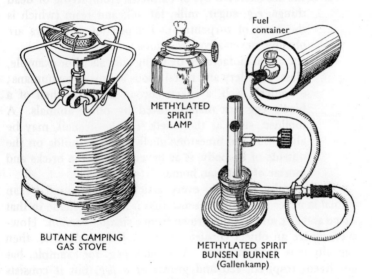

METHYLATED
SPIRIT
LAMP

Fuel
container

BUTANE CAMPING
GAS STOVE

METHYLATED SPIRIT
BUNSEN BURNER
(Gallenkamp)

The figures in the following table were obtained during an experiment conducted in order to compare the efficiency of various heating methods. In each case, an attempt was made to raise the temperature of one-third of a pint of water from a temperature of 70°F (21°C) to boiling point.

The single candle, the bundle of six candles, and the fuel in the methylated spirit lamp were all eventually consumed without boiling the water. In their case, the maximum temperature attained is given. The butane gas stove, and the methylated spirit bunsen burner boiled the water, and in their case the time taken is compared with that taken by a standard laboratory bunsen burner.

One Candle	Bundle of 6 Candles	Spirit Lamp (Recommended make)	Butane Gas Camping stove	Methylated Spirit Bunsen	Standard Lab. Bunsen Burner
144°F	180°F	180°F	5¼ minutes	5 minutes	5¼ minutes

THE TINIEST NEVER-ALIVE THINGS

MOLECULES AND ATOMS

DEMONSTRATION MATERIAL

1 Jars of water; potassium permanganate or Dettol
2 Screw-topped jars; objects with strong odours, *e.g.* onion, mothballs
3 Jam jars, sugar and water; paper handkerchiefs, or filter funnels and filter paper
4 Different colours of plasticine

SAMPLE LINK QUESTIONS

1 What are the three forms of never-alive things? (*Solid, liquid and gas*)
2 Although most gases cannot be seen, how can we sense some of them? (*By means of smell*)
3 When a solid substance melts, how is that different from dissolving? (*When a solid melts, it changes to the liquid form*)
4 When sugar is mixed in a cup of tea, does it melt or dissolve? (*It dissolves*)
5 What is the commonest solid dissolved in sea water? (*Common salt*)
6 What name do we give to a mixture in which something is dissolved? (*A solution*)
7 When something dissolves and breaks up into the tiniest possible bits of itself, what do we call those bits? (*Molecules*)

RELEVANT INFORMATION

Children are usually interested in tiny things, and not infrequently in the possibility of the ultimately small. The purpose of this and the next lesson is to show that all substances are made up of ultimately small parts, and to serve as a simple introduction to molecules and atoms in general.

The Smallest Possible Complete Particles

If it were possible to divide, subdivide and continue to subdivide a very small portion of a substance, there would ultimately be a particle which would be the tiniest possible. That is to say, the next subdivision would result in particles which would lack the properties of the original substance. For example, if a drop of water could be continually subdivided there would eventually be a minute particle whose further subdivision would result in particles which would not be water. A molecule, then, is the smallest portion capable of existing in a free and natural state while retaining the properties of the original substance.

Normally, free and separate molecules only exist either when a substance is in the gaseous state, or when it is dissolved in some other substance, *i.e.* forming a solution. In a solution, the molecules of a solid, liquid or gas are dispersed throughout some other solid, liquid or gas, and the result is a molecular mixture. The substance whose molecules are dispersed is the solute, and the one throughout which the molecules are dispersed is the solvent. For example, sugar dissolves in tea, its particles dispersing throughout the tea. Likewise, cooking fat and oil dissolve in petrol.

When two liquids are able to form a solution, the molecules of either may disperse throughout the other. For example, if a thimbleful of methylated spirit is mixed with a bucketful of water, the molecules of methylated spirit will be dispersed throughout the water. On the other hand, if a thimbleful of water is mixed with a bucketful of methylated spirit, the molecules of water will be dispersed throughout the methylated spirit. Most solids and liquids will dissolve to at least a slight extent in water, which is why distilled water is difficult to maintain as such.

The gases in the air form a molecular mixture (and are therefore strictly a solution). Molecules of the gases in the air also mix with water. It is the molecules of oxygen dispersed throughout water that are so important to animals and plants which absorb their oxygen from water.

Dissolving, of course, is not the same as melting. Melting occurs when, owing to a rise in temperature, a substance changes from the solid to the liquid state. For example, at temperatures above freezing point, ice melts and becomes water. It melts from the solid to the liquid state. It does not dissolve.

Molecules of different substances are of different sizes, but for the great majority, the molecular diameter is such that there could be between 25 million to 250 million to the inch.

Sensing Molecules

Although an individual molecule is far too tiny for the human eye to see, we are aware, by means of our sense of taste or our sense of smell, of the molecules of some substances when these are dispersed throughout some other medium. By means of taste we sense the sugar molecules dispersed throughout tea or coffee. Most solids and liquids exposed to the air are constantly losing molecules to the air. This is particularly apparent with liquids where the steady loss of molecules results in evaporation. The air-borne molecules of some of these substances can be sensed by means of smell. The odours of a mothball, an onion, petrol, perfume or new-mown hay are due to molecules of these substances dispersing through the air and affecting our sense of smell.

Simple and Compound Molecules

A molecule itself consists of one or more particles called atoms. An atom is the smallest particle which can take part in a chemical change. A number of elements, *e.g.* certain gases and metals, have only one atom per molecule, and these are known as monatomic molecules. In such instances, the atom and the molecule are one and the same. However, the molecules of most substances consist of two or more atoms. A molecule of hydrogen or a molecule of oxygen consists of two atoms, and a molecule of sulphur consists of eight atoms. Certain elements can possess molecules consisting of differing numbers of atoms. For example, a normal molecule of oxygen consists of two atoms (chemical formula O_2), but there is a rarer form (known as ozone) which consists of three atoms (chemical formula O_3).

Most substances are compound substances, and the molecule of a compound substance always consists of two or more atoms, these being of different elements. In an element the atoms in a molecule are of the same kind.

Notes

1 An element (elementary substance) is a simple substance. There are 92 elements which occur naturally. A few of these are found in a free state on their own, but most are found in combination with other elements forming compounds. These 92 natural elements are listed in the next chapter.

2 A compound (compound substance) is a chemical combination of two or more elements. Water (H_2O) is a compound consisting of the two elements, hydrogen and oxygen. A molecule of water consists of two atoms of hydrogen and one atom of oxygen. Similarly, carbon dioxide (CO_2) is a compound consisting of the two elements, carbon and oxygen, in chemical combination; and a molecule of carbon dioxide consists of three atoms. Sugar ($C_{12}H_{22}O_{11}$) is a more complex compound. A molecule of sugar consists of 45 atoms, *i.e.* twelve atoms of carbon, twenty-two atoms of hydrogen and eleven atoms of oxygen. The large complex molecules of which the living cells of animals and plants are built, may contain up to hundreds of thousands of atoms.

3 As stated, a molecule may consist of a single atom, but unfortunately there is a misleading tendency to describe the smallest particle of an element as an atom, and to restrict the term *molecule* to the smallest particle of a compound.

CODE

1 Observe the dispersal of molecules in a solution.

e.g. (*a*) Allow a drop of Dettol to fall into a jar of water, and observe:

(i) the milky 'streamers' of molecules spreading through the water;

      (ii) that these disappear as they disperse throughout the water, demonstrating that the individual molecules are too tiny to be seen.

  (*b*) Stir one solitary particle of potassium permanganate into a jar of water and observe the diffusion of colour throughout the water.

Note. In neither of these cases will the *individual* molecules be seen, but 'streamers' of vast numbers will be apparent.

2 Observe that although molecules are too tiny to be seen, we can sense some kinds by means of smell.

  (*a*) Observe (without being personal) that it is possible to sense odours from various things in the classroom, such as ink, pencil shavings.

  (*b*) Enclose various objects with strong odours, *e.g.* onion, mothballs, camphor, in screw-topped jars. Empty out after a while, and observe that molecules of these substances remain in the jars, *i.e.* they can be sensed by means of smell.

3 Demonstrate that the molecules of a solid are very tiny.

  (*a*) Mix sugar and water to make a solution.

  (*b*) Place a paper handkerchief over the mouth of a jar, and make a slight hollow in it.

  (*c*) Pour the solution gently into the hollow so that it filters through into the jar.

  (*d*) Taste the filtered water, and observe that the sugar molecules were small enough to pass through the paper.

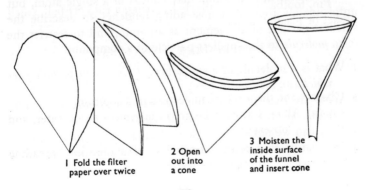

I Fold the filter paper over twice

2 Open out into a cone

3 Moisten the inside surface of the funnel and insert cone

Plastic filter funnels and filter paper may be used instead of a paper handkerchief.

4 Observe that molecules of gas are very tiny, *e.g.* that an inflated balloon or tyre gradually becomes deflated owing to molecules of the different gases which make up air escaping through minute holes in the rubber walls.

NOTEBOOK WORK

Answers should be along the following lines.

1 A molecule is the tiniest bit of a substance that can exist on its own.

2 Every molecule consists of one or more particles called atoms.

3 We can sense molecules by means of taste and by means of smell.

4 (*a*) The atoms in the molecule of an element are all of the same kind.

   (*b*) The atoms in the molecule of a compound are of different elements.

2) MOLECULES AND ATOMS

INSIDE DIFFERENT ATOMS

DEMONSTRATION MATERIAL

Pin, football or large playball; string, a rubber; ball, small basket or plastic bucket

SAMPLE LINK QUESTIONS

1 What is a molecule of a substance? (*The tiniest possible part which can exist on its own*)

2 What are two ways in which we can sense molecules? (*By means of taste and by means of smell*)

3 Why can we not see a single molecule? (*It is far too tiny*)

4 Of what does a molecule consist? (*One or more particles called atoms*)

5 How many atoms are there in a molecule of iron? (*One*)
6 How many atoms are there in a molecule of oxygen? (*Two*)
7 When each molecule in a substance consists of atoms of the same kind, what do we call that substance? (*An element*)
8 When each molecule in a substance consists of atoms from two or more different elements, what do we call that substance? (*A compound*)
9 Of what does a molecule of water consist? (*Two atoms of hydrogen and one atom of oxygen*)
10 Of what does a molecule of carbon dioxide consist? (*Two atoms of oxygen and one atom of carbon*)

RELEVANT INFORMATION

An atom is the smallest possible part of an element which can take part in a chemical change.

Perhaps the most remarkable thing about atoms is that so much has been found out about them without a single atom being actually seen. It has been estimated that there are about 35,000 million million million atoms in a single breath of air inhaled by a normal human being. (This is about a pint of air.) Another analogy is that it would take as many atoms to fill a cricket ball as it would take cricket balls to fill the world.

The Nature of an Atom

An atom was once considered to be spherical, solid throughout, and impossible of division. Subsequent research has shown it to be otherwise. It is now known that most of an atom—like most of the solar system—consists of empty space. The centre or dense part is termed the nucleus, and in this almost the whole mass of an atom is concentrated. Even so, the size of the nucleus is more than 10,000 times smaller than that of the whole atom.

Round the nucleus revolve incredibly small particles called electrons. The simplest kind of atom known is the commonest atom of hydrogen. It would take 250 million hydrogen atoms in line to measure one inch. In a hydrogen atom the nucleus consists of a single particle called a proton, and round this revolves one electron. The relative distance between nucleus and electron is such that they may be compared to the

35

sun with the earth going round it, or to a grain of sand at the centre of a football. If the nucleus could be imagined as being the size of a pea, then the electron going round it would be the size of a grain of salt revolving round the pea in an orbit which would enclose the school. It has been said that if all the molecules which go to make up a camel could be compressed so that there were no space in their atoms, the resultant dot would be so small that it could be passed through the eye of a needle. Likewise, if all the molecules which go to make up a school, the children and its teachers could be compressed so that there were no space in their atoms, the result could be very comfortably housed in a matchbox. This would not be practical, of course, as the weight of the camel and the weight of the school would remain the same.

An electron repels other electrons but attracts protons. A proton repels other protons but attracts electrons. An electron is said to be negatively charged; a proton is said to be positively charged. As a proton and an electron attract each other, only the motion of the rapidly orbiting electron keeps the two particles apart. The situation is analogous to that of the moon going round the earth. The speeding moon is tending to travel in a straight line away from the earth, but owing to the force of gravity, it is also tending to be pulled towards the earth. The two forces cancel out, and the moon orbits round the earth.

In so small a particle as an atom the speed of the revolving electron has to be terrific in order to maintain its distance from the protons in the nucleus which attract it. It has been calculated (by Niels Bohr) that in a hydrogen atom the electron whirls round the nucleus at least seven thousand million million times per second.

As the moon revolves round the earth, its orbit remains in the same plane, but this is not so with an electron. The orbit of a speeding electron is constantly changing position, so that the electron seems to weave a continuous, spherical, protective shell round the nucleus. Any external particle would have to travel at enormous speed in order to penetrate this shell without being intercepted by the electron.

The common atom of hydrogen consists of one proton and

one revolving electron. In the nucleus of the atom of any other element there is more than one proton, and for every proton there is correspondingly one revolving electron. In fact the difference between one element and another element is simply a matter of different numbers of protons in the atoms of these elements. Helium (a very light gas formerly used in some airships) consists of atoms containing two protons per nucleus and two revolving electrons. Carbon has 6 protons per nucleus and 6 electrons. Nitrogen has 7 protons and 7 electrons. Oxygen has 8 protons and 8 electrons, and so on. Altogether, there are 92 natural elements ranging from hydrogen with one proton and one electron, to uranium with 92 protons and 92 electrons. During research into atomic energy additional elements have been made artificially. These are known as transuranic elements, and each has its own number of protons per nucleus in excess of 92 and a corresponding number of electrons.

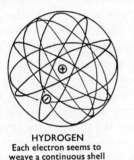

HYDROGEN	HELIUM
Each electron seems to weave a continuous shell	More than one electron can orbit in the same shell

Larger atoms with more electrons have more shells. There can be up to 2 electrons in the first shell, up to 8 in the second shell, up to 18 in the third, up to 32 in the fourth, and up to 50 in the fifth. Sample diagrams are shown overleaf.

Elements are given atomic numbers, and these correspond to the number of protons per nucleus. Thus hydrogen, having one proton, has the atomic number 1. Uranium with 92 protons is given the atomic number 92, and fermium (a transuranic element) with 100 protons per nucleus is given the atomic number 100.

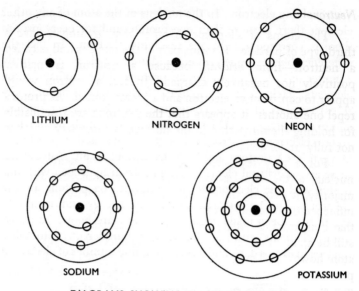

DIAGRAMS SHOWING ELECTRON SHELLS

As the number of protons in the nucleus determines to which element an atom belongs, it follows that if that number can be changed, then the atom concerned will become an atom of a completely different element. Thus it is possible to change one element to another element merely by changing the number of protons in the nuclei of its atoms. In fact every known element can be transformed into some other element.

The alchemists of old dreamed of making gold. The alchemists are long dead, but their dream did not die. A gold atom has 79 protons in its nucleus. If the number of protons in the nuclei of the atoms of another element can be altered to 79, that element will become gold. This transmutation has now been accomplished. An atom of mercury has 80 protons in its nucleus. By using a cyclotron (a machine for producing high energy particles) to bombard a thin film of mercury, the 80 protons have been reduced to 79, and the age-old dream of the alchemists has been finally realised. The expense of achieving it, however, is not worth it.

Neutrons

The atoms of all elements other than hydrogen have a third type of particle. It forms part of the nucleus and is called a neutron—from *neutral*, because a neutron is neither positively nor negatively charged. In fact a neutron would appear to consist of an electron and a proton joined. As protons repel one another, it appears that the neutrons are responsible for holding them together in the nucleus in some way which is not fully understood.

For a very few elements, the number of neutrons per nucleus is the same as the number of protons, but for the majority, it exceeds the number of protons. Neutrons do not influence the chemical properties of an atom as protons do, so that if an atom of helium had 3 neutrons instead of 2, it would still be an atom of helium. Neutrons do affect the weight of an atom however. The weight of an atom is obtained by adding its protons and neutrons together. For example, a normal hydrogen atom with one proton has a weight of 1 unit, whereas a normal oxygen atom with 8 protons and 8 neutrons weighs sixteen times as much. This is why, volume for volume, oxygen is a heavier element than hydrogen. Almost the whole weight of an atom is concentrated in the nucleus. As a proton is nearly 2,000 times heavier than an electron, the effect of the electron on the atomic weight is negligible.

In the table of 92 natural elements on page 40, the figure in the third column stands for three things—the element's *atomic number*, which is of course also the number of *protons* in its nucleus, and the number of orbital *electrons* in a normal atom of that element. To obtain the approximate atomic weight of a normal atom, add the figures in colums 3 and 4 (number of protons plus number of neutrons). For example, the atomic weight of helium is 4, and of lithium 7.

Isotopes

In the table, the neutrons column shows the number of neutrons for a normal (ordinary) atom of each element. However, most elements have amongst their normal atoms a small percentage which do not possess the normal number of neutrons.

Element	Symbol	P., E. & At. No.	Neutrons	Element	Symbol	P., E. & At. No.	Neutrons
Hydrogen	H	1	0	Silver	Ag	47	60
Helium	He	2	2	Cadmium	Cd	48	66
Lithium	Li	3	4	Indium	In	49	66
Beryllium	Be	4	5	Tin	Sn	50	70
Boron	B	5	6	Antimony	Sb	51	70
Carbon	C	6	6	Tellurium	Te	52	78
Nitrogen	N	7	7	Iodine	I	53	74
Oxygen	O	8	8	Xenon	Xe	54	78
Fluorine	F	9	10	Caesium	Cs	55	78
Neon	Ne	10	10	Barium	Ba	56	82
Sodium	Na	11	12	Lanthanum	La	57	82
Magnesium	Mg	12	12	Cerium	Ce	58	82
Aluminium	Al	13	14	Praseodymium	Pr	59	82
Silicon	Si	14	14	Neodymium	Nd	60	82
Phosphorus	P	15	16	Promethium	Pm	61	86
Sulphur	S	16	16	Samarium	Sm	62	92
Chlorine	Cl	17	18	Europium	Eu	63	90
Argon	A	18	22	Gadolinium	Gd	64	94
Potassium	K	19	20	Terbium	Tb	65	94
Calcium	Ca	20	20	Dysprosium	Dy	66	98
Scandium	Sc	21	24	Holmium	Ho	67	98
Titanium	Ti	22	26	Erbium	Er	68	98
Vanadium	V	23	28	Thulium	Tm	69	100
Chromium	Cr	24	28	Ytterbium	Yb	70	104
Manganese	Mn	25	30	Lutecium	Lu	71	104
Iron	Fe	26	30	Hafnium	Hf	72	108
Cobalt	Co	27	32	Tantalum	Ta	73	108
Nickel	Ni	28	30	Tungsten	W	74	110
Copper	Cu	29	34	Rhenium	Re	75	112
Zinc	Zn	30	34	Osmium	Os	76	116
Gallium	Ga	31	38	Iridium	Ir	77	116
Germanium	Ge	32	42	Platinum	Pt	78	117
Arsenic	As	33	42	Gold	Au	79	118
Selenium	Se	34	46	Mercury	Hg	80	122
Bromine	Br	35	44	Thallium	Tl	81	124
Krypton	Kr	36	48	Lead	Pb	82	126
Rubidium	Rb	37	48	Bismuth	Bi	83	126
Strontium	Sr	38	50	Polonium	Po	84	126
Yttrium	Y	39	50	Astatine	At	85	126
Zirconium	Zr	40	50	Radon	Rn	86	136
Niobium	Nb	41	52	Francium	Fr	87	136
Molybdenum	Mo	42	56	Radium	Ra	88	138
Technetium	Tc	43	56	Actinium	Ac	89	138
Ruthenium	Ru	44	58	Thorium	Th	90	142
Rhodium	Rh	45	58	Protactinium	Pa	91	140
Palladium	Pd	46	60	Uranium	U	92	146

When an atom of an element contains more than the normal number of neutrons, its atomic weight is greater than normal, and the atom is said to be heavy. For example, about 1 in 5,000 atoms of hydrogen has a neutron as well as a proton in the nucleus. This means that it is a hydrogen atom in all respects except that it has an atomic weight of 2 instead of 1. Similarly, in every 5,000 oxygen atoms, about two have 9 neutrons instead of 8, and about 10 have 10 neutrons instead of 8. Such neutrons only increase the atomic weight; they do not alter the charge of the nucleus, nor do they change the atom chemically. When atoms differ only in their number of neutrons, they are termed isotopes. Thus a normal atom of hydrogen and a 'heavy' atom of hydrogen are both isotopes of hydrogen. 'Heavy water' is a compound whose hydrogen atoms are 'heavy'.

It is also possible for isotopes to contain fewer than the normal number of neutrons. A normal atom of uranium contains in its nucleus 92 protons and 146 neutrons, but it has isotopes with fewer, *e.g.* uranium 235, which has 143 neutrons. Some elements are known to have a number of isotopes. Tin for example has 10.

Isotopes do not normally occur separately. They are mixed together in the general mass of an element, and if they are to be separated, they must be extracted in some way.

Natural Radioactivity

A number of the heavier elements are radioactive. A radioactive element is one whose atoms tend to disintegrate spontaneously, so that the element changes into a different element over a period of time. Both uranium and radium break down through a series of elements over a period of time, finally ending up as lead. Disintegration by radioactivity can take place in either of two ways.

1 By the ejection of a particle consisting of two protons and two neutrons. Such a particle is known as an alpha particle and is of the same constitution as a helium nucleus.

2 By the ejection of an electron from one of the neutrons in the nucleus. An electron ejected in this way is known as a beta particle. As a neutron contains an electron and a proton, the emission of a beta particle leaves an additional proton in the nucleus, so that the atom concerned becomes the atom of a different element.

The emission of either an alpha or a beta particle may be

accompanied by the emission of short electromagnetic waves, known as gamma rays (γ rays).

Atomic Energy

The energy released during burning or any other chemical reaction is derived from the forces that hold atoms together in the form of molecules. Atomic energy is derived from the vastly stronger forces (more than a million times stronger) which hold together the nucleus of an atom. This energy can be released as the result of the splitting of a nucleus (nuclear fission). Nuclear fission in 1 lb of uranium can yield the same amount of energy as the burning of 3 million lbs of coal. Atomic energy can also be released as the result of the union (nuclear fusion) of nuclei as in a hydrogen bomb.

The fission of a nucleus can take place naturally, but in order that sufficient energy can be made available for use as a source of power, it has to be promoted artificially. For example,

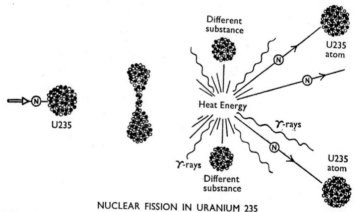

NUCLEAR FISSION IN URANIUM 235
Here the splitting of a nucleus is shown. The orbiting electrons have been omitted

when an atom of uranium 235 (the uranium isotope with 143 neutrons) splits, energy is released in the form of heat, and 2 or 3 neutrons are ejected. If these ejected neutrons strike the nuclei of other similar uranium atoms, the process is repeated, *i.e.* more heat is evolved, and more ejected neutrons become available for striking other nuclei. In a sufficient mass of uranium 235, the repeated splitting of nuclei multiplies rapidly in a chain reaction. The ordinary atoms of uranium, *i.e.* those with 146 neutrons (uranium 238), do not support a chain reaction; and as uranium 235 atoms are scarce (only about 7 in every thousand), a suitable mass of this isotope has to be accumulated by artificial means.

The chain reaction in a suitable mass of uranium 235 builds up in a fraction of a second, and the tremendous heat released results in a devastating explosion. The two bombs which fell on Hiroshima and Nagasaki in Japan in 1945 killed between them 105,000 people, injured another 94,000, and ended World War II. Since then, atomic reactors have been developed for controlling the rate at which nuclear fission takes place so that the heat can be released slowly and in consequence used as a source of power.

With atomic reactors substances can be made radioactive artificially. For example, an element may be made radioactive by exposing it in a reactor. During such exposure a number of the atoms in the element absorb additional neutrons, thus forming unstable isotopes which disintegrate over a period of time by radioactivity. Radio-isotopes have many uses in science, from the study of diseases to tracing a leak in an underground pipe.

Atomic energy has provided the means for the destruction of the world; it has also provided the means for furnishing it with benefits as yet undreamed of.

CODE

1 Demonstrate the relative size of an atom, *e.g.* with a pin-head and a football. The football represents a hydrogen atom, with a seemingly solid shell. The pin-head represents its nucleus (one proton).

2 Demonstrate how an electron seems to make a continuous shell. Fix a rubber or suitable weight to the end of a length of string. Whirl it round rapidly, and observe the circular 'shell'. An electron, of course, makes a spherical shell.

3 Demonstrate why an electron does not fall into the nucleus. Place a ball in a small basket or plastic bucket. Whirl overhead. Observe that when basket or bucket is upside down, the ball does not fall out. This is also why the moon does not fall to the earth.

NOTEBOOK WORK

Answers should be along the following lines.
1 Most of an atom is empty space.
2 The centre of an atom is called a nucleus.
3 The atoms of different elements have different numbers of protons.
4 If the nucleus in a uranium atom is upset, some stray neutrons from it may split the nuclei in other uranium atoms.
5 Nuclear fission causes tremendous heat.

(3) THE SOLAR SYSTEM

ASTEROIDS, COMETS AND METEORS

DEMONSTRATION MATERIAL

Wall-frieze or chart to show positions of the asteroid belt in the solar system. (See page 51 for scale)

SAMPLE LINK QUESTIONS

1 How many planets go round the sun? (*Nine*)
2 What are their names in order from the sun? (*Mercury, Venus, Earth, Mars, Jupiter, Saturn, Uranus, Neptune, Pluto*)
3 What are the names of the four giant planets? (*Jupiter, Saturn, Uranus, Neptune*)
4 Which of these is the largest? (*Jupiter*)
5 Which is the smallest planet in the solar system? (*Mercury*)
6 What is the name of the planet with rings? (*Saturn*)

7 What do we call things which go round a planet? (*Satellites*)
8 What are the rings of Saturn believed to be? (*The remains of a satellite which broke into pieces long ago*)
9 Which three planets have no satellites as far as we know? (*Mercury, Venus and Pluto*)
10 Why would we find it hard to live on any of the other planets or their satellites? (*None has enough oxygen gas and a suitable temperature*)

RELEVANT INFORMATION

The main points of a lesson in Pupils' Book 3 were that
1 the solar system consists of the sun and everything that goes round it. This includes the nine major planets and their satellites;
2 the farther a planet has to travel in its orbit, the longer it takes to go round the sun;
3 planets are of different sizes. Five are 'small', and four are giants;
4 human beings would find it hard to live on the other planets and their satellites.

The main points of this lesson are that
1 in addition to the nine major planets, there are asteroids, comets and meteors going round the sun;
2 most asteroids are in a belt between the orbit of Mars and the orbit of Jupiter;
3 part of a comet's orbit is near the sun, and part is far out in space;
4 meteors are the bits and pieces of space. 'Shooting stars' are meteors falling into the earth's atmosphere.

Asteroids

These are also known as minor planets, or planetoids. The word *asteroid* means *starlike*, but whereas stars are spheres of glowing gases, asteroids are lumps of barren rock, lacking in air and water. It has been estimated that there are well over 40,000 of them—all of them insignificant. The majority are small rough solids, and even the largest known—Ceres—has an estimated diameter of only 485 miles. Ceres was the first asteroid to be discovered. So far as is known, all asteroids revolve round the sun in the same direction as the planets, but each has its own orbit and travels at its own speed. Some asteroids have orbits which are slanted above or below those of the major planets.

Although most asteroids remain between the orbits of Mars and Jupiter, some do not. Odd ones have erratic orbits which take them well away from the rest of the asteroid belt. Icarus is an example, travelling from beyond the orbit of Mars to within 19 million miles of the sun (which brings it closer to the sun than Mercury). The asteroid which comes nearest the earth is Hermes, which approached to within half a million miles of the earth in 1937. Collisions between erratic asteroids and planets are very unlikely, as in most cases the orbits of such asteroids are slanted above or below those of the planets. Two groups of asteroids revolve in the orbit of Jupiter itself—one group ahead of the giant planet, and one group behind it. These two groups are called the Trojans.

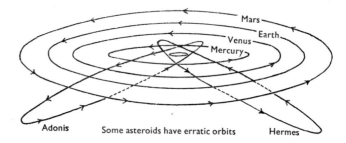
Some asteroids have erratic orbits

The force of gravity of the major planets—especially of Jupiter—is believed to have affected the orbits of some asteroids. Of the twelve satellites of Jupiter, the four which are farthest away from the giant planet revolve in the opposite direction from all the others, and are believed to be asteroids which have been 'captured' by Jupiter. This belief also applies to Phoebe, the outermost of Saturn's nine satellites, which revolves round its planet in a direction opposite to the others.

The force of gravity of most asteroids is too weak to overcome the effects of centrifugal force set up by rotation, so that anything landing on the surface would probably be sent drifting back into space. Some names of asteroids are Adonis, Eros, Apollo, Pallas, Vesta, Juno, Hermes, Fanny and Agnes.

According to one creditable theory, asteroids are the fragments of a small broken planet that once revolved between the orbits of Mars and Jupiter. But whatever their origin, asteroids now form part of the general debris of space.

Comets

Comets are seen as luminous bodies, travelling round the sun in elongated, elliptical orbits. One end of a comet's orbit may be close to the sun, and the other far out in space. In most

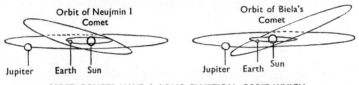

MOST COMETS HAVE A LONG ELLIPTICAL ORBIT WHICH SLANTS AT AN ANGLE TO THE ORBITS OF THE PLANETS

cases, these orbits are not in the plane of the sun's equator like those of the planets, but slanting at an angle to those of the planets. The head of a comet is believed to consist of solid particles from which gases are given off as the comet approaches the sun and becomes affected by its heat. These gases form a glowing tail which may stretch back into space for about 50 to 150 million miles, and be up to 10 million miles wide. The tail always points away from the sun.

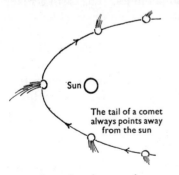

The tail of a comet always points away from the sun

The time taken to complete an orbit varies greatly with each comet. Encke's comet has the shortest known revolution period. It takes only 3·3 years to go once round the sun. It is believed that there are comets which will take thousands of years to complete an

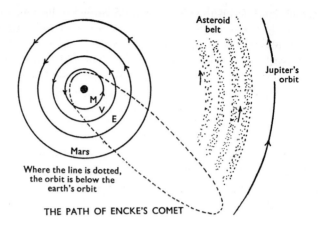

Asteroid belt

Jupiter's orbit

Mars

Where the line is dotted, the orbit is below the earth's orbit

THE PATH OF ENCKE'S COMET

orbit, and the orbits of some are such that they may never return. The closest a comet has been known to approach the earth was when Lexell's comet passed within 1,500,000 miles in 1770. Halley's comet is perhaps the most famous of comets. It travels along its orbit in a direction opposite to that taken by the major planets and is visible from the earth about every 76 years. Records of the appearance of this comet have been traced back to 240 B.C. Its appearance in 1066 is shown on the famous Bayeux tapestry. When it appeared in 1910, its tail extended for well over 35 million miles. The earth actually passed through this tail, but there were no observable effects. Its next appearance is due in 1985.

If a comet passes sufficiently close to a planet, the force of gravity of the planet will cause part of the comet to break off in the form of meteors. It is believed that there are more than 100,000 comets revolving round the sun, but very few are bright enough to be seen without a telescope.

Meteors

Meteors are the dust of space. In the solar system, they orbit round the sun, and although a few may weigh several tons, the majority are assumed to be extremely small—no larger than a pin-head. Probably the tiny meteoric particles originate from comets, and the larger fragments from asteroids.

As the earth travels along in its orbit, it attracts meteors by its force of gravity. As these meteors are pulled towards the earth, they become heated by friction between them and the atmosphere. The air in front of the meteor becomes compressed and luminous. The surface of the meteor melts in the heat, and glowing particles stream off and form the fiery tail which has resulted in the name 'shooting star'. Larger ones which may be visible for some time are called 'fireballs'. The majority of meteors which fall into our atmosphere are reduced to gas and dust, and it has been estimated that some 2,000 tons of this meteoric dust settles on the earth each day. Although few are actually seen, probably well over 100 million meteors a day fall from outer space towards our planet, and if it were not for the protection which the atmosphere affords, the surface of the earth would probably be pitted with craters like the surface of the moon.

When a meteor is large enough to penetrate the atmosphere and land on the earth's surface, it is called a meteorite. Most meteorites are probably no bigger than small pebbles. A number of these falling together can however do a certain amount of damage. In 1908 a shower of meteorites landed in Siberia, laying waste some 20 miles of forest, and in 1947 another forest in the U.S.S.R. suffered from a shower of meteorites of an iron and nickel nature. From this second shower, some 30 tons of meteoric material were eventually collected. There is evidence of an occasional large meteor falling to the earth. Meteor Crater in Arizona, which is ¾ mile across and some 600 feet deep, is believed to have been caused by a meteorite which fell some thousands of years ago. The largest crater known to have been caused by a single meteorite is Chubb Crater in Ungava. This is 3 miles across. When a large meteorite lands, it may be shattered into smaller pieces. However, there is one embedded in South Africa which weighs some 60 tons. One theory holds that the craters on the moon have been caused by meteorites. It is not the only theory which seeks to account for the moon craters, but meteorites could certainly have caused some of the moon craters, especially in view of the fact that the moon does not have a protective atmosphere like that of the earth.

The composition of meteorites seems to be of three main kinds.

1 Iron meteorites, in which a certain amount of nickel is also usually present

2 Stony meteorites, which are composed mainly of silicates

3 Stony irons, which are a mixture of irons and silicates

Although meteors fall into the atmosphere all the year round, the most brilliant showers occur during August, October, November and December. During these months it is usually quite easy to see falling meteors (or 'shooting stars') on any clear starry night.

Thunderbolts

There is no such thing as an actual thunderbolt. The term has been applied somewhat indiscriminately to shafts of lightning, to hollow fused tubes produced in sandy soil by the action of lightning and known as fulgurites, and also to rough cylinders of iron pyrites sometimes found in chalk cliffs and quarries and admired for their radiating structure. In the past various unusual objects found in the earth, e.g. belemnites (see lesson on fossils), meteorites and even flint tools and spearheads have been termed thunderbolts. This was due to a belief that such objects had been flung down to the earth as the result of thunder and lightning.

CODE

A. Demonstrate the distances of the planets from the sun, together with the position of the asteroid belt, using a large blackboard, wall-chart or frieze. The figures in columns 3 to 6 in the table opposite are approximately to scale, and based on mean average distances from the sun. (From 1969 to 2009, the distance of Pluto will be less than the distance of Neptune. This is due to the orbit of Pluto intersecting that of Neptune.) The planets may be illustrated by discs. Obviously these cannot be shown to the same scale as the distances, but their diameters, relative to one another, are given in columns 8 and 9. A length of wallpaper makes a convenient frieze in place of the sheets of imperial paper mentioned in the key.

		Distances from the Rim of the Sun (4 scales. See key)					*Diameters (to scale)*	
1	2	3	4	5	6	7	8	9
SUN						864,000	17″	34″
MERCURY No satellites	36	½″	1″	1½″	2″	3,100	$\frac{1}{16}$″	⅛″
VENUS No satellites	67	1″	1⅞″	2⅞″	3¾″	7,700	⅙″	$\frac{5}{16}$″
EARTH 1 satellite	93	1¼″	2½″	3¾″	5″	7,900	⅙″	$\frac{5}{16}$″
MARS 2 satellites	142	2″	4″	6″	8″	4,300	$\frac{1}{12}$″	$\frac{3}{16}$″
JUPITER 12 satellites	484	6¾″	1′ 1½″	1′ 8¼″	2′ 3″	89,000	1¾″	3½″
SATURN 9 satellites	887	1′ 0¼″	2′ 0½″	3′ 0¾″	4′ 1″	75,000	1½″	3″
URANUS 5 satellites	1,790	2′ 1″	4′ 2″	6′ 3″	8′ 4″	32,000	⅝″	1¼″
NEPTUNE 2 satellites	2,800	3′ 3″	6′ 6″	9′ 9″	13′ 0″	31,000	⅝″	1¼″
PLUTO No satellites	3,680	4′ 2″	8′ 4″	12′ 6″	16′ 8″	8,000 (est.)	⅙″	$\frac{5}{16}$″

Key to Columns of Table

1 Sun and planets
2 Mean distance from the sun in millions of miles
3 For a length of 5 ft, *e.g.* a large blackboard, or two sheets of imperial paper placed end to end
4 For a length of 10 ft, *e.g.* four sheets of imperial paper end to end
5 For a length of 12 ft 6 in, *e.g.* five sheets of imperial paper end to end

6 For a length of 17 ft 6 ins, *e.g.* seven sheets of imperial paper end to end

7 Diameter at the equator in miles

8 Suitable diameters for use in conjunction with columns 3 and 4

9 Suitable diameters for use in conjunction with columns 5 and 6

Notes

1 For Saturn's ring system use an overall diameter of $3\frac{1}{2}$ inches for the column 8 scale, and an overall diameter of 7 inches for the column 9 scale.

2 Show the asteroid belt as a band, or a number of speckles between the orbits of Mars and Jupiter.

3 In view of the relatively large size of the sun, it may be better shown as an arc. As an alternative it may be symbolised by a mere dot, in which case the elongated elliptical orbit of a comet may also be marked on the completed chart.

NOTEBOOK WORK

Answers should be along the following lines.

1 (*a*) Asteroids are believed to be the remains of a broken planet which once existed between the orbits of Mars and Jupiter.

(*b*) A comet is believed to be a mass of gas and bits of solid.

(*c*) Meteors are believed to be bits broken from asteroids and comets.

2 An asteroid is a lump of barren rock.

3 A meteorite is a meteor which is big enough for part of it to reach the earth's surface.

4 The asteroid belt is in the space between the orbits of Mars and Jupiter.

5 Part of a comet's orbit is near the sun, and part is far out in space.

6 Friction between a falling meteor and the earth's atmosphere makes it hot enough to glow.

4 THE STARS ARE FAR AWAY

GALAXIES AND CONSTELLATIONS

DEMONSTRATION MATERIAL

Globe of the world, or a pupil; black paper; large sheet of black card with holes indicating the Plough and pole star

SAMPLE LINK QUESTIONS

1 What does the solar system consist of? (*The sun and everything that goes round it*)
2 What is an asteroid? (*A lump of barren rock in space*)
3 What is a comet? (*A mass of gas and bits of solid*)
4 What are meteors? (*Bits broken from asteroids and comets— the odds and ends of space*)
5 What is a 'shooting star'? (*A meteor falling towards the earth*)
6 What do we call a meteor if it lands on the earth? (*A meteorite*)
7 What is a star made of? (*Hot, glowing gases*)
8 Which star is nearest to the earth? (*The sun*)
9 Why does the sun seem larger than the other stars? (*It is very much nearer*)
10 What is the earth doing to cause us to have night-time and daylight? (*Spinning (turning on its axis)*)

RELEVANT INFORMATION

The main points of this lesson are:
1 Stars are in giant collections called galaxies;
2 They appear to be in patterns called constellations;
3 Because the earth is spinning, the patterns do not always seem to be the same way up;
4 From a constellation called the Plough, we can find the pole star which indicates the north of the earth.

Stars in General

Stars are spheres of glowing gases. They do not burn in the same way as a fire burns, however. Their energy is not produced chemically but is believed to be the result of a prolonged nuclear reaction similar to that which takes place in a hydrogen bomb. The apparent twinkling of a star is due to turbulence in the layers of the earth's atmosphere causing the rays of light from the star to be bent this way and that.

The sun is the star nearest to the earth. Its distance is approximately 93 million miles, but this is short compared with the distance of other stars. The next nearest are Proxima Centauri, visible from the southern hemisphere, and Alpha Centauri visible from the northern hemisphere. Both of these stars are about 25 million million miles away—nearly 270,000 times the distance to the sun. The distances to other stars is so incredibly great that it is expressed in terms of light years. Light travels at 186,000 miles per second, and one light year is the distance which light could cover in a year—roughly 6 million million miles. All the stars visible to the naked eye lie within 3,000 light years of the sun, *i.e.* some 18,000 million million miles. Telescopes reveal that beyond that there are stars for as far as you can possibly imagine.

In most respects the sun is just an average star. It has a diameter of 864,000 miles, but there are many stars smaller, and many stars bigger. Some stars are even smaller than the earth. Kuiper's star, for example, has a diameter of only about 4,000 miles—about that of the planet Mars. On the other hand, there are stars big enough to contain the sun many millions of times over. The largest known of these is Epsilon Aurigae with an estimated diameter of 2,500 million miles. Nearly 2,800 stars the size of the sun could stand in line along its diameter.

Only the relative nearness of the sun makes it look so much larger and brighter than any of the other stars. It is because of this that we see them only at night, when the light from the sun no longer outshines them. Some stars are not so bright as the sun, and others are far brighter. For example, the star known as Wolf 359 has a luminosity which is only 1/50,000 that of the sun, whereas many stars are 50,000 times brighter than the sun. The *apparent* brightness of a star is, of course, governed by its distance. Sigma Doradus, for example, looks very faint because of distance and is visible only through a telescope, yet it has been estimated that its brightness is more than 300,000 times that of the sun. The star which appears to be the brightest in the sky, apart from the sun, is Sirius, visible from the northern hemisphere. This star, also known as the dog star, is actually about 26 times brighter than the sun, but it appears to be brighter than other stars because it is comparatively near—a mere 8½ light years away, *i.e.* 50 million million miles.

Many stars are hotter than the sun. The surface temperature of the sun is estimated to be some 6,000°C, but the hottest stars have surface temperatures estimated to be well over 35,000°C. Other stars are cooler than the sun, and the coolest of these—the dark stars—are not visible to the eye. The temperature of a star is not relative to its size. Epsilon Aurigae, the largest star known, is also one of the coolest, with an estimated surface temperature of only 1,700°C, while there are white-hot dwarf stars, far smaller than the sun, with surface temperatures far greater than that of the sun. The colour of a star is affected by its temperature—just like a poker in a fire—and ranges from red (the coolest) through orange, yellow and white, to blue-white (the hottest). The sun is classed as a yellow star.

Many stars are in pairs, revolving round their common centre of gravity. They are known as double or binary stars. Mizar, the second star in the tail of the Plough, is an example. Sirius, the dog star, is another; its companion star is a white-hot dwarf many times smaller than the sun, and commonly known as the Pup. Triple star systems are also known, *e.g.* Alpha Centauri, and there are also star systems containing four or more stars. Despite the vast distances of interstellar space between one star and the next, they are nevertheless collected into giant groups known as galaxies.

Galaxies

There are three general shapes of galaxies.
1 Elliptical, *i.e.* something like an oval disc
2 Spiral—usually in the form of a circular disc with a central bulge

3 Irregular, *i.e.* with no obvious symmetry, and not similar to either of the above two.

The sun itself is one of 100,000 million stars forming a spiral galaxy, the Milky Way. About half of the stars of the Milky Way are single stars; the rest are in pairs or in other multiple systems. Seen from the side, this galaxy is expected to be roughly the shape of two soup plates—one inverted on top of the other. Its greatest diameter, *i.e.* from rim to rim, is estimated to be in the region of 100,000 light years, and its depth is probably about one-fifth of this. The whole galaxy rotates about its centre, something like a huge catherine wheel.

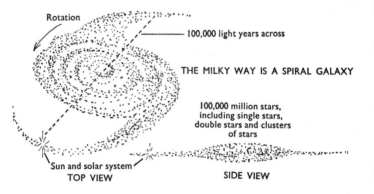

Rotation

100,000 light years across

THE MILKY WAY IS A SPIRAL GALAXY

100,000 million stars, including single stars, double stars and clusters of stars

Sun and solar system
TOP VIEW

SIDE VIEW

The sun is located in one of the spiral arms of the Milky Way—more than half way from the centre of the galaxy (*i.e.* about 27,000 light years from the centre)—and together with the stars in its vicinity it travels in its galactic orbit at about half a million miles an hour. Even at this speed, it takes some 200 million years to complete one orbit, so that it has been round only once since the Coal Age.

As we are within the Milky Way, we can look outwards from it, and on a clear starry night we can see the rim of the galaxy as a faint misty band stretching down the sky. This misty effect is due to the light from millions of stars in the rim, which are too far away to be seen individually.

Just as the sun is an ordinary star, so the Milky Way is just an ordinary galaxy. There are smaller galaxies, and there

are larger galaxies. For example, the two nearest galaxies outside the Milky Way are much smaller, each consisting merely
of hundreds of thousands of stars. Both these galaxies are
irregular in shape. They are visible from the southern hemisphere and are believed to be companions of the Milky Way.
They are called the Large Magellanic cloud and the Small
Magellanic cloud, after Magellan who noticed them on his
voyage round the world.

Somewhere between 900,000 and 2,000,000 light years
away is the Great Nebula in Andromeda—a very impressive
galaxy which is probably larger than the Milky Way. It is a
spiral galaxy, and like the Milky Way has two smaller companion galaxies. Both of these are elliptical. These six galaxies
—the Milky Way and its two irregular neighbours, and the
Great Nebula in Andromeda with its two elliptical neighbours—
belong to a cluster of about twenty galaxies referred to by
astronomers as the 'local group'.

Beyond this local group of galaxies, and incredibly far out
across the vast deeps of space, are other galaxies and other
clusters of galaxies. There may be some 500 million galaxies
within the range of the 200-inch telescope, and many of them
belong to clusters, some of which may have up to a thousand
members. Some 3,000 galaxy clusters have been catalogued.
Galaxies have been discovered at distances of 2,000 million
light years, and beyond these far horizons of space there may
be untold millions of them. This then is the universe, and it
would seem that the whole of it is in motion. Rotating satellites orbit round planets. Rotating planets orbit round stars,
and rotating stars orbit round the axis of the galaxy to which
they belong. As the galaxies rotate, and as they are in motion
relative to one another, it is not inconceivable that they too
revolve round some hypothetical point in the universe.

One minor part of all this is the sun—an ordinary, middle-
aged star on the fringe of an ordinary, average-sized galaxy of
100,000 million stars, a galaxy so vast that it would take a shaft
of light travelling at 186,000 miles per second a full 100,000
years to cross it, a galaxy which is as an infinitesimal speck of
dust in the interminable reaches of space.

57

Constellations

The galaxies are too far away to be distinguished as such by the naked eye, and even through an ordinary telescope a galaxy seems no more than a small luminous cloud or a fuzzy star. To us, looking at the canopy of the sky on a starry night, it would seem that the stars are in a variety of formations. These apparent formations are constellations, and although all the stars in all the constellations are at different distances they appear to be at the same distance. This is because our eyes cannot obtain a three-dimensional picture of the vast gulfs of space.

A constellation then is really an arbitrary grouping of stars based on perspective. Nevertheless these apparent groupings are useful to astronomers for the purpose of easy reference and for the identification of stars. The ancients named the constellations after various gods and animals, but it is not easy to see any resemblance.

The panorama which an observer sees on a clear starry night depends on three main factors.

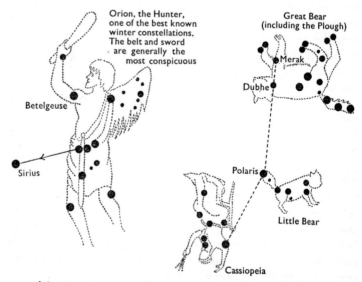

It is not easy to see a resemblance between a constellation and the figure after which it is named

1 The position of the observer on the earth. An observer in the northern hemisphere will not see the same constellations as an observer in the southern hemisphere.

2 The time of night. The turning of the earth about its axis makes the constellations seem to turn instead. Only the pole star, which is almost exactly in line with the earth's axis, seems to remain in the same position while the other stars *seem* to revolve in an anti-clockwise direction round it. Stars which appear to be near to the pole star seem to describe a small circle round it. Stars which appear to be much farther away from the pole star seem to describe a much larger circle, so that a star which is overhead at midnight will be low in the western sky five hours later, while other stars which were not visible at midnight will have climbed into the eastern sky.

3 The position of the earth in its path round the sun. We see the stars only at night, *i.e.* when we are looking away from the sun. The winter and summer positions of the earth are on opposite sides of the sun. Therefore when we look away from the sun in winter, we cannot see all the constellations that we see when we look away from the sun in summer. The same applies to spring and autumn. Those constellations which are near the pole star are visible from our hemisphere all the year round, but those which are far away from the pole star are seen according to season. Those which we see in winter are below our horizon in summer, and vice versa.

It is because the earth is moving round the sun, that for each month of the year a different constellation serves as a background for the rising and setting sun. In ancient times the name Zodiac was given to these twelve constellations.

The Plough and the Pole Star

Among the best known constellations is Ursa Major, or the Great Bear. The main part of this constellation is separately named the Plough. It is also known as the Dipper, Charles' Wain, David's Car, and the Bier of Lazarus. The Plough consists of seven white stars. It is in the far north of the sky and always above the horizon as seen from Britain, so that it is visible on starry nights all the year round. Owing to the earth's rotation, it appears to make a complete circuit round the pole star in a 24-hour period. Two of its stars—Merak and Dubhe—are known as the pointers, because a straight line taken from them leads to the pole star.

The pole star (Polaris) is a fairly bright star, but not as bright as the stars of the Plough. As Polaris lies virtually on the same line as the axis of the earth, a line dropped vertically from it to the earth always indicates the approximate position of the true north. This of course applies only to an observer in the northern hemisphere.

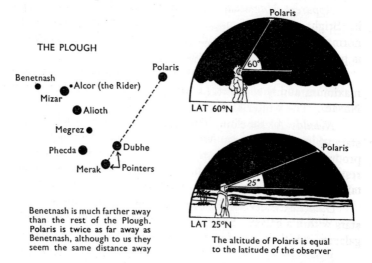

THE PLOUGH

Benetnash
Alcor (the Rider)
Mizar
Alioth
Megrez
Phecda
Merak Dubhe
Pointers
Polaris

Polaris

LAT 60°N

Polaris

LAT 25°N

Benetnash is much farther away than the rest of the Plough. Polaris is twice as far away as Benetnash, although to us they seem the same distance away

The altitude of Polaris is equal to the latitude of the observer

The apparent height in the sky of Polaris depends on which latitude of the earth it is viewed from. To an observer at the north pole, Polaris would seem vertically overhead. The nearer the observer is to the equator, the lower in the sky Polaris seems to be, so that to an observer on the equator, Polaris would seem to be right on the skyline. South of the equator, it is never seen at all. An observer in the southern hemisphere is rather unfortunate in that there is no bright star conveniently positioned above the south pole. In the southern hemisphere it is possible to find the way towards the south by means of a group of stars known as the Southern Cross.

From early times the pole star has served as a very useful guide to those travelling by sea or by land, and it is believed that the Greek astronomer, Thales, recommended it for navigational purposes as early as the seventh century B.C. Even today, in an age equipped with modern direction-indicating instruments, Polaris is useful to navigators on land and sea and in the air, and is a means for checking their instruments.

Brief Glossary

Apparent Magnitude: The brightness of a star, as we see it. Bright stars are of magnitude 1. The faintest visible to the normal eye are of magnitude 6. With powerful telescopes it is possible to detect stars of magnitude 21.

Nova: A star which brightens temporarily to a brilliant maximum and then fades. Large examples are termed Super Novae.

Nebula: A vast cloud of gaseous matter illuminated by the stars which it enshrouds. May be compared to the bright patch produced by a car headlamp in fog. The term is now usually restricted to such clouds within the Milky Way, those beyond taking the more general name of galaxy.

Galactic Cluster: A loose aggregation of up to a few hundred stars within a galaxy. Should not be confused with a cluster of galaxies, which is, of course, an aggregation of entire galaxies.

Extragalactic: Beyond the limits of the Milky Way galaxy.

Parsec: Unit of 19,150,000,000,000 miles, *i.e.* slightly more than three light years. (A light year is nearly 6 million million miles.)

Radio Telescope: An instrument for receiving any radiant energy travelling from stars in the form of radio waves instead of light waves.

CODE

1 Demonstrate why the pole star always appears to be above the north pole of the earth, and why the constellations appear to revolve round it.

(*a*) Place a globe of the world so that its axis points towards one of the lights in the room. Let this light stand for the pole star. Let other lights or various objects in the room stand for other stars. Observe:

    (i) that the 'pole star' is visible from the northern hemisphere but not from the southern hemisphere;

    (ii) the direction from the globe of the other 'stars'.

(*b*) Rotate the globe slowly in an anti-clockwise direction and observe:

    (i) that the 'pole star' remains in the same direction, *i.e.* above the north pole;

    (ii) that the direction of the other 'stars' from points on the globe changes as it rotates.

One complete rotation represents a 24-hour period.

A similar impression may be obtained by allowing a pupil to stand below the light which represents the pole star. As he rotates, the direction of the other 'stars' changes, but the 'pole star' is always seen in the same direction, *i.e.* overhead.

2 (*a*) Mark in chalk, on a large sheet of black card, the outline of the Plough and pole star.

(*b*) Pierce holes through the 'stars'.

(*c*) Fix the chart over a window so that the light shining through the holes gives the appearance of the stars in the night sky.

A similar idea is suggested in the Pupils' Book. Pupils should start by ruling a line on which to mark the positions of the pointers and the pole star. The rest of the Plough can then be outlined. A pupil's paper model can be rotated about the pole star to give an impression of the different appearances of the Plough.

NOTEBOOK WORK

Answers should be along the following lines.

1 A star is a huge mass of gases which are hot enough to glow.

2 A galaxy is a collection of stars.

3 A constellation is a pattern of stars.

4 We see constellations in different positions because the earth spins.

5 An imaginary line drawn through two of the stars in the Plough leads to the pole star. We call these two stars the pointers.

5) SOME HERBS STORE FOOD

SWOLLEN ROOTS: SWOLLEN STEMS: SWOLLEN LEAVES

DEMONSTRATION MATERIAL

Leaf succulents and cacti; swollen roots, *e.g.* taproots of carrot, turnip, beetroot, parsnip, swede, fibrous roots of dahlia; swollen underground stems, *e.g.* iris rhizome, crocus corm, primrose rootstock, potato; bulb, *e.g.* onion, daffodil, hyacinth, tulip

SAMPLE LINK QUESTIONS

1 What are the three main parts that most plants have? (*Roots, stems, leaves*)
2 What do we call plants that have no true roots, stems or leaves? (*Simple plants*)
3 What are the three main kinds of plants with roots, stems and leaves? (*Herbs, trees and shrubs*)
4 Which of these have not got woody stems? (*Herbs*)
5 Are all stems above ground level? (*No*)
6 What are the four main needs of living things? (*Oxygen, food, to grow, to have young*)
7 What is a food which all living things need? (*Water*)
8 What happens to a living thing if its body temperature becomes too low? (*It dies*)
9 Some plants die in winter. What do other plants do? (*Rest*)

RELEVANT INFORMATION

A lesson in Book 2 indicated that some plants have underground stems.

A lesson in Book 3 indicated that a plant becomes less active as its body temperature falls.

The main points of this lesson are that

1 many plants are forced to rest because of either a periodic shortage of water or a periodic fall in temperature;

2 some of the herbs whose rest is enforced by a shortage of water are able to store food in swollen stems or leaves above ground level;

3 some of the herbs whose rest is enforced by a drop in temperature are able to store food in swollen roots, stems or leaves below ground level.

Plants in General

There are two kingdoms of living things—the animal kingdom and the plant kingdom. Although the term *plant* is unfortunately misused on occasions to segregate one group of plants from another in phrases such as 'weeds and plants' and 'trees and plants', such things as weeds, trees and vegetables are, of course, all plants. Throughout this series of books, the plant kingdom has been divided into two major groups according to simple observable characteristics.

1 Plants with true roots, stems and leaves—the herbs, trees and shrubs

2 Plants with no true roots, stems and leaves—the simple plants. These are the subject of Lessons 29 and 30 in this book.

On trees and shrubs, the stems are comparatively stout and woody and remain above ground level during winter. Herbs have stems which are comparatively soft and which are not regularly persistent above ground in the way that those of trees and shrubs are. For further information, see Teacher's Book 2, pages 43-4 on herbs, trees and shrubs, pages 209-10 on leaves and pages 217-21 on stems and roots.

A herb that begins as a seed, grows to maturity, produces flowers, fruit and seeds, and then dies all in one year is an *annual*. Its seeds remain dormant throughout the winter to begin proceedings the following spring. Some, *e.g.* common groundsel, have more than one generation within the year. A *biennial* lives for two years. The seed puts out roots and the plant grows during the first year, and then stores food to use the following year for flowers and seeds. Swedes, turnips, beetroots, parsnips and carrots are biennials whose swollen roots are lifted at the end of the first year of growth and used for food. A *perennial* lives for more than two years. Many of the herbs including those with bulbs, corms, rhizomes and rootstocks are perennials. As trees and shrubs live for more than two years, they too are perennial plants.

Climatic conditions and the situation of plants influence their behaviour. Biennials and perennials which grow naturally in positions where they regularly experience a shortage of moisture or a lowering of temperature need to be adapted in order to survive. Some herbs have adaptations in the form of roots, stems or leaves specially modified into swollen parts for the purpose of storing reserves of food.

Swollen Parts above Ground Level

Herbs adapted to living through dry periods, or in soils where there is little available moisture, tend to build up reserves of water in swollen leaves or swollen stems above ground level. The leaf succulents of dry, rocky, and alpine regions, and the stem succulents of the desert are well-known examples of such plants, equipped to survive periods of drought. Stonecrops (*Sedums*), house leeks and other *Sempervivums*, and the live-forevers (*Echeveria*) are popular as cultivated varieties of leaf succulents. Herbaceous cacti are popular as cultivated varieties of stem succulents. Cacti are perennial plants modified to exist in hot desert conditions where water is plentiful only during the few rainy days of the year. The thick juicy stems of cacti are sometimes cylindrical, sometimes columnar and sometimes flattened, and their storage capacity is such that well over 90% of the total weight of the stem may consist of water. These stems are green and carry out the functions of a leaf. The leaves themselves, when present, are reduced to short spines, and these serve to protect the plant against browsing animals. The flowers, when they appear, are extremely beautiful.

Swollen Parts below Ground Level

In general, plants in temperate and arctic regions are inactive in winter. Biennial and many of the perennial herbs adapted to regions where the climate imposes seasonal growth, die down to ground level after a period of growing, and in certain of these food is stored underground in specially swollen parts.

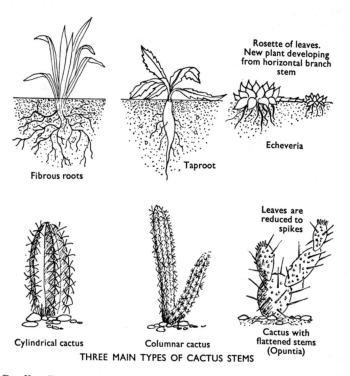

Fibrous roots

Taproot

Rosette of leaves. New plant developing from horizontal branch stem

Echeveria

Leaves are reduced to spikes

Cylindrical cactus

Columnar cactus

Cactus with flattened stems (Opuntia)

THREE MAIN TYPES OF CACTUS STEMS

Swollen Roots

1 *Root tubers* occur when swellings are formed on fibrous-rooted systems. The dahlia, the lesser celandine and the British orchids store food in this way.

2 *Swollen taproots.* When modifications for food storage occur in the roots of a herb with a taproot system, it is the main

taproot which swells. This type of food storage is a characteristic of biennials. During the first season of growth, the herb produces roots, stem and leaves, and builds up a store of food in the taproot. With the approach of winter, the stem and leaves die down to ground level. During the following season of growth, a new stem and leaves are produced, and subsequently flowers, fruit and seeds. Thus the plant reproduces itself at the expense of the food store and then dies. Examples of herbs which follow this procedure (if allowed) are carrot, turnip, beetroot, parsnip and swede. Dandelions and docks are perennial herbs with swollen taproots.

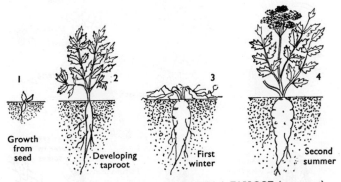

STAGES IN THE GROWTH OF A HERB WITH A TAPROOT (e.g. carrot)

Swollen Stems

1 *Rootstock.* In most perennial herbs the main stem has become an underground one, sending up leaves, or branch stems bearing leaves, each year. On herbs where this underground stem is an upright structure, it is often termed a rootstock. A rootstock may become noticeably swollen with food as on the primrose and some ferns.

2 *Rhizome.* A rhizome is an underground stem growing horizontally. On some herbs it becomes swollen throughout its length, as on the flowering rush, iris and Solomon's seal. The rhizomes of iris and Solomon's seal are only partly covered by

67

the soil, so that the leaves which grow directly from them appear above ground level. A water-lily has a swollen rhizome from which it sends up leaves with long leaf stalks.

3 *Stem tuber*. When a swelling occurs at the growing tip of an underground rhizome instead of throughout its length, it is known as a stem tuber. Examples are potatoes, perennial sunflowers and Jerusalem artichokes. On a potato, the eyes are reduced buds in the axils of tiny scale-like leaves. It is from these buds that the aerial stems develop when a potato is planted.

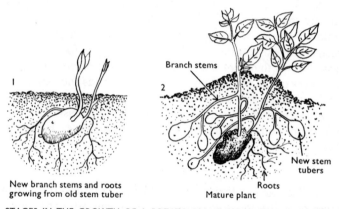

New branch stems and roots growing from old stem tuber

Branch stems

New stem tubers

Roots

Mature plant

STAGES IN THE GROWTH OF A POTATO PLANT FROM AN OLD POTATO

4 *Corm*. A corm is a short thickened underground stem surrounded by a few thin scaly leaves. In spring an aerial stem develops from the centre of the corm which then shrivels gradually as its food is used up. Later in the spring food manufactured by the leaves passes to the base of the aerial stem, forming a new corm on top of the old one. The new corm rests until the following year. Stout roots which are sent out by new corms eventually contract in length, pulling the new corms to a lower level in the soil. Examples of herbs which store food in the form of corms are the gladiolus, crocus and montbretia. Meadow saffron or autumn crocus also grows from a corm, but should not be confused with the ordinary crocus.

Swollen Leaves

It is in bulbs that swollen modified leaves are used for the underground storage of food. A bulb bears a superficial resemblance to a corm but may be easily distinguished from a corm if it is cut open. The greater portion of a bulb consists of fleshy colourless, scale-like leaves growing from a small modified stem. Roots emerge from the base of this contracted stem. The modified leaves may be complete leaves, as in a tulip bulb, or consist of the swollen bases of foliage leaves from the preceding season, as in the onion. Both types of leaves occur in the daffodil bulb. From the contracted stem in a bulb appears the bud from which the aerial stems bearing leaves and a flower or flower cluster develop. After the flowers have died down, the foliage leaves become larger, manufacturing food which is passed down to one or more buds in the axils of the old withering leaves of the original bulb. These new buds then swell with the food which is being stored and form new bulbs. Examples of herbs storing food in the form of bulbs are narcissi (daffodils, etc) onions, tulips, hyacinths, snowdrops, bluebells and certain lilies.

Notes

1 Because of their food-building activities, the foliage leaves of bulbs and corms should not be cut after the flowers have died but should be left until they have withered.

2 Although some corms and bulbs, *e.g.* crocus, bluebell, daffodil and snowdrop, may be left where they are in the garden, others, *e.g.* gladioli corms, Spanish iris and ixias, are better lifted and stored after their season of growth as they are not vigorous enough to withstand local conditions of frost and excessive damp.

CODE

1 Observe herbs which store food in swollen leaves or stems above ground level, *e.g.* leaf succulents and cacti.

2 Observe swollen roots used for food storage, *e.g.* taproots of carrot, turnip, beetroot, parsnip, swede; and fibrous roots of dahlia.

3 Observe swollen underground stems used for food storage, *e.g.* rhizome as on iris, corm as on crocus, stem tuber as on potato, rootstock as on primrose.

4 Observe differences between a bulb and a corm.
   (*a*) New corm forms on top of the old corm, whereas new bulbs form at the base of the old bulb.
   (*b*) Cut open bulb and corm, and observe that bulb consists mainly of swollen leaves, whereas corm consists of swollen stem. Cutting down a hyacinth bulb may expose stem with embryo flowers inside.

5 Observe swollen underground parts which have to be lifted for the winter because local conditions are too severe.

6 Plant a piece of potato with several buds about 3 inches down in a pot of garden soil. Water regularly.

7 Observe the development of leaves from the contracted stems at the tops of swollen taproots, *i.e.* cut off the tops and 'grow' in tin lids or saucers containing a little water. Carrot is an obvious example. Turnip, parsnip and swede should produce similar results.

Brief Notes on Care of Cacti

1 *Compost*: John Innes Compost No. 1, or a mixture of fibrous loam, small bits of broken brick and coarse sand.

2 *Water* twice weekly from about March to September, but not at all during winter months.

3 Transplant or re-pot in early spring. Change soil about every 2 years. Detached sections of stem may be pushed into compost at any time.

Brief Notes on Care of Leaf Succulents

1 *Compost*: as above

2 *Water* with discretion throughout the year; less in winter.

3 Transplant or re-pot as above.

Brief Notes on Indoor Bulbs and Corms

1 *Compost*: commercially prepared fibre (usually coconut fibre containing small pieces of oyster shell and charcoal, the latter keeping the mixture sweet). The mixture should

first be soaked and then pressed hard to remove surplus moisture. Press this down into bulb container to the depth at which the bulbs, resting on the fibre, just show their tips above the rim of the bowl. Space bulbs a little way apart, and press more fibre round them until almost covered. Avoid mixing varieties, because of different flowering times.

2 Store containers in a cool dark place, *e.g.* outside under pile of ashes, or indoors in a dark cupboard. Ensure good ventilation. Darkness encourages development of root system prior to development of stems, leaves and flowers.

3 Moisten fibre every ten days or so with tepid water to prevent drying out. Do not over-water, as this leads to root destruction.

4 Remove from darkness after 10 weeks or so, and grow on at room temperature.

Peat, or a composition of three parts soil, two parts peat and one part sand may be used instead of commercial mixture. Chief advantage of commercial mixture is that it does not discolour pottery bowls.

After flowering, the bulbs and corms can be planted out-of-doors where, given suitable conditions, they will establish themselves.

Various bulbs, potatoes, etc, may be grown on glasses containing water provided they are just clear of the water. As roots develop and absorb water, more water (preferably at room temperature) should be added. A piece of charcoal in the water will keep it sweet.

NOTEBOOK WORK

Answers should be along the following lines.

1 Plants are forced to die or rest if the weather becomes too dry or too cold.

2 Succulents store water in swollen leaves or swollen stems above ground.

3 The leaves of a cactus have become spines.

4 Some herbs store food below ground where the temperature does not fall too low.

5 Rhizomes, corms and rootstocks are all forms of swollen underground stems.

6 A tuber is a swelling developed on part of a root or at the end of an underground stem.

7 In a bulb, food is stored in a cluster of swollen underground leaves.

6 THE THINGS WE SEE

LUMINOUS AND NON-LUMINOUS

DEMONSTRATION MATERIAL

1 Objects to show light being emitted, *e.g.* classroom light, candle, torch

2 Objects to show transparency, *e.g.* clear glass, perspex, polythene, cellulose tape, acetate sheeting

3 Objects to show translucency, *e.g.* tracing paper, frosted glass, thin exercise book paper

SAMPLE LINK QUESTIONS

1 What is the sun? (*A star*)
2 What are stars made of? (*Hot and glowing gases*)
3 What is a flame made of? (*Burning gases*)
4 When a substance is burning, what is it changing into? (*Other substances*)
5 What do we get from burning fuels in addition to heat? (*Light*)
6 Why is it dark at night? (*Because the sun is on the other side of the earth*)
7 Why can we not see the stars during daylight? (*Because the sun outshines them*)

RELEVANT INFORMATION

The main purpose of this lesson is to show that when we say an object is visible to us, the object is either giving out light or reflecting light. The emphasis of the lesson is more on seeing than on light.

Light is a form of radiant energy. Radiant energy has a wavelike motion and travels along straight paths called rays. There is a great number of these rays, and they include x-rays, infra-red rays, ultra-violet rays, and those used by radio and radar. They all travel at the same speed (approximately 186,000 miles per second through air), but each has its own particular wavelength. Wavelength is the distance from one wave crest to the next wave crest.

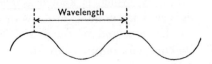

In our eyes are nerve endings which are capable of being stimulated by rays whose wavelengths fall within a certain limited range. This stimulation of nerve endings is what we term *seeing*. Thus, when we say that we can see something or that it is visible to us, what is really happening, is that we are being made aware of it by means of our sense of sight, *i.e.* our eyes and their immediate nervous connexions in the brain are reacting to one or more of these rays of energy. These particular rays are generally known as light rays, and in this book and the Pupils' Book, the term *light* is confined to them, although the rays which have shorter or longer wavelengths, *e.g.* x-rays, infra-red rays, are sometimes discussed under the heading of light, as (apart from not affecting our eyes) their behaviour is similar.

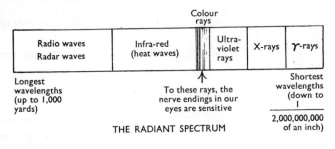

THE RADIANT SPECTRUM

Things which Give out Light Themselves

When a substance emits light itself (that is to say it could be seen on its own in the dark), it is said to be luminous. Luminosity is usually accompanied by high temperature, but this is not always so.

Luminosity without High Temperature

The general term for this is *luminescence*. An example is the property of shining after exposure to light. Luminous paints, especially prepared for use on some watch and clock dials, have this property, which is known as *phosphorescence* but which in this sense has nothing to do with phosphorus. Certain species of bacteria and of fungi and a number of animals are able to emit light (a procedure known as *bioluminescence*). Glow-worms, fireflies, deep-sea fish, and certain protozoa on the surface of the sea are amongst the best-known examples, but there are others—among them certain worms, molluscs, crustaceans and jellyfish—which are self-luminous in this way. The glow-worm is not actually a worm; it is a beetle and emits light during all four stages of its life, *i.e.* egg, larva, pupa and adult. Both male and female are able to glow, but the female (a wingless insect) has the brighter light. Deep-sea fish which possess luminous parts live at depths where light from the sun does not penetrate. Bioluminescence is due to the slow oxidation of a substance known as luciferin, which is manufactured by the plant or animal concerned. Almost all the energy resulting from this oxidation appears in the form of light. *Fluorescence* is the property possessed by certain substances, *e.g.* quinine sulphate solutions, paraffin oil and fluorescein solutions, of absorbing light of one wavelength, and in its place emitting light of another wavelength, *i.e.* colour. Unlike phosphorescence, the phenomenon ceases immediately the source of light is cut off. The inside of a cathode ray tube, as used in a television or radar set, is coated with a fluorescent paint which emits light when bombarded with electrons.

Luminosity at High Temperatures

Most things that give out light give out heat at the same time, *i.e.* they are hot enough to glow, or they are burning. The general term for this is *incandescence*. Many solids, such as a poker, a piece of rock or an old-fashioned gas mantle, can be heated to the temperature at which they eventually emit light. The filament in an electric light bulb and the element of an electric fire are both lengths of metal wire which become hot enough to glow owing to the resistance which they offer to an electric current passing through them. The phrase *in the limelight* comes from the days when a piece of lime (calcium oxide) was heated until it became sufficiently hot to give out a whitish light which could be reflected as a spotlight on to an actor on a stage. A number of substances can be made hot enough to glow in the liquid form, *i.e.* at temperatures below those at which they are completely converted into gas. Molten iron and molten lava are liquids which are hot enough to glow. We see the sun itself and other stars because they consist of gases which are hot enough to glow. In daylight we do not see the other stars because the light from the sun outshines them.

When a substance is burning, it is also incandescent. Burning is the term given to any chemical reaction during which heat and light are evolved. Generally (but not always), burning involves a chemical reaction of something with oxygen. A piece of red-hot wood and a piece of red-hot coal are burning. A flame itself is generally understood to consist of burning gases, although the colour of the flame may be influenced by the presence of glowing particles of solid, *e.g.* carbon.

Things which Reflect Light

Our eyes can be sensitive to non-luminous bodies only when they are reflecting light. We become aware of them only when some of the light which they reflect reaches our eyes. Those that we see in daylight are reflecting light from the sun. As they give out no light of their own, they cannot be seen in darkness. They are visible only when light from some luminous body falls on them, *i.e.* when they are illuminated. The objects in a darkened room become apparent only when a light is switched on. They remain apparent only for as long as the light illuminates them. Such things as these—the circle of faces round the flickering light from a camp fire, the rocky wall of a cave revealed by the light from a torch, a cat's eye on the road at night, picked out for a moment by a headlight—can be sensed by our eyes only while there is light to be reflected.

At night a scene may reflect light from the moon, but the moon has no light of its own. We see the moon only because it reflects light from the sun; and moonlight, therefore, is sunlight reflected by the moon to the earth. The moon also reflects light from the earth (earthshine). Earthshine is light which the earth itself reflects from the sun. This reflection of earthshine results in the darkened part of the moon being faintly visible when only a thin crescent of the sun's reflected light can be seen. The darkened portion of the moon is not due to a shadow of the earth, as is sometimes supposed, but due to the angle from which we see the light which the moon is reflecting from the sun. The shadow of the earth across the moon appears only during an eclipse of the moon by the earth.

There are three possible reactions of a non-luminous object to that part of the radiant spectrum which we term light. They are:

1 Reflection,   2 Absorption,   3 Transmission.

If an object which is reflecting light also transmits some of it, *i.e.* permits its passage, then it is possible to see through the object. If the passage of light is permitted in such a way that the object can be seen through clearly, then the object is transparent. Clear glass and clear water are examples. If the passage of light is permitted in such a way that an object cannot be seen through clearly, then it is translucent. Frosted glass, tracing

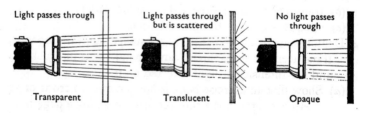

| Light passes through | Light passes through but is scattered | No light passes through |
| Transparent | Translucent | Opaque |

paper and many lampshades are examples. If an object is neither transparent nor translucent, *i.e.* it does not permit the passage of any light, it is opaque. Whether a particular object appears transparent, translucent or opaque may depend on various factors, *e.g.* the brightness and nature of the light illuminating it and the thickness of the actual substance. A wad of paper held in front of an electric light bulb may appear opaque, whereas a thin sheet of the same material would appear translucent.

Because our eyes are a little distance apart, each receives a slightly different picture. These two pictures are co-ordinated by the brain, so that we get a three-dimensional impression. This enables us to form an estimate of the relative distances of different things. This advantage diminishes with distance, however, which is why distant objects tend to have a flat appearance. The sun and the moon, for example, appear as flat discs instead of as spheres. A stereoscope is a device which enables two similar pictures to be presented, one to each eye, in such a way that the brain is able to co-ordinate them and form a three-dimensional impression.

CODE

1 Observe the sources of light in the classroom, *e.g.* sunlight alone, or electric light.
2 Observe examples of light being given out
   (*a*) by something burning, *e.g.* candle flame, lighted match;
   (*b*) by something hot enough to glow without burning, *e.g.* the filament in a torch bulb or electric light bulb.
3 Observe which things in the room appear to be
   (*a*) transparent, *e.g.* clear glass, water, perspex, polythene, cellulose tape, acetate sheeting;
   (*b*) translucent, *e.g.* frosted glass, tracing paper;
   (*c*) opaque, *e.g.* most things in the room.
4 Demonstrate that whether a substance appears opaque, translucent or transparent can depend upon its thickness and the intensity of light directed on it.
   (*a*) Show that an exercise book is opaque even in front of an electric light, but a thin section, *i.e.* a single page from

the book, is translucent when placed in front of an electric light. (This principle of directing a strong light on to a thin slice is used in microscope work.)

(b) A single thin sheet of polythene is transparent in ordinary light, a thickness of a few sheets together appears translucent, and a thickness of a larger number of sheets appears opaque.

5 Experiment to show that each eye sees its own picture.

(a) Close the left eye. Hold up one finger in front of the right eye, and sight it on some object beyond the finger—as in sighting a rifle.

(b) Now close the right eye, and open the left. Observe that the finger is no longer in line with the object beyond it. By closing and opening each eye alternately, the finger can be made to give the impression of moving from side to side.

6 The use of two eyes enables us to obtain a three-dimensional picture instead of a flat picture, and so to judge the relative distances of different objects. Experiment to show that the view obtained by one eye does not enable us to judge distance as well as the combined view obtained by two eyes.

Close one eye, and place a pencil, point uppermost, in a vertical position on the desk. Still with the eye closed, try to bring the point of a second pencil vertically down to touch the point of the first. Repeat with both eyes open.

7 Experiment to show how an illusion can be obtained as a result of the different views obtained by the eyes.

(a) *Floating finger tips.* Hold both hands up in front of the face, point the two index fingers towards one another, and then bring their tips together. Look directly at the finger tips. Separate the tips by about half an inch, and then look through the gap at something beyond the fingers. Observe that there now appears to be a joined pair of finger tips floating in the gap.

(b) *Looking through a hole in a hand.* Roll a sheet of paper into a tube. (A sheet about 8″ long is suitable.) Place this tube to one eye, and look through it towards the light. Now place the edge of the other hand against the side of the tube, and about half way along. With both eyes open, observe the illusion of looking through a hole in the hand.

NOTEBOOK WORK

Answers should be along the following lines.

1 When we see a thing, either it is giving out light itself, or it is reflecting light given out by something else.
2 (*a*) When something is luminous, it is giving out light itself.
  (*b*) A non-luminous thing can be seen only when it is reflecting light from something else.
  (*c*) If we can see through something clearly, we say it is transparent.
  (*d*) When we can see through something, but only faintly, we say it is translucent.
  (*e*) Anything which we cannot see through at all is said to be opaque.

7) THE STRAIGHT PATHS OF LIGHT

SHADOWS AND REFLECTIONS

DEMONSTRATION MATERIAL

Drinking straws; candles, sheets of white paper, plasticine; an old spoon, jar of water; mirrors—separate and hinged together with tape; a periscope; a kaleidoscope, *e.g.* as sold as toys

SAMPLE LINK QUESTIONS

1 When we see a thing, it is for one of two reasons. What are they? (*Either it is giving out light itself, or it is reflecting light given out by something else*)
2 When something is giving out light itself, what is it said to be? (*Luminous*)
3 Are most of the luminous things we see at high temperatures or low temperatures? (*High temperatures*)

4 Name some things which are luminous at low temperatures. (*Luminous paint, glow-worm, deep-sea fish*)

5 Are the gases of which a star is made hot enough to burn or hot enough to glow? (*Hot enough to glow*)

6 What are the only times that non-luminous things can be seen? (*When they are reflecting light*)

7 What is the difference between the light from the sun and the light from the moon? (*Light from the sun is given out by the sun. Light from the moon is light from the sun reflected by the moon*)

8 When something lets enough light through for us to see through it clearly, what is it said to be? (*Transparent*)

9 If something can be seen through, but not clearly, what is it said to be? (*Translucent*)

10 When we can see something without being able to see through it what is it said to be? (*Opaque*)

RELEVANT INFORMATION

The main points of this lesson are that

1 light travels along straight paths;

2 shadows are caused by objects in the light's path;

3 the way an object reflects light depends on its surface;

4 the reflection of an object in a mirror is called an image;

5 we can see the reflection of an image just as we can see the reflection of an object.

Light from a luminous object is radiated in all directions along straight paths. Similarly the light which is reflected by non-luminous objects is reflected along straight paths. This is evident when something opaque is placed between the eye of an observer and a luminous object. The object is cut off from view, because light radiated by it cannot curve round the obstruction and reach the eye. We have visual evidence that light is radiated along straight paths when we see a beam of light, *e.g.* the beam from a torch, searchlight, lighthouse or car headlight at night, or a sunbeam slanting through a gap in the clouds or through the keyhole of a partly darkened room.

When we say that we see a beam of light, we do not actually see light. The phenomenon of the beam is due to particles which are in the light's path being illuminated by the light which strikes them, *i.e.* the nerve endings in our eyes are being stimulated by the rays which are reflected by those particles.

It is because light is radiated along straight paths that we see shadows—dark patches resulting from something obstructing the passage of part of the light. The length of a shadow depends on the angle of the source of light in relation to the object. Shadows which are due to the obstruction of the sun's light lengthen in the evening as the sun sinks lower in the sky. Similarly the shadow of, say, a post will be longer at midday in winter than it will be at midday in summer, because the sun is lower in the sky at midday in winter. Long ago men working in the fields judged the time by watching the changing length of the shadow cast by an upright stick in the ground. A sundial is a device for measuring apparent solar time by means of shadow. It consists of a gnomon (the rod which casts the shadow), and a dial marked in divisions to represent the hours. Sundials are more ornamental than useful. The gnomon has to be at the correct angle, the dial in a suitable position, the sun has to be shining, and artificial summertime has to be allowed for.

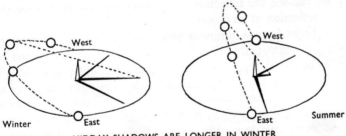

MIDDAY SHADOWS ARE LONGER IN WINTER

An eclipse of the sun is due to the moon passing between the sun and the earth in such a position that it causes a shadow on the earth. The eclipse is seen from that part of the earth which is in the moon's shadow. An eclipse of the moon is due to the earth being in such a position between the sun and the

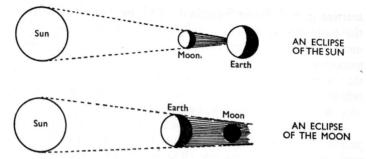

AN ECLIPSE
OF THE SUN

AN ECLIPSE
OF THE MOON

moon that the earth's shadow appears across the moon. This is not the same as seeing the 'old moon in the new moon's arms'. On such an occasion, we see a brilliant new moon, together with the ghostly outline of the full moon. Then, the sun, moon and earth are so positioned that the dark part of the moon facing the earth is being faintly illuminated by earthshine, *i.e.* sunlight being reflected from the earth to the moon. Eclipses are only

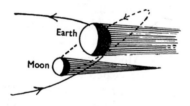

THE MOON'S ORBIT IS
NOT IN THE SAME PLANE
AS THE EARTH'S ORBIT

occasional. This is because the moon's orbit is not in the same plane as that of the earth.

The manner in which an object reflects light depends on its surface. A rough surface reflects the light unevenly, *i.e.* it

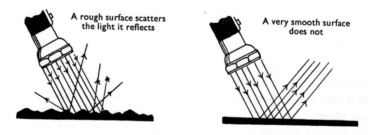

A rough surface scatters
the light it reflects

A very smooth surface
does not

scatters it in different directions. The smoother the surface, the more evenly the light is reflected. A wet road shines more than a dry road because the film of water provides a smoother surface which therefore reflects the light more evenly than a rough dry surface. A sufficiently smooth surface will reflect light evenly enough for us to see the reflections of objects clearly. We call these reflections images.

The light reflected from the smooth flat surfaces of transparent substances such as clear glass and still water may be sufficient to provide images. The clarity of such images is influenced by the relative intensity of the light coming from the object. Thus an image is very clear in a still pool on a sunny day when the object is reflecting plenty of light from the sun. The clarity of the image is also influenced by the background against which it is observed. For example, an image that is faint against a light background may be much clearer against a dark background. The image of a passenger's face may be observed faintly in a train or bus window against the details of the passing scene during daylight, but is more apparent at night.

Images are often apparent in smooth metal surfaces, and the first mirrors are supposed to have been made of bronze with a flat, highly polished surface. Modern mirrors are made of thin polished glass with one surface coated with a fine even layer of silver or some other suitable metal. The back of this layer is then varnished and painted. The metal layer provides the reflecting surface. The glass enables it to remain smooth and rigid.

A mirror image is an optical illusion. When seen in a flat (plane) mirror, it appears to be as far behind the mirror as the object is in front. It is also reversed in such a way that it bears to the object the same relation as a right hand does to a left hand.

Just as the light from an object can be reflected from one mirror, so the light from its image can be reflected from a second mirror. The two mirrors used in a periscope are set so that each can reflect, at an angle of 90°, the light received from the other. Essentially, such a periscope consists of a tube with the mirrors at opposite ends, each being at an angle of 45° to the main axis of the tube. Each mirror has an opening opposite to its reflecting face, so that the eye of an observer sees in one mirror the reflection of the image produced by the other mirror. A periscope enables an observer to view objects which are above eye level and situated so that direct vision is obstructed in some way. In the best periscopes, *e.g.* those used on submarines and on tanks, glass prisms are used in place of mirrors.

If two mirrors are placed together at an angle to each other, each will produce an image of any object which is between them. If the angle is narrow enough, an observer will see in each mirror, not only an image of the object, but also the reflection of the image produced by the other mirror. As the angle between the mirrors is made narrower, the observer sees even more reflections of images. A kaleidoscope uses this phenomenon to produce symmetrical patterns from these repeated images.

CODE

1 Experiment to show that light travels along straight paths,
    (*a*) with drinking straws as suggested in the Pupils' Book,
    (*b*) by discovering the three ways to avoid seeing a luminous object which is in front of you (*e.g.* candle flame or electric light) without actually looking away from it. The three ways are to shut your eyes, to extinguish the light, or to put something large and opaque between the source of light and the eyes. The point is that light does not curve round the intervening object.

2 Experiment to show that shadows are caused by something which is in the path of light.
    (*a*) Light a candle. Hold a sheet of plain white paper a short distance from it, and place suitable objects in between, *e.g.* a ball of plasticine on the end of a pencil. Observe different ways in which the shadow can be altered by moving the object.
    (*b*) Observe shadows in the room. Discover the source of light which is responsible for them, and find out how the shadows may be altered or eliminated.

84

3 Demonstrate that the way an object reflects light depends on the smoothness of its surface.

Hold the bowl of an old spoon in a candle flame until black. The soot provides a rough surface. Now dip the spoon in a jar of water, and observe that its bowl now appears silver. This is due to the fact that tiny bubbles of air trapped between the particles of carbon provide a smooth surface which reflects light so well that the bowl appears to shine.

4 Observe surfaces in the room from which light is reflected evenly enough to provide a reasonable image, e.g. the glass front of a cupboard, a window, shiny tin lids or other metal surfaces.

5 Experiment to show that the image seen in a flat mirror is the reverse of the object.

(a) Observe that the image of the palm of one hand in a mirror is similar to the actual palm of the other hand.

(b) Using pen and ink, print name on writing paper and blot quickly. Hold writing paper to mirror and observe how printing is reversed. Hold blotting paper impression to mirror, and observe that this is no longer reversed.

6 Experiment to find how mirrors may be used to obtain reflections of images.

(a) Place two mirrors (the larger the better) a short distance apart and directly facing each other. Put an object, e.g. a toy, between them. Observe, in each mirror, an image and a series of reflections of images.

(b) Use a periscope to see over the top of a table or screen.

(c) (i) Hinge two mirrors together with a strip of tape (as shown in the Pupils' Book). Place a suitable object, e.g. toy figure or a piece of coloured chalk, in front of them.

(ii) Angle the mirrors slightly so that only the image of the object is seen in each mirror.

(iii) Narrow the angle (to 90°) until one reflection of an image is seen in each.

(iv) Narrow the angle further until two reflections of images are seen.

(v) Continue to narrow the angle, observing the increase in the number of reflections of images.

(*d*) Use a kaleidoscope (*e.g.* as sold as toys) to observe the patterns obtained from object, two images, and a number of reflections of images. Look through the bottom of the kaleidoscope to see how the two mirrors are positioned.

NOTEBOOK WORK

Answers should be along the following lines.

1 A beam of light shows that light travels along straight paths.

2 Shadows are caused by things which are in the path of the light.

3 A mirror image is reversed.

4 (*a*) Two mirrors are used in a periscope so that we can see a reflection of an image.

(*b*) Two mirrors are used in a kaleidoscope so that we can see an object, its images, and the reflections of its images.

8 THE SOUNDS WE HEAR

VIBRATIONS AND SOUNDS

DEMONSTRATION MATERIAL

Elastic bands; tuning fork, table-tennis ball; metal or wooden ruler, or hacksaw blade, or dinner knife or nail file

SAMPLE LINK QUESTIONS

1 What are the three kinds of things in the world? (*Alive, dead, never alive*)

2 What are the three forms of never-alive things? (*Solid, liquid, gas*)

3 How does a gas differ from a solid and a liquid? (*A gas has neither size nor shape*)

4 Which is the commonest mixture of gases? (*Air*)
5 What do we call the tiniest possible part of a never-alive
  thing which can exist on its own? (*A molecule*)
6 What are the two main ways in which we may sense the
  molecules of something? (*By tasting and by smelling*)
7 How else may we sense things apart from tasting and smelling?
  (*By seeing, feeling and hearing*)
8 When we see a thing it is for one of two reasons. What are
  they? (*Either it is giving out light itself, or it is reflecting
  light given out by something else*)
9 What can you sometimes feel when you pick up a purring
  cat?

RELEVANT INFORMATION

The main points of this lesson are that
1 sound is caused by something vibrating;
2 big vibrations cause loud sounds, and little vibrations cause
  soft sounds;
3 quick vibrations cause high notes, and slow vibrations cause
  low notes.

Human beings interpret their physical surroundings by
means of five senses—by feeling, tasting, smelling, seeing and
hearing. Human ears are organs which are sensitive to particular to-and-fro movements of molecules. These particular
movements may occur in solids, liquids or gases and are known
as vibrations.

Sometimes it is possible to *feel*, as well as hear, that something is vibrating. For example, a passenger at the front on the
top deck of a bus may feel vibrations through his feet when the
driver sounds the horn. More commonly vibrations are felt
when you touch a washing machine, a refrigerator, a piano, or a
purring cat, and sometimes when you touch a radio or television
set. Occasionally it is possible to *see* that an object which is the
source of a sound is vibrating. Examples are when an elastic
band is twanged, or when, say, a ruler is held on a table with part
of the length projecting, and flipped.

Mostly, however, the vibrations responsible for the sounds
we hear are sensed by the ears alone. Every sound we hear is

caused by vibration—the singing of telegraph wires in the wind, the blast of an explosion, the roar of surf, the discordant hub-bub of a busy city, the rustling of paper, the scream of a seagull, the whirr of machinery, the music of a band, the noise of children in a playground, and the harsh jangling of a bell.

If a vibrating object is to serve as a source of sound to the ear, either it must be in direct contact with the ear, or it must set into vibrating motion whatever medium intervenes between it and the ear. Most of the sounds we hear are due to some vibrating object causing the air itself to vibrate. To take a simple example: if the face of a gong is struck, it moves out-wards, compressing the layer of molecules of air in contact with it. This in turn compresses the next adjacent layer of molecules, and so the compressed area (compression) is passed on, not unlike the way in which a line of stationary railway trucks bump one another if the end one is suddenly pushed. The next movement of the gong face is inwards past its initial position of rest to the limit of its movement. This causes the molecules of the layer of air in contact with it to spread out and results in a rarefied area. This in turn allows the next adjacent layer of molecules to spread out, and so the rarefied area (rare-faction) is passed on in the wake of the compressed area. The alternate pushing and pulling of the air, resulting in com-pressions and rarefactions, constitutes a sound wave. It is noteworthy that it is the compressions and rarefactions which travel away from the vibrating source, not the molecules of air themselves; they merely oscillate about their original positions. In a similar way, if a stone is dropped into still water, ripples travel outwards from the point where the stone strikes, but the water itself does not flow, so that a cork floating on the surface would merely bob up and down and would not be carried along.

If vibrations are to be detected, they have to be made perceptible to the senses by some kind of receiver. On human beings and other mammals, these receivers take the form of ears. Vibrations entering a human ear, pass along the passage leading from the outer ear, and cause the membrane known as the eardrum to vibrate. From the eardrum, these vibrations are transmitted across the middle ear by means of three small contacting bones, to the inner ear, where they stimulate the sensitive endings of nerves which are connected to the brain. It is the brain which interprets them as sound. Possession of two ears enables a human being to ascertain the direction from which the vibrations approach.

Different Kinds of Vibrations Cause Different Kinds of Sounds

Sounds differ in quality, loudness and pitch.

The *quality* of a sound is its character, and this depends on the shape of vibrations produced. This in turn depends on the voice or instrument producing the vibrations. For example, middle C on two different pianos have the same pitch and can be sounded just as loudly as one another, but they may differ in quality—also known as *timbre*.

The *loudness* or intensity of a sound depends on the size of the vibrations. The bigger the vibration, the louder the sound; the smaller the vibration, the softer the sound. If you strike a drum hard, the skin of the drum moves through a greater distance than if you strike it gently. In consequence, the vibration and the resulting compression wave are bigger, and the sound which is heard is louder. Similarly if you drop a tiny pebble into a still pool, the ripples are smaller than they would be if you dropped in a large boulder. Just as the ripples on a pond become shallower as they spread out from their source, so compression waves gradually fade out as they travel away from the source of vibration. Consequently, the greater the distance of the listener, the fainter the sound he hears. Sound also grows fainter as the vibrations become smaller. The vibrations of the drum, for example, gradually become smaller until they cease so that, for the listener, the sound gradually fades or dies down. It is possible, of course, for vibrations to be too small for us to be sensitive to them. A record player or a tape recorder can be turned down to the point where the vibrations continue but sound is no longer heard.

The *pitch* of a sound depends on the speed of the vibrations, and sounds caused by different speeds of vibrations are interpreted as high notes and low notes accordingly. The faster an object vibrates, the greater the number of compression waves per second, *i.e.* the more frequently they occur. The higher the *frequency*, the higher the note is pitched; and the lower the frequency, the lower the note is pitched. In other words, quick vibrations cause high notes, and slow vibrations cause low notes. Pulling the edge of a card across the teeth of a comb at different speeds produces different notes. If the card is pulled slowly, it vibrates at a slower speed and the note is lower. If it is pulled quickly, it vibrates at a faster speed and the note is higher.

When an object or a portion of an object vibrates, the actual speed of the vibrations is influenced by three factors, namely the length of the section which is vibrating, the thickness of that section, and its tension.

If two unequal *lengths* of the same material, having the same thickness and tension, are made to vibrate, the shorter length will vibrate more quickly, and produce the higher note.

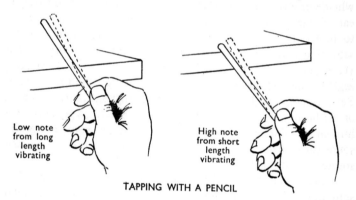

Low note
from long
length
vibrating

High note
from short
length
vibrating

TAPPING WITH A PENCIL

On a piano, high notes are obtained from short wires, and low notes from long wires. On a double bass the strings are longer than on a violin, and it produces lower notes than a violin's. A xylophone is a good example of an instrument on which the lowest notes are obtained from the longest lengths and the highest from the shortest. In wind instruments, long columns of vibrating air give lower notes than short columns of vibrating air. Blowing across the top of a cycle pump with the handle in different positions demonstrates this.

If two unequal *thicknesses* of the same material, having the same length and tension, are made to vibrate, the thinner of the two will produce the higher note. On a stringed instrument, the thinnest string is used for the highest notes, and the thickest string for the lowest notes.

If two sections of the same material, having the same length and thickness, are made to vibrate, the one with the greater *tension* will produce the higher note. If, for example, an elastic band is stretched and then plucked, it will vibrate and produce a note. If it is stretched farther and plucked, the note will be higher because the tension will be greater. On instruments using strings or wires, higher notes can be obtained by tightening the strings, and lower notes by slackening the strings. Stringed instruments are tuned by tightening or slackening the strings.

Dogs are able to hear higher notes than humans, and a dog whistle produces a note which is too high for the average human ear. Some vibrations are too slow and others too fast for humans to interpret as sounds. The fluttering wings of a butterfly vibrate too slowly to affect the human eardrum, whereas the very rapid vibrations of a bat's vocal cords when it emits a high-pitched squeak are too rapid for most people to interpret. Sensitivity in the human ear decreases with age, and the limits of audibility vary with different individuals, but very few human ears can detect vibrations below 20 per second (*e.g.* the sound of a deep growl), or above 30,000 per second (*e.g.* the sound of a shrill whine).

Sounds higher in pitch than human ears can detect are sometimes called supersonic sounds, but are better termed ultrasonic sounds. Speeds which are faster than the vibrations can be transmitted through the air are known as supersonic speeds. The sonic bang (due to an aircraft 'breaking the sound barrier') is caused by a shock wave passing through the air to the ear. The shock wave is set up when the air in front of the aircraft is considerably compressed owing to the great speed at which it is flying. The bang which is heard when a balloon or paper bag is burst is also caused by a shock wave set up by compressed air.

CODE

1 Experiment to show that sound is caused by something vibrating.

(a) Stretch a rubber band and twang it. Observe that the sound ceases as the vibration ceases.

(b) Strike a tuning fork, and with the vibrating end, gently touch a suspended table-tennis ball. The ball may be suspended by fastening with cellulose tape to the end of a length of thread.

(c) The vibrations may be felt if the end of a vibrating tuning fork just touches a finger nail. (Children should not be allowed to place a tuning fork to their teeth, as the vibrations may damage the enamel.)

2 Experiment to show that big vibrations cause loud sounds, and little vibrations cause soft sounds.

(a) Hold a wooden or a flat metal ruler firmly on a table or desk so that about 8 inches projects over the edge. Flip the projecting end so as to observe big vibrations. Flip again so as to observe little vibrations. Observe that the sound is louder on the first occasion.

(b) Pluck an elastic band so as to obtain big vibrations, and again so as to obtain small vibrations. Observe the difference in sound.

(c) Place a number of lightweight objects, e.g. tiny balls of paper, on a table or desk. Tap the surface gently, and observe no apparent movement of the objects. Then strike a heavy blow, and observe how the objects jump because of the bigger vibrations.

3 Experiment to show that quick vibrations give high notes, and sLOW vibrations give LOW notes.

Hold a hacksaw blade, ruler, nail file, or the blade of a dinner knife firmly against a table or desk so that a short length projects. Flip, and observe the speed of vibration and the note. Repeat with a longer length projecting, and observe that the vibrations are slower, and that the note is lower.

Where rulers are used for these experiments, it is better, for obvious reasons, if only ONE is heard at a time.

92

4 Observe examples of the speed of vibration being controlled by the tension, length or thickness of the vibrating material.

(*a*) Stretch an elastic band across an open tin and pluck. Pull the band tighter and pluck again. Observe that the note is higher when tension is increased. Tightening a violin string has the same effect.

(*b*) Stretch an elastic band across an open tin and pluck. Now grip the band in the middle and pluck again. Observe that the note is higher when the length of vibrating material is less. The same effect is obtained when playing a violin by placing the fingers in different positions on the string.

(*c*) Stretch a thin elastic band and a thick elastic band across the tin so that the tension is about the same. The two bands should be about the same length to begin with. Pluck each, and observe that the note obtained from the thicker band is lower, *i.e.* the thicker the vibrating material, the slower the vibrations. The same effect is obtained on stringed instruments, where thicker strings are used for the lowest notes.

(*d*) Construct a crude musical instrument. See the diagrams overleaf for examples showing how different lengths may be used to obtain different notes.

NOTEBOOK WORK

Answers should be along the following lines.

(*a*) Every sound is caused by vibration.
(*b*) A loud sound is caused by big vibrations.
(*c*) A soft sound is caused by little vibrations.
(*d*) A high note is caused by quick vibrations.
(*e*) A low note is caused by slow vibrations.

SOLUTIONS TO PUZZLES

1 The drum on which the seeds are bouncing higher would be making the louder sound, as the vibrations would be bigger.
2 The short lengths vibrate faster.

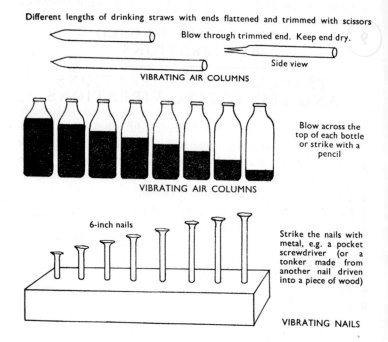

Different lengths of drinking straws with ends flattened and trimmed with scissors

Blow through trimmed end. Keep end dry.

Side view

VIBRATING AIR COLUMNS

Blow across the top of each bottle or strike with a pencil

VIBRATING AIR COLUMNS

6-inch nails

Strike the nails with metal, e.g. a pocket screwdriver (or a tonker made from another nail driven into a piece of wood)

VIBRATING NAILS

Notes

1 The bottles should be as similar as possible. The height of water determines the length of the air column, *e.g.* the bottle containing the most water has the shortest air column and should therefore produce the highest note.

2 Blowing across the top of a bottle containing water produces a lower note than if the bottle is tapped. This is because in the first instance a column of air is vibrating, whereas in the second instance the bottle is the initial source of vibration.

3 Neither bottles nor nails are likely to be identical in tension and thickness, and it will usually be necessary to make adjustments to compensate for individual differences.

SOUNDS ARE CAUSED BY VIBRATIONS

TRANSMITTING VIBRATIONS AND REFLECTING VIBRATIONS

DEMONSTRATION MATERIAL

As many as possible of the following groups:

1 Tuning fork and a number of hard solid objects, *e.g.* empty jars, tins, bottles
2 Two spoons or forks, a length of string
3 Watch, jam jar, soft material to stuff jar
4 Two cardboard tubes, a cushion or thick garment
5 Material for making a simple telephone, *e.g.* thin string or wire, small empty cocoa tins, nails or buttons
6 Plastic funnels, plastic or rubber tubing, *e.g.* bunsen tubing
7 Empty bucket
8 Ruler

SAMPLE LINK QUESTIONS

1 What are the five ways in which we sense things? (*By feeling, tasting, smelling, seeing and hearing*)
2 What causes sound? (*Something vibrating*)
3 Most of the sounds we hear are caused by something making the air vibrate. What happens to make us become aware of these vibrations as sound? (*The vibrating air makes the eardrum vibrate*)
4 What kind of vibrations cause loud sounds? (*Big vibrations*)
5 What kind of vibrations cause soft sounds? (*Little vibrations*)
6 As the vibrations which are causing a particular sound become smaller what happens to the sound we hear? (*It becomes softer*)
7 What kind of vibrations cause high notes? (*Quick vibrations*)
8 What kind of vibrations cause low notes? (*Slow vibrations*)
9 Why can you hear a sound from the vibrating wings of a bee, but not from the vibrating wings of a butterfly? (*The*

vibrations of a butterfly's wings are too slow to affect our eardrums)

10 Which will reflect light better—a rough surface or a smooth surface? (*A smooth surface*)

The main points of this lesson are that

1 vibrations can be transmitted through solids, liquids and gases;

2 vibrations can be reflected from surfaces.

When a vibrating object is in contact with the air, it causes the surrounding molecules of air to move rhythmically forward and backward. These molecules of air affect the adjoining molecules of air, and so the movement is transmitted as a compression wave. Similarly a vibrating object can set up compression waves in other solids, liquids or gases with which it is in contact. Such compression waves can be transmitted in all directions.

Transmission through Solids

Primitive tribesmen—either hunting or being hunted—have been known to detect animals at a considerable distance by placing their ears to the ground so as to become aware of the vibrations being transmitted through the solid earth. The sound of distant tapping on iron railings, steel girders and metal pipes can be heard by placing an ear to the metal. A plumber, trying to locate an underground burst, may detect the sound of water running through the pipe by placing one end of a piece of wood to the pipe and the other end to his ear. Vibrations can also be transmitted to the inner ear through the bones of the skull. Even when the ears are plugged with cotton wool, it is possible to hear the tapping of a pencil on the teeth or the ticking of a watch held against the forehead.

Transmission through Liquids

Fish in particular are sensitive to vibrations transmitted through water. It is inadvisable to tap on the sides of an aquarium, for the effect on a fish can be compared to striking a human being on the head with a brick. Some children will have heard sounds under water, *e.g.* when their ears have been below the surface of the water in a swimming bath and a coin has struck the tiled bottom of the bath.

For vibrations to be transmitted in the form of compression waves, it is always necessary for them to have a contacting medium to be transmitted through. If there were nothing in contact with a vibrating object, there would be nothing in which compression waves could be set up, nothing would reach the eardrums, and consequently no sound would be heard. This is often illustrated by the well-known experiment of suspending a vibrating bell inside a jar from which the air has been evacuated. The bell is seen to be ringing without being heard.

How efficiently or how quickly vibrations are transmitted through a medium depends on various factors, such as the continuity of the medium, its temperature, density, the weight of its molecules, and their resistance to compression. The denser a particular medium, *i.e.* the more closely the molecules are packed together, the more intensely the vibrations are transmitted. For men working in compressed air, *e.g.* in a caisson on the bottom of a river bed, sounds are easier to hear; whereas to men working in rarefied air, *e.g.* at high altitudes, sounds are more difficult to hear.

How far a compression wave is transmitted depends on how rapidly it is absorbed by the solid, liquid or gas through which it is travelling. Materials such as sawdust, cotton wool, rubber, felt, or a pillow filled with feathers are poor transmitters. In general, transmission through liquids is better than through gases, and transmission through hard and firm solids is best of all.

The expression 'sound is conducted' is often used for 'vibrations are transmitted'. It should be remembered that vibrations are not conducted in the sense that heat or electricity is conducted, and that sound is only the term we give to those vibrations which are sensed by the ears.

When a compression wave encounters a surface, the following can occur.

97

1 Transmission through the surface
2 Reflection
3 Absorption
4 The object whose surface is encountered may itself be forced to vibrate by the compression wave. This is what happens to an eardrum.

Transmission

Although vibrations may be transmitted easily from, say, one hard solid to another hard solid, they are not easily transmitted from one medium to another, e.g. from solid to liquid, or from liquid to gas. The Red Indian has to put his ear to the ground to listen for the sound of distant hoofbeats being transmitted through the solid earth. Without doing so, he will not be aware of them, because vibrations are not easily transmitted from ground to air. Similarly, the plumber with his ear to the length of wood will be aware of the vibrations transmitted from the solid metal of the pipe via the solid wood, but if he removes his ear, he will no longer hear the sound of running water, because the vibrations will not easily be transmitted from solid to air.

Reflection

A ball will bounce better from a hard surface than from a soft one. A number of spherical balls travelling along parallel paths will, if they strike a smooth surface, bounce off along parallel paths. If they strike a rough surface, they will bounce in a variety of different directions. The same may be said of the molecules in a compression wave, i.e. that they bounce better from hard surfaces than from soft ones, and more evenly from smooth surfaces than from rough ones. Thus, generally speaking, smooth hard surfaces are the best reflectors, and soft rough surfaces, such as those of clothing, are the best absorbers.

If any vibrations which have been reflected are transmitted to our ears, they may cause us to hear extra sound. Three general effects of reflected vibrations are:

1 *to cause the sound to be amplified*, i.e. *made louder*. Here a reflected compression wave strikes the eardrum while it is still

vibrating from the effects of a direct compression wave, thus accentuating the vibrations of the eardrum. This is something like giving a child on a swing a push in order to make it swing higher. The sounds we hear when someone speaks in a room are caused by vibrations from the speaker plus vibrations reflected from various surfaces in the room, *e.g.* walls, ceiling and floor. This is why a voice sounds louder in a room than in the open air, and also why songs sound better when sung in a tiled bathroom.

2 *to cause the sound to be intensified*, i.e. *to be transmitted farther*. In a megaphone, a doctor's stethoscope or a speaking tube, vibrations are reflected from side to side of the interior so that their energy tends to be concentrated in one direction, instead of spreading out equally in all directions. They are transmitted more intensely in that direction, so that they travel a greater distance before fading out.

3 *to cause the sound to be repeated*. The farther away the reflecting surface, the farther the vibrations have to travel before and after being reflected. At a distance, the reflected vibrations arrive noticeably later than those which have been

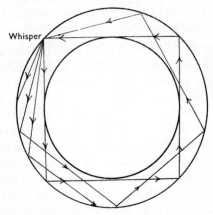

In a whispering gallery, e.g. in St Paul's Cathedral, vibrations are reflected from point to point round the circular wall and so returned to the whisperer

directly transmitted, so that, instead of amplifying the sound, they cause it to be repeated. We call this an echo. Echoes are sometimes heard in large buildings such as churches and old theatres where the sound of a footfall or a speaker's voice is repeated a fraction of a second after it has first been heard. Generally a reflecting surface needs to be over 56 feet away for a distinctly separate sound to be heard.

When there is more than one surface from which vibrations can be reflected, *e.g.* the inner surface of a tunnel, or the steep sides of a narrow gorge, then a multiple echo can result. Some of the reflected vibrations are themselves reflected. The rumble of a train in a tunnel is an example of multiple echoes. A clap of thunder may develop into a long peal if vibrations are reflected to and fro. As vibrations—like light—can be absorbed as well as reflected, echoes grow fainter with each rebound.

Absorption

The rate of absorption depends on various factors such as the density of the transmitting substance. As most of the sounds we hear result from compression waves transmitted through the air, we customarily compare absorption with absorption by the air. The study of acoustics is concerned with absorption. Materials which are good absorbers of transmitted vibrations depend in general on porosity. Examples of good absorbers are cork, various textiles and materials with specially made perforations or fissures. It is because soft rough surfaces such as clothing are good absorbers that a speaker's voice which would echo in a large empty hall does not echo in the same hall filled with people.

Enforced Vibration of the Object which the Compression Wave Encounters

In certain circumstances an object can be made to vibrate by compression waves striking it. When this happens, the vibrating object will set up its own compression waves in the surrounding medium, *e.g.* air, so that a sound may be heard from it. Examples of this are when a violin or piano string are made to 'vibrate in sympathy', or when a wine glass is made to shake itself to pieces. Sounding boxes, sounding boards, reverberation and resonance are all associated with reflection or enforced vibrations.

Music and Noise

Vibrations which occur at regular intervals tend to be pleasing to the ear, and are responsible for the sounds we describe as musical. On the other hand, vibrations which do not occur at regular intervals, *e.g.* those set up by a pneumatic drill, tend to be displeasing to the ear, and are referred to generally as noise. The purpose of most musical instruments is to cause regular vibrations in the air.

CODE

1 Demonstrate how a vibrating object can cause something which it touches to vibrate.

(*a*) Arrange a number of different hard solid objects, *e.g.* empty bottles, jars and tins along a table top. Invite a pupil to place an ear to any one of the objects, suggesting that you will try to throw vibrations into it.

Cause a tuning fork to vibrate, *e.g.* strike it on a rubber. No sound will be heard from the selected object.

Cause the tuning fork to vibrate again, and this time pretend to throw vibrations into the selected object. At the same time touch the haft of the tuning fork to the table top. This time sound will appear to come from the object.

Repeat with different pupils and different objects until it becomes apparent that sound is heard from the objects only when the haft of the vibrating tuning fork is touching the table, *i.e.* vibrations are transmitted through the table top to the objects.

(*b*) Observe also that vibrations are transmitted through the table in all directions, *i.e.* that sound can be heard from all the objects at the same time.

(*c*) Touch the metal parts of a watch to the teeth and observe that ticking can be heard, because vibrations are transmitted through the teeth and the bones in the head.

2 Experiment to show that vibrations can be transmitted better through some things than through others.

(*a*) Tie two spoons or forks in the centre of a length of string. Swing the string so that the two jangle together. Observe the sound. Now hold the ends of the string to each ear, and jangle the spoons again. This time observe that the sound is louder. The vibrations which were transmitted through the air spread out and were diminished. Those transmitted through the string arrive relatively undiminished.

(*b*) Hold the metal parts of a ticking watch against the bottom of an empty jar. Place the open end of the jar over the ear. Observe that ticking is heard. Place soft material, such as a pair of woollen gloves, in the jar and repeat. Observe that the ticking is inaudible owing to the soft material in the jar absorbing vibrations.

3 Experiment to show that vibrations can be reflected from a surface. Arrange two tubes, *e.g.* of cardboard, as shown in the diagram. Place a ticking watch at the end of one, and listen at the end of the other. Observe that ticking is heard through the tubes, although it may not be heard directly through the air between the watch and the ear.

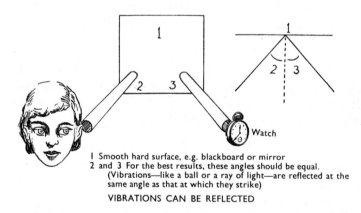

Watch

I Smooth hard surface, e.g. blackboard or mirror
2 and 3 For the best results, these angles should be equal.
(Vibrations—like a ball or a ray of light—are reflected at the same angle as that at which they strike)

VIBRATIONS CAN BE REFLECTED

Note. Rubber or plastic tubing and plastic funnels can be used to make the simple stethoscope and speaking tube illustrated in the Pupils' Book.

4 Experiment to show that vibrations are reflected from some surfaces better than from others. Repeat the experiment with the watch and tubes, but replace the hard smooth surface with a soft rough one such as a jacket or cushion.

NOTEBOOK WORK

Answers should be along the following lines.

1 Vibrations are transmitted when anything which is vibrating causes something which it touches to vibrate.
2 Vibrations may be transmitted in all directions.
3 Some solid, liquid or gas is needed for transmission.
4 When you speak through a megaphone, the extra sound is caused by vibrations reflected from the sides of the megaphone.
5 An echo is due to reflected vibrations causing us to hear a separate sound.

10 REFLECTING LIGHT FROM DIFFERENT MIRRORS

IMAGES AND ALTERED IMAGES

DEMONSTRATION MATERIAL

Flat mirrors, *e.g.* pocket mirrors; ball or electric torch; candle, jar of water, small sheet of clear glass; any curved surface in which an image can be seen, *e.g.* convex mirror, concave mirror, smooth metal can or polished spoon

SAMPLE LINK QUESTIONS

1 When we see a thing it is for one of two reasons. What are they? (*Either it is giving out light itself or it is reflecting light given out by something else*)
2 When is the only time that a non-luminous thing can be seen? (*When it is reflecting light given out by something else*)
3 Is the direction in which light travels straight or curved? (*Straight*)

4 What is a shadow caused by? (*Something in the path of light*)
5 What does a rough surface do to the light which it reflects? (*It scatters it*)
6 When a surface is smooth enough to reflect the light from an object without scattering it, what does it act as? (*A mirror*)
7 When we see the reflection of an object in a mirror, what do we call it? (*An image*)
8 What do we see in a kaleidoscope besides the object? (*Its images and the reflections of its images*)

RELEVANT INFORMATION

The main points of this lesson are that
1 we see images because rays of light are bent before they reach our eyes;
2 in flat mirrors, images appear the same size and shape as their objects;
3 in curved mirrors, images appear altered in size or shape.

When we say we can see an object, what is actually happening is that some of the rays of light emitted by the object, or reflected from it, are entering our eyes. These rays always appear to have come in a direct path from the object.

If, for some reason, some of the rays from a particular point on an object are bent out of their direct path, and if these particular rays enter our eyes, then we still see that point, but it appears to be in a different position. When we are aware of these circumstances, we term what we see an image.

Three things may cause the bending of light rays.
      1 Gravity
      2 Reflection at a surface
      3 Transmission through a surface
It is with the last two that this and the next lesson in the Pupils' Book are concerned.

Change of Direction caused by Gravity

The theory that light is affected by gravity was first propounded by Einstein and confirmed in 1919 during an eclipse of the sun. The illustration shows rays from a distant star being bent from their direct path as they pass the sun, so that the star appears in a slightly different position. From this it was inferred that light has mass, and that energy and mass are interconvertible.

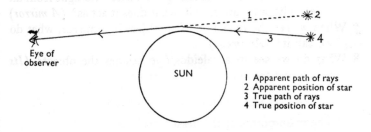

Eye of observer

SUN

1 Apparent path of rays
2 Apparent position of star
3 True path of rays
4 True position of star

Change of Direction caused by Reflection

The simplest example of this is when light is reflected from a flat (plane) mirror. When light strikes a flat mirror, all the rays are bent back at an angle equal to that at which they make contact. If a ray strikes the mirror at right angles to the surface, it is reflected, *i.e.* bent back, along the same path. Any line drawn at right angles to the surface of a flat mirror is known as the normal. If a ray of light strikes the mirror at an angle to the normal, it will be reflected at the same angle to the normal but in the opposite direction, just as a ball striking the surface of a smooth wall will bounce away at the same angle. When parallel rays of light make contact with a smooth flat surface, those which are reflected are bent back along parallel paths. For this reason the image seen in a flat (plane) mirror is always the same size as the object. It is always upright, and it always appears to be as far behind the mirror as the object is in front.

When parallel rays of light make contact with a smooth curved surface, those which are reflected are not bent back along parallel paths. All the rays are bent back at an angle equal to that at which they make contact, as is the case with a plane mirror, but the angle of contact is different for each ray. A curved mirror can be imagined to consist of innumerable tiny flat mirrors, each facing in a slightly different direction. Because of this, when parallel rays strike a curved mirror, each ray is received at a different angle from the others, and is therefore reflected at a different angle from the others. For the same reason, some of the rays whose paths are not parallel can be bent back along paths which *are* parallel.

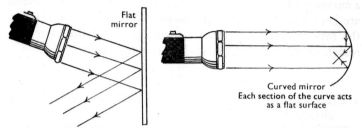

THE REFLECTION OF PARALLEL RAYS FROM FLAT AND CURVED MIRRORS

The image seen in a curved mirror may differ in size from the object. It may appear the right way up, or upside down, and at a different distance from the mirror than the object. It will also be reversed, as is the image seen in a flat mirror. The most important kinds of curved mirrors are convex and concave mirrors.

A convex (curving outward) mirror bends back the rays in such a way that an image always appears the right way up but reduced in size, *i.e.* it is upright and diminished. Some driving mirrors are convex. As the images produced by a convex driving mirror are smaller than those produced by a flat mirror, the driver's field of view is increased. Convex mirrors are also used in buses to let the conductor view the upper deck from the platform.

A concave (curving inward) mirror bends back the rays in such a way that two kinds of images are possible. If an object is a long way from a concave mirror, its image will appear inverted and diminished. If it is close to the mirror, it will appear the right way up and magnified. Concave mirrors may be used to provide an enlarged image of a small part of a person's face, *e.g.* some shaving mirrors and some make-up mirrors. The reflectors used in searchlights, car headlights and torches are concave mirrors positioned so that the rays of light which they reflect are bent back in a concentrated beam. Some curved mirrors are so shaped that they may be regarded as parts of a hollow spherical glass ball, and are termed convex spherical or concave spherical according to which side they are silvered.

Note. When parallel rays of light make contact with a flat or a curved surface which is *not* smooth, those which are reflected are bent back in all sorts of different directions. We say that the rays are scattered or that the light is *diffused*. For this reason we do not see an image in a rough surface.

CODE

1 Experiment with flat mirrors to show how rays of light change direction when they are reflected.

Equip children in different parts of the room with flat mirrors. Let each child position his mirror so as to obtain an image of a selected fixed object. Observe how all the mirrors are at different angles. Trace the paths of light from the object to each mirror, and from each mirror to the eye of the observer.

Repeat for other selected fixed objects.

2 Demonstrate how light is reflected from a flat mirror.

(*a*) Drop a ball on to a smooth surface, *e.g.* floor or table, and observe how it bounces back along the same path. Now direct the ball so that it strikes the surface at an angle, and observe how it bounces away at an angle along a different path.

(*b*) Shine a torch on to a mirror so that the light is reflected on to a wall. Turn the mirror through different angles, and observe where the light is reflected in each case.

Note. Children are experimenting in this way when they use smooth shiny surfaces such as those of tin lids and mirrors to reflect light on to walls, ceilings and one another.

3 Demonstrate that an image appears behind a mirror, *e.g.* by seeing the image of a lighted candle in a jar of water.

Light a candle and stand it in front of a sheet of clear glass. Observe the image of the candle in the sheet of glass. Position a jar of water behind the glass so that the image of the candle appears to be inside it.

This illusion can also be used to show that an image is as far behind a flat mirror as the object is in front.

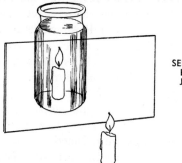

SEEING A CANDLE
BURNING IN A
JAR OF WATER

4 Observe how images appear altered in curved mirror surfaces.
  (*a*) Upright and diminished in a convex spherical mirror
  (*b*) Upright and magnified in a concave spherical mirror held close
  (*c*) Inverted and diminished in a concave spherical mirror held at a distance
  (*d*) Upright, diminished and distorted in the back of a polished spoon
  (*e*) Inverted, diminished and distorted in the front of the spoon
  (*f*) Upright, diminished and possibly distorted in the side of a smooth metal can

NOTEBOOK WORK

Answers should be along the following lines.
1 (*a*) We see an object when some of the rays of light from that object travel straight to our eyes.
  (*b*) We see an image if the rays have changed direction before they reach our eyes.
2 The image in a flat mirror is the same size and shape as the object. The image in a curved mirror is altered.
3 (*a*) If the image appears larger than the object, we say it is magnified.
  (*b*) If it appears smaller, we say it is diminished.
  (*c*) If it differs in shape from the object, we say it is distorted.

IMAGES AND ALTERED IMAGES

SEEING THROUGH TRANSPARENT SURFACES

DEMONSTRATION MATERIAL

1 For demonstrating the bending of light, *e.g.* square jar or glass tank, water tinted with red ink, electric torch, sheet of white paper
2 For observing simple images, *e.g.* sheets of lined writing paper, square jars, water; ruler and a bowl of water
3 For observing distorted images, *e.g.* bowl of water, pencil, drinking straw
4 For observing magnified images, *e.g.* round jam jars filled with water, pencils, rulers; specimen tubes (*e.g.* $3'' \times 1''$) filled with water and corked; magnifying glasses (convex lenses)
5 For observing diminished images, *e.g.* convex lenses (magnifying glasses), white paper; concave lenses (as in some spectacles)

SAMPLE LINK QUESTIONS

1 What is light made up of? (*Rays*)
2 When do we see an object? (*When some of the rays of light from the object travel straight to our eyes*)
3 When do we see an image? (*When the rays of light have changed direction before they reach our eyes*)
4 When rays of light are being bent back from an object what do we call this? (*Reflection*)
5 From which part of an object are rays of light reflected? (*Its surface*)
6 What kind of surface reflects rays of light without scattering them in all directions? (*A very smooth surface*)
7 How does the image seen in a flat mirror differ from the image seen in a curved mirror? (*The image in a flat mirror is the same size and shape as the object*)

8 How does a magnified image differ from an object? (*It is larger*)

9 How does a diminished image differ from an object? (*It is smaller*)

10 In what way does a distorted image differ from an object? (*It differs in shape*)

The main points of this lesson are that

1 images can result from light being bent as it passes through a transparent surface;

2 images seen through a transparent substance which is thicker in some parts than in others appear altered in size or shape.

Change of Direction caused by Transmission through a Surface

The simplest example of this is when light passes from one transparent substance to another through a smooth flat surface. If a ray passes through the surface at right angles to it (*i.e.* along the normal), then it continues in the same direction, *i.e.* at right angles to the surface. However, any ray which passes through such a surface at an angle to the normal is bent in another direction or *refracted*. This kind of bending takes place when light passes from water to air, or from glass to air, or from water to glass.

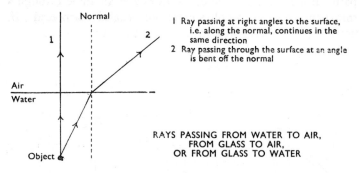

1 Ray passing at right angles to the surface, i.e. along the normal, continues in the same direction
2 Ray passing through the surface at an angle is bent off the normal

RAYS PASSING FROM WATER TO AIR, FROM GLASS TO AIR, OR FROM GLASS TO WATER

This is why, if you look at a sloping stick which is partly in air and partly in water, it looks as though it is bent at the surface of the water. The stick is not bent; only the rays from the stick which reach your eye are bent as they pass from water to air. The eye makes no allowance for this bending; it sees the stick as though all the rays of light from it travelled in a direct line. Those reaching the eye from the section above the surface do travel in a direct line. Those reaching the eye from the section below the surface do not, so that section appears in the wrong place, *i.e.* we see an image.

It is because light is bent as it passes from water to air that a pond of water seems shallower than it is, and that the back of an aquarium seems nearer to the front than it actually is. The bottom of the pond and the back of the aquarium are both seen as images.

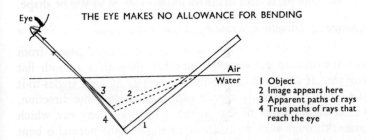

THE EYE MAKES NO ALLOWANCE FOR BENDING

Air
Water

1 Object
2 Image appears here
3 Apparent paths of rays
4 True paths of rays that reach the eye

The wider the medium through which the deflected ray has to pass, the greater becomes its distance from its original path. If a point on an object is viewed at an angle through a thin pane of glass, it will appear only slightly displaced. If, however, it is viewed at an angle through a very thick block of

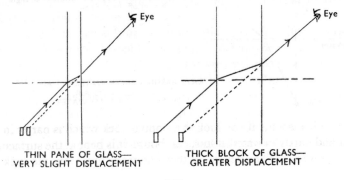

THIN PANE OF GLASS—
VERY SLIGHT DISPLACEMENT

THICK BLOCK OF GLASS—
GREATER DISPLACEMENT

glass, it will appear more displaced. Similarly, a line of print will seem only slightly displaced when viewed at an angle through the thin flat walls of a square jar, but will appear more displaced if viewed from the same angle after the jar has been filled with water.

If a transparent substance is wider in some parts than in others, the light rays passing through it may be bent in such a way that the image may appear distorted, magnified or diminished, according to circumstances. A simple example is the view of an object seen through a pane of cheap window glass which has slight irregularities in its surface. As the glass is not of uniform thickness, parts of an object viewed through it will appear out of shape, *i.e.* will be seen as a distorted image. Similarly a bather may see a distorted image of part of his own body through the disturbed surface of the water.

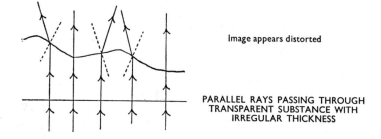

Image appears distorted

PARALLEL RAYS PASSING THROUGH
TRANSPARENT SUBSTANCE WITH
IRREGULAR THICKNESS

A magnified or a diminished image may be seen by looking at an object through a transparent substance which has a smooth curved surface. Any portion of transparent material which has either both surfaces curved, or one surface curved and the other flat, can alter an image in this way and is known as a lens. There are two main kinds of lenses—convex (outward curving) and concave (inward curving).

A convex lens is thicker at the centre than at the outside edges, and is sometimes known as a converging lens, as parallel rays passing through it converge to a point. Two main kinds of images may be seen through a convex lens. If the object is sufficiently close to the lens, the image will appear upright and magnified. If the object is some distance from the lens, the

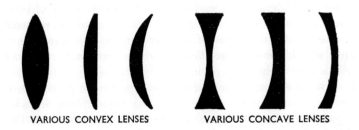

VARIOUS CONVEX LENSES   VARIOUS CONCAVE LENSES

image will appear inverted and diminished, like those seen in a *concave* mirror.

A concave lens is thinner at the centre than at the outside edges, and is sometimes known as a diverging lens, as parallel rays passing through it diverge. The image seen through a concave lens is always of the same kind—upright and diminished, like that seen in a *convex* mirror.

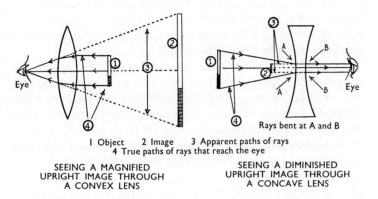

1 Object   2 Image   3 Apparent paths of rays
4 True paths of rays that reach the eye

SEEING A MAGNIFIED
UPRIGHT IMAGE THROUGH
A CONVEX LENS

SEEING A DIMINISHED
UPRIGHT IMAGE THROUGH
A CONCAVE LENS

Lenses are used in spectacles—a convex lens to correct long sight, and a concave lens to correct short sight. A simple magnifying glass is a convex lens; compound microscopes and telescopes consist of two or more lenses. Opera and field glasses are in effect double telescopes with a set of lenses for each eye.

Refraction of light takes place at the surface. Once a ray has been bent, it continues in its new direction until it meets another surface. However, if the transparent substance through which a ray is passing is not the same density all the way through, then the ray will be bent as it passes from a layer of one density to a layer of another density. For example, a layer of cold air is denser than a layer of warm air, and a ray will be bent at the surface where the two layers meet. Distorted images are sometimes seen through warm air rising from a hot stove. A mirage is an image seen as the result of light from an object being bent by layers of air of different densities. The shimmering patch some distance ahead on a tarred road heated by the sun is also due to the bending of light as it passes through layers of air of different densities. The impression that a star is twinkling is due to light rays from the star being refracted irregularly as they pass through the various shifting layers of air in the atmosphere. At heights above 30,000 feet the stars no longer appear to twinkle.

When rays of light pass through a curved or flat surface which is not smooth, they are refracted unevenly, *i.e.* they are scattered in a variety of different directions. We say that the light is diffused. The ground-glass, translucent surface of a pearl electric light bulb diffuses light in this way.

Light can therefore be diffused by both reflection and refraction, and most of the light by which we see is scattered by one of these means. Daylight itself is light from the sun diffused by clouds in the air, by dust and other particles in the atmosphere, and subsequently, when it reaches earth, by most of the surfaces which it strikes. This is why a room at the front of the house is not in darkness when the sun is at the back of the house. Even the soft light of twilight and the first light of dawn are due to diffusion of light by the atmosphere while the sun is below the horizon.

Notes

1 It is possible to see an image through a convex lens which is the same size and shape as the object. This is only at one particular point—when the object is at twice the distance of the focal length of the lens. The image at this point does, however, appear inverted.

2 *Reflect* means to bend back after striking a surface.

3 *Refract* means to bend from a straight line, *i.e.* to break the natural course.

4 The speed of light through air is 186,000 miles per sec approx. Through water it is 139,000 miles per sec approx ($\frac{3}{4}$ of its speed through air). Through glass it is 124,000 miles per sec approx ($\frac{2}{3}$ of its speed through air).

CODE

1 Demonstrate how light may be bent as it passes through a transparent surface.

Fill a large square jar or a small glass tank with water, and tint with red ink. Stand the jar on a sheet of white paper. Cut a narrow slit in a piece of thin card or thick paper and fasten round the end of a torch.

Direct a beam of light from the slit so that it passes through the side of the jar or tank at an angle.

Observe how the beam is bent from its original path as it passes through the inky water. Observe how the emerging beam is again bent as it re-enters the air. This can be shown by adjusting the torch so that a pinkish line appears on the paper.

2 Experiment to obtain simple images.

(a) At an angle look through the front of a partly-filled aquarium at one of the back corners, and observe the apparent position of the corner seen through the water. Observe that the image appears in different positions when viewed from different angles.

(b) Place a sheet of ruled paper, with the lines horizontal, behind a flat-sided glass container, *e.g.* a medicine bottle or a square jar. Observe how the section of lines viewed through the jar appear displaced when jar and paper are tilted towards viewer and when tilted away from viewer. Fill container with water and repeat.

(c) Place a ruler in a bowl of water so that it breaks the surface at an angle. Observe that it appears bent at the surface of the water.

Observe that, when the ruler is upright, the section below the surface appears shortened, *i.e.* the inch marks seem closer together.

3 Experiment to obtain distorted images.

(*a*) Look at various objects through any window with a flaw in it.

(*b*) Place an object, *e.g.* coin or pencil, in a bowl of water and observe its image through the surface. Now blow through a drinking straw into the water so as to disturb the surface. Observe how the image now becomes distorted.

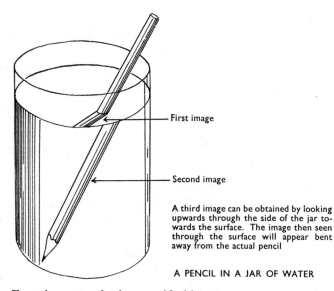

First image

Second image

A third image can be obtained by looking upwards through the side of the jar towards the surface. The image then seen through the surface will appear bent away from the actual pencil

A PENCIL IN A JAR OF WATER

4 Experiment to obtain magnified images.

(*a*) Stand a pencil or ruler upright in a round jam jar of water, and move it from front to back.

(*b*) (i) Roll a corked specimen tube filled with water over printed words, and observe the upright magnified images.

(ii) Place a second similar tube filled with water on top of the first, and observe that the magnified images become reversed and inverted.

(c) Look through a magnifying glass (convex lens) to observe upright magnified images of objects on the desk.

5 Experiment to obtain diminished images.

(a) Look through a concave lens to obtain upright diminished images.

(b) Through a magnifying glass (convex lens) observe inverted diminished images of objects across the room.

(c) Hold a magnifying glass between a sheet of white paper and a source of light, e.g. a lighted lamp or a well-lit window. Adjust the position of the lens until an inverted and diminished image of the lamp or window is obtained on the paper.

Notes

1 A convex lens (magnifying glass) placed on a flat mirror can be made to serve as a *concave* mirror.

2 A concave lens placed on a flat mirror can be made to serve as a *convex* mirror.

NOTEBOOK WORK

Answers should be along the following lines.

1 The corner of an aquarium seen at an angle through water may be called an image because it appears in the wrong place.

2 We can see a distorted image through a window when the window has a flaw in it.

3 Lenses are used in spectacles to see magnified or diminished images.

4 Images seen through a concave lens and in a convex mirror are diminished.

SPLITTING LIGHT INTO DIFFERENT KINDS OF RAYS

COLOUR RAYS

DEMONSTRATION MATERIAL

Glass prism; small mirror, shallow bowl of water, plasticine; torch, coloured transparent material; materials for colour tops and whizzers—thick white card (*e.g.* from a round cheese box), wax crayons, sharpened pencil stubs, fine string

SAMPLE LINK QUESTIONS

1 What do we mean when we say that something is luminous? (*It is giving out light itself*)

2 From which luminous object do we get most of the light on earth? (*The sun*)

3 When is the only time a non-luminous object can be seen? (*When it is reflecting light from something else*)

4 On what does the way in which an object reflects light depend? (*Its surface*)

5 When do we call an object transparent? (*When we can see through it clearly*)

6 When we can see through an object but not clearly, what is it said to be? (*Translucent*)

7 When do we say an object is opaque? (*When we cannot see through it at all*)

8 What is light made up of? (*Rays*)

9 What are the two main occasions when rays of light from an object are bent so that we see an image? (*When the rays are reflected from a very smooth surface, and when the rays are bent as they pass through a transparent surface*)

10 What are the three main kinds of altered images which can result from the bending of rays of light? (*Magnified, diminished, and distorted images*)

RELEVANT INFORMATION

The main purpose of this lesson is to show that the different colours we see are caused by different kinds of rays of light.

The wavelengths of the different rays of light to which most human eyes are sensitive, range from approximately 1/30,000 of an inch to 1/60,000 of an inch. We see an object when any of these rays travel from the object, enter our eyes, and stimulate the nerve endings inside them. Each ray has its own particular wavelength, and the nerve endings in most human eyes are capable of reacting to these different wavelengths and also to different mixtures of these wavelengths, so as to produce different sensations. These different sensations are interpreted by the brain as colours.

These rays which stimulate human eyes may be roughly divided into seven bands of wavelengths, according to the seven main colour sensations which the human brain interprets as red, orange, yellow, green, blue, indigo and violet. An object appears red because the rays travelling to the eye from that object belong to the band of wavelengths whose stimuli cause the special sensation which the brain has come to interpret as redness. For convenience, we call this particular band of rays the red colour rays. Red colour rays have the longest wavelengths; violet colour rays have the shortest wavelengths. The usual mnemonic for the seven main colours is 'Richard Of York Gave Battle In Vain'.

The Apparent Colour of Luminous Objects

The light given out by most luminous objects is composed of a mixture of these different colour rays. This mixture, however, is not the same for all luminous sources, and depends on factors such as temperature and the kind of substance from which the light is being radiated. For example, the light from a torch has a larger proportion of yellow colour rays than sunlight. Likewise, the mixture from a sodium vapour lamp contains a large proportion of orange colour rays and that from a mercury vapour lamp contains a large proportion of blue colour rays. A red-hot poker is at a temperature at which it emits chiefly red colour rays, whereas a white-hot poker is hot enough to be emitting a mixture of all the colour rays, so balanced as to produce the sensation that we interpret as whiteness. If the poker is cooled to the point where it cannot be seen in darkness, it continues to emit rays of energy, but their wavelengths are too long to stimulate the nerve endings in our eyes. They may stimulate other nerve endings however. We may feel them as heat, and we term them infra-red rays.

Separating the Colour Rays

It very frequently happens that the light which reaches our eyes from an object has been forced to change direction on the way, *i.e.* it has been reflected or refracted. Under certain circumstances, where a mixture of colour rays is reflected or refracted, one or more of the colour rays may be separated from the others. Perhaps the best-known demonstration of this is when a beam of light consisting of a mixture of all the colour rays (*e.g.* a beam of sunlight) is made to pass through a glass prism at such an angle that the beam is split into separate rays, which fan out as they emerge from the prism. We do not actually see these separate rays of light, of course, but we do see individual colours when the rays strike a surface which reflects the rays to our eyes. The separating of the rays in this case is due to the fact that the shorter the wavelength of a ray, the greater is the angle through which it is bent during refraction. Violet colour rays are bent more than indigo colour rays, and red colour rays are bent least of all. This splitting of a mixture of rays into its different components is known as dispersal, and the range of colours seen is known as a spectrum. In a spectrum the colours are not sharply defined but merge gradually into one another.

A rainbow is perhaps the most spectacular example of a spectrum and is caused by sunlight being reflected and refracted by millions of raindrops. Each droplet of water acts as a tiny prism, with the main difference that the light is reflected within the raindrop instead of passing through it. As the colour rays fan out when they emerge from a droplet, they will obviously not all reach the same eye from the same raindrop. The different colour rays which enter the eye of an observer come from many raindrops at varying distances. In fact, each observer sees his own bow. It is not easy to see seven colours in a rainbow; indigo is especially elusive.

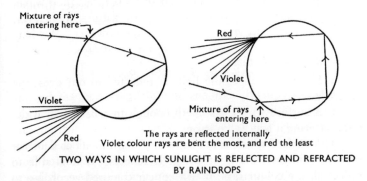

TWO WAYS IN WHICH SUNLIGHT IS REFLECTED AND REFRACTED BY RAINDROPS

As the light responsible for the illusion of a rainbow is reflected to the observer, the sun will be behind the observer when the rainbow is seen in front. A rainbow is part of a circle, and an imaginary line drawn from the sun to the centre of this circle would pass through the eye of the observer. Double rainbows are occasionally seen, and the colours seen in one will be in reverse order from those seen in the other. A partial rainbow may be seen by an observer standing with his back to the sun and spraying water into the air from a garden hose held in front of him.

The splitting of light into separate colour rays does not always result in the eye seeing a complete spectrum. More often than not, only certain colours are seen according to which of the colour rays enter the eye. Very fine grooves on a surface may be responsible for the separation of certain colour rays as light is reflected from the surface. The sheen of colour on many beetles and on mother-of-pearl is an example. The iridescent colours of a peacock's tail in sunlight are due to the splitting of light reflected from the edges of very fine slits in its feathers. Thin layers of oil or grease on water and the surface of soap bubbles are also responsible for the splitting of reflected light so that certain colours are seen.

The Apparent Colour of Non-Luminous Objects

When light strikes the surface of a non-luminous object, there are three possible reactions.

1 Reflection, *i.e.* some or all of the light is bent back

2 Transmission, *i.e.* some or all of the light passes through

3 Absorption, *i.e.* some or all of the light is neither reflected nor transmitted.

Effects due to Reflection

1 If some or all of the light is reflected to our eyes, the object is seen.

2 A surface which is smooth enough to reflect light without scattering it acts as a mirror.

3 A surface which is not smooth enough to act as a mirror scatters (diffuses) the light which it reflects. If it is able to reflect all the colour rays, it will appear coloured according to those which strike it. For example, if a balanced mixture of all the colour rays strike it (as in sunlight), it will appear white. This is why a balanced mixture of colour rays is often termed white light. But if only blue colour rays strike it, it will appear blue, if only red colour rays strike it it will appear red, and so on. This is why a white surface is the best one on which to project or paint colours.

Effects due to both Reflection and Absorption

1 Many surfaces reflect only certain colour rays and absorb the rest. Such surfaces appear coloured according to the colour rays they reflect. The skin of an orange appears orange because it reflects orange colour rays, and a leaf looks green when it reflects green colour rays. Common language masks the real state of affairs, and we tend to think of colour as being part of the physical make-up of a thing, and to overlook the fact that if the colour rays were not there to be reflected, the colour would not be apparent. For example, the skin of an orange would not look orange in the light from a blue lamp, and a leaf would not look green in the light from a neon lamp. With nothing for them to reflect, they would in fact appear black.

2 If none of the light is transmitted (*i.e.* all is reflected or

absorbed), the object will appear opaque; if some of the light is transmitted, it will appear transparent or translucent.

Effects due to Transmission

1 If the object transmits light without diffusing it, it appears transparent. If it scatters the transmitted light, it appears translucent.

2 A transparent object that transmits a mixture of colour rays appears colourless, *e.g.* a clear glass window.

3 A translucent object that transmits a balanced mixture of colour rays but diffuses them, appears white. Frost on a window pane gives this effect.

Effects due to both Transmission and Absorption

Certain transparent or translucent objects, *e.g.* coloured glass and coloured cellophane, transmit only certain colour rays and absorb others. Such objects are termed colour filters, and a lamp viewed through such a filter would appear coloured according to which colour rays were transmitted. Green glass in front of a lamp makes it appear green, and red glass makes it appear red. Colour filtering is used in a number of ways—for various vehicle and traffic lamps, for fairy lights, stained glass windows, and certain attractive wrapping materials.

Notes

1 Anything which transmitted all the light without absorbing or reflecting any would be colourless, and would not be seen. Most gases are colourless and cannot be seen, although even, through these, total transmission of all the light is an unlikely occurrence.

2 Anything which reflected all the light without absorbing or transmitting any would, in the case of a smooth surface, act as a mirror, and in the case of an unsmooth surface, appear coloured according to the colour rays striking it. Total reflection by an unsmooth surface is unlikely. For example, most of the surfaces which we accept as white are absorbing anything up to 20% of the light which strikes them. This is why white surfaces are hard to match.

3 Anything which absorbed all the light without reflecting or transmitting any, would appear black. Total absorption of all the light is unlikely, which is why pure black—like pure white—is rare. A pure black surface would reflect no light to our eyes, but we might be aware of its presence by comparison with its surroundings.

4 The whiteness of snow and the foam on the crest of a breaking wave is due to the surface being broken up to such an extent that most of the light is reflected instead of being transmitted. Glass wool, or a pile of powdered glass appears white for the same reason.

Colour Effects in the Atmosphere

When light passes through a transparent or a translucent medium containing transparent particles differing in density from the medium, those rays which pass through the particles will be refracted at the surface through which they enter, and again at the surface through which they leave. This will cause the light to be diffused, and may also lead to the dispersal of certain of the component rays. Again, if the medium contains particles which reflect some of the rays, a certain amount of diffusion and dispersal may occur, and rays of some wavelengths may not get through. Even on a relatively clear day, the atmosphere contains very tiny suspended particles of dust and droplets of water, and sunlight passing through the atmosphere is diffused by these sub-microscopic particles. Even the molecules of gases making up the air itself assist in this scattering, during which they are responsible for the dispersal of those with the shortest wavelengths, *i.e.* the blue colour rays, which is why the sky appears blue. If there were no atmosphere, the sky would appear black, as it does at night or in outer space.

The proportions of different particles in the atmosphere through which light has to pass vary from time to time and from place to place and are responsible for varying colour effects. To take a simple example, the smoke from the burning tip of a cigarette appears blue, owing to the dispersal of the blue colour rays passing through it; but the smoke in exhaled breath appears whitish, owing to water vapour molecules in the

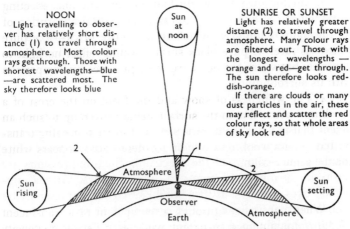

NOON

Light travelling to observer has relatively short distance (1) to travel through atmosphere. Most colour rays get through. Those with shortest wavelengths—blue—are scattered most. The sky therefore looks blue

SUNRISE OR SUNSET

Light has relatively greater distance (2) to travel through atmosphere. Many colour rays are filtered out. Those with the longest wavelengths — orange and red—get through. The sun therefore looks reddish-orange.

If there are clouds or many dust particles in the air, these may reflect and scatter the red colour rays, so that whole areas of sky look red

THE SKY IS NOT BLUE : THE SUN IS NOT ORANGE

exhaled breath diffusing other colour rays as well. In a fog, the red and orange colour rays from a lamp penetrate better than the other colour rays, because, having the longest wavelengths, they are the least likely to be reflected by the suspended particles. This is why orange filters are used in fog lamps. Variations in the proportions of atmospheric particles are responsible for different phenomena in the sky, such as the haloes round the sun or the moon, the grey horizon and the red glow of dawn.

Brightness and Darkness

An object appears brighter or darker according to the total amount of light it is able to reflect.

The difference between white, grey and black is one of brightness. A surface which reflects a proportion of all the colour rays and absorbs a proportion will appear whitish, greyish or blackish according to the proportion of light reflected. The greater the proportion reflected, the whiter the surface will appear. The greater the proportion absorbed, the blacker it will appear. White chalk stands out against the surface of a blackboard because it is able to reflect a greater proportion of the light which strikes it than can the surrounding surface of the board. So too does the white line on the dark road at night stand out in the light from a vehicle's headlamps.

As the amount of light striking an apparently white surface is reduced, it will appear darker, *i.e.* it will shade gradually from white through grey to black.

Tints, Shades and Colour Pigments

More often than not, the light reaching our eyes from an object consists of colour rays mixed in such proportions that we have an impression of something other than white and other than the pure colours of the spectrum. Such impressions are the result of mixing pigments in different ways. Artists' pigments, dyes, paints and inks stimulate colour impressions by their particular ability to reflect certain colour rays.

A tint is obtained by mixing white with a standard colour. For example, pink is obtained by adding white to red, and a surface which appears pink is reflecting the red colour rays together with a balanced mixture of all the others which normally give the impression of white. As a pink surface is reflecting more light than a red one, it will appear brighter.

A shade is obtained by mixing black with a standard colour. If black is added to red, the red will become a shade darker, because some of the red colour rays are being absorbed, *i.e.* the total amount of light reflected is less. Adding grey to a standard colour also results in a darker shade, and this is sometimes termed a *tone*. The impression of brown may be obtained from a mixture of orange and black.

It is estimated that the human eye is able to distinguish more than two million tints and shades.

When two different pigments are mixed together, the resultant colour appearance will be that of the colour rays which both can reflect, and will differ from the colour seen when the light from two coloured lamps is projected on to the same area on a white screen. For example, if red and green paint are mixed, the mixture will appear to be a dark muddy colour because each will absorb most of the colour rays normally reflected by the other. On the other hand, if light from red and green lamps are shone together on to a white screen, the screen will reflect a mixture of red colour rays and green colour rays, and the eye interprets such a mixture as yellow.

Pigments however are not generally pure, and they usually reflect certain colour rays in addition to those which are primarily responsible for their particular colour appearance. For example, a yellow pigment reflects some green colour rays and some orange colour rays in addition to the yellow ones. If two different pigments reflecting the same additional colour rays are mixed, only these additional colour rays will be reflected, and the mixture will appear coloured accordingly. A blue pigment reflects some green colour rays, so if yellow and blue pigments are mixed, the yellow will absorb the blue colour rays, the blue will absorb the yellow colour rays, but each will continue to reflect green colour rays, so that the mixture will appear green. Similarly, as a red pigment reflects some orange colour rays, a mixture of yellow and red pigments appears orange. These are comparatively simple examples. Most of the tints, shades and tones of colour which we experience in our modern world are caused by the reflection of far more complicated mixtures of colour rays.

Although human eyes are sensitive to a range of colour rays, the eyes of other animals are not necessarily so. Most mammals and many other animals are sensitive only to light without being able to distinguish separate colour rays. Such eyes see their world in terms of white, grey and black. A bull cannot distinguish between a red rag and one of any other colour. The eyes of honey bees are believed to be sensitive to blue and yellow colour rays, but not to green and red. Even some human beings have eyes which are not fully sensitive to all the colour rays, and they are said to be colour blind.

CODE

1 Observe examples of colours being seen as a result of light being split into colour rays.

   (a) Look through the edge of a glass prism towards a lamp with a translucent shade, or a window with daylight coming through. Turn the prism slowly until bands of colour are seen.

Mirror rests against plasticine, under water in shallow dish

(b) Place a mirror at an angle in a shallow dish of water as shown in the diagram. Use in any of the following ways.

(i) Position dish with mirror facing a window, so that the image of the window is seen in the mirror by looking at an angle through the surface of the water. Observe the colour bands edging the window frame.

(ii) Position so that, by looking into the mirror at an angle through the surface of the water, it is possible to see the image of a lamp surrounded by a translucent shade. Observe the colour bands on the edge of the shade.

(iii) Position facing strong sunlight slanting through a window so that the sunlight can be reflected from the mirror and out through the surface of the water at an angle. Place a sheet of white card or paper in the path of this reflected light. Observe the colour band obtained. By a little manipulation, it is possible to obtain a complete spectrum band in which only the indigo will be difficult to discern.

Note. When direct sunlight strikes the end of an aquarium at an angle, it is sometimes possible to see bands of colour by looking through the front of the aquarium towards the sunlit end. Bands of colour are sometimes seen incidentally by looking at the edge of a bevelled mirror or a piece of broken glass, or by looking through a prism of glass from a chandelier.

2 When children next see a rainbow, they should observe the position of the sun, *i.e.* that it is behind them when the rainbow is in front. A rainbow will be in the east in the evening, and in the west in the morning.

3 Experiment by shining a light through coloured glass or cellophane to show that only part of the light passes

through. Observe in each case that the light is reduced in brightness.

4 Experiment to show that the apparent colour of a surface is caused by the colour rays it is able to reflect. Shine a light through coloured transparent material on to a white card or paper.

5 Experiment to show that when a surface reflects a mixture of all the colour rays to our eyes, it appears white. Colour a disc of thick white card (*e.g.* from cheese box) as shown in the diagrams, and make into a top or a whizzer. Observe the whitish appearance when spun.

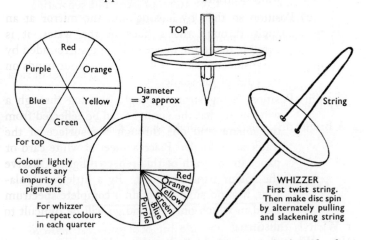

6 Experiment to show that different tints and shades of colour are caused by different mixtures of colour rays entering our eyes. Make up colour tops or whizzers, as shown in the diagrams, but select different colour combinations, *e.g.* colour alternate segments black and white and spin to obtain impression of grey. Similarly use red and white segments to obtain pink, orange and black to obtain brown, blue and red to obtain purple.

Note. It is often stated that a surface that reflects only one kind of colour ray looks black if observed through a colour filter which transmits only another kind of colour ray, *e.g.* a red rose would look black through green glass, as the green glass would not transmit the red colour rays. However, as tints and shades are more common than pure pigments, most of the reflecting surfaces we experience will reflect a mixture of colour rays, and most of the colour filters will transmit a mixture of colour rays. Consequently, experiments to show this kind of thing with ordinary materials are more than likely to prove confusing.

NOTEBOOK WORK

Answers should be along the following lines.

1 (a) A rainbow is caused by millions of raindrops in the air bending sunlight towards our eyes and separating the different rays at the same time.

(b) The colour of a non-luminous surface is caused by which-ever colour rays are reflected from it to our eyes.

(c) Tints and shades are caused by different mixtures of rays in the light entering our eyes.

(d) Darkness is caused by little or no light entering our eyes.

2 A bright tint reflects more light than a dark shade.

QUESTIONS ON LESSONS 1 TO 12

1 What is the tiniest possible bit of a sub-stance that can exist on its own? — *A molecule of the substance*

2 What are the two means by which we can sense molecules? — *Taste and smell*

3 Every molecule consists of one or more particles. What are these particles called? — *Atoms*

4 What name do we give to a substance when its molecules consist of atoms which are all of the same kind? — *Element*

5 What name do we give to a substance when its molecules consist of atoms of two or more different kinds? — *Compound*

6 Is oxygen an element or a compound?   *An element*

7 Is water an element or a compound?   *A compound*

8 What does the greater part of an atom consist of?   *Empty space*

9 What is the centre of an atom called?   *A nucleus*

10 Which particles revolve round the nucleus
of an atom?   *Electrons*

11 What is the energy released when the
nucleus of an atom is split?   *Atomic energy*

12 What is an asteroid a lump of?   *Rock*

13 The asteroid belt is between the orbits of   *Mars and*
two planets. Which planets?   *Jupiter*

14 What are asteroids believed to be the re-
remains of?   *A planet*

15 A shooting star is something falling into the
earth's atmosphere, but it is not a star.
What is it?   *A meteor*

16 If part of a meteor lands on the surface of
the earth, what do we call it?   *A meteorite*

17 What go round the sun in addition to the
planets and their satellites, the asteroids
and meteors?   *Comets*

18 Which galaxy does the sun belong to?   *The Milky
Way*

19 What name do we give to a pattern of stars
in the sky?   *Constellation*

20 Towards which star does the earth's north   *Pole star*
pole always point?   *(Polaris)*

21 Which constellation helps us to find this
star?   *The Plough*

22 Which part of a cactus is swollen with food
—the roots, the stem, or the leaves?   *The stem*

23 What are cactus spines—roots, or stems or
leaves?   *Leaves*

24 Is a carrot a swollen root, a swollen stem, or
a swollen leaf?   *A swollen root*

25 Is a potato a swollen root, a swollen stem, or a swollen leaf? *A swollen stem*

26 Which of the following stores food in the form of specially swollen underground leaves—a corm, a tuber, or a bulb? *A bulb*

27 What are the five ways in which we sense things? *Feeling, tasting, smelling, seeing, hearing*

28 What are sounds caused by? *Vibrations*

29 Which kind of vibrations cause loud sounds? *Big vibrations*

30 Which kind of vibrations cause low notes? *Slow vibrations*

31 Which reflects vibrations better—a smooth hard surface, or a rough soft surface? *A smooth hard surface*

32 When any reflected vibrations cause us to hear a separate sound, what do we call it? *An echo*

33 Which word describes an object that gives out its own light? *Luminous*

34 From what do we get most of the light by which we see? *The sun*

35 If you could switch off the sun, would you still be able to see the moon? *No*

36 If you could switch off the moon, would you still be able to see the sun? *Yes*

37 Which word describes an object that can be seen through clearly? *Transparent*

38 Which word describes an object that lets no light through at all? *Opaque*

39 Is the path of light straight or curved? *Straight*

40 Which reflects light better—a smooth surface or a rough surface? *A smooth surface*

41 What does a rough surface do to the light it reflects? *Scatters it*

42 What name do we give to the reflection of an object which we see in a mirror? *An image*

43 When an image appears larger than the object, what is it said to be? *Magnified*

44 When an image differs in shape from the object, what is it said to be? *Distorted*

45 What do we call the transparent glass objects through which we see magnified or diminished images? *Lenses*

46 What do we call the rays that give us an impression of colour? *Colour rays*

47 When we see a rainbow, what is causing the colour rays to be bent back and separated? *Raindrops*

48 When a surface appears yellow, which colour rays is it reflecting to our eyes? *Yellow*

49 Which makes white look whiter—bright light or dull light? *Bright light*

50 Which colour rays does a piece of pure red glass let through? *Red*

(13) TEMPERATURE AND NEVER-ALIVE THINGS

EXPANDING AND CONTRACTING

1 Materials for demonstrating that air expands when heated and contracts when cooled; water (as hot as possible) and (a) plastic liquid-soap container with airtight cap; (b) medicine bottle and balloon; (c) balloon and dried-milk tin; (d) dented table-tennis ball

2 Materials for demonstrating that some liquids expand when heated, and contract when cooled: (a) see CODE 2(a) on page 140, and Pupils' Book; (b) school thermometer

SAMPLE LINK QUESTIONS

1 What are the three forms of never-alive things? (*Solid, liquid, gas*)

2 What does anything which is colder than its surroundings gain from its surroundings? (*Heat*)

3 What does anything which is hotter than its surroundings lose to its surroundings? (*Heat*)

4 If a solid gains enough heat to melt, what does it change to? (*Liquid*)

5 What causes a liquid to freeze—losing heat or gaining heat? (*Losing heat*)

6 If a gas becomes cold enough to condense, what does it change to? (*Liquid*)

7 If a substance becomes hot enough to burn what does it change into? (*Other substances*)

8 What does temperature mean? (*How hot (or how cold) something is*)

9 What do we use to measure temperature? (*A thermometer*)

10 What do the marks on the scale of a thermometer stand for? (*Degrees (of hotness)*)

RELEVANT INFORMATION

In Pupils' Book 2 it was shown that the three forms in which never-alive things are found are solid, liquid and gas.

In Pupils' Book 3 it was shown that

1 a change in form (*i.e.* a change in state) may be brought about in a substance by a change in its temperature;

2 when a substance is hot enough to burn, it is changing into other substances.

The main points of this lesson are that

1 gases and most liquids begin to expand as soon as they begin to gain heat; they likewise contract as they lose heat.

2 change of size is most obvious in gases; it is less obvious in liquids.

Three possible changes may result from a substance incurring a change in temperature.

1 A change in form (*i.e.* state), *e.g.* from solid to liquid or from liquid to solid

2 A change in chemical structure, *e.g.* during burning

3 A change in actual size (*i.e.* volume)

The volume of most substances varies according to temperature. If the temperature increases, the volume increases. If the temperature decreases, the volume decreases. Change of size continues with change of temperature, unless there is either a change of state or a chemical change. For example, a strip of iron will continue to expand until it reaches the temperature at which it melts; a strip of magnesium will continue to expand until it reaches the temperature at which it burns, *i.e.* combines with oxygen.

Change of Size in Gases

Change of size is most obvious in gases. The expansion of a gas due to a rise in temperature is apparent when the steam in a kettle of boiling water forces the lid to rise. A balloon may burst if it goes too near a fire, because the heat causes the air inside the balloon to expand. Likewise, the air in tyres expands in hot weather, possibly resulting in a burst. An explosion is the result of the *rapid* expansion of gases. An explosion (chemical, not nuclear) can result from the very rapid burning of a substance in a confined space, *e.g.* in a bomb or firework. Gases released during burning expand with the heat and break the walls of their container with considerable force.

When a gas which is being heated is trapped inside a rigid container so that it cannot expand, it builds up pressure instead. If the fire for a domestic boiler is lit when the boiler is not full of water, the steam inside the boiler (together with any trapped air) expands as the temperature rises, until the walls of the boiler can no longer withstand the pressure and the whole boiler bursts. After a freeze-up, it is wise to ensure that the hot-water system is in working order before lighting a fire beneath the boiler.

Because gases expand so much when heated, they can be used to provide the power to force pistons to move and wheels to turn. Both steam engines and internal combustion engines are operated by expanding gases.

Unlike liquids and solids, gases all expand at the same rate.

Change of Size in Liquids

Change of size is less obvious in liquids than in gases, *i.e.* liquids expand less for a given rise in temperature, and contract less for a given fall in temperature. The expansion of a liquid due to a rise in temperature is apparent when a kettle is filled right up with water, and then heated. The water overflows long before it boils. Because of the expansion of water as it gains heat, hot-water cylinders are fitted with overflow pipes, so that some of the expanding hot water can escape and drop into the cold water tank.

As liquids expand when heated and contract when cooled, they can be used in glass tubes to indicate changes of temperature, *i.e.* on thermometers. (A thermometer is an instrument designed to measure temperature, and consists basically of a scale, together with some means of indicating degrees of hotness on that scale.) The most suitable liquids for this purpose are mercury and coloured alcohol. Mercury is used where accurate measurements are required, *e.g.* on a clinical thermometer. It conducts heat better than alcohol, expands more uniformly, and its boiling point (357°C) is much higher than that of water (100°C). Unfortunately its rate of expansion is not great, so that the bore in the glass tube of a mercury thermometer has to be narrow to enable the expansion to be appreciated. This is one reason why mercury thermometers are not generally so easy for children to read as alcohol thermometers. Alcohol has the advantage that it expands about six times as much as mercury for the same rise in temperature. It is better for measuring low temperatures since its freezing point is − 112°C, whereas that of mercury is − 39°C. However, the boiling point of alcohol is only 78°C, so that it cannot be used for temperatures above that.

Different liquids expand at different rates. Alcohol and paraffin, for example, both expand more than water for the same rise in temperature.

Water is Odd

When water is cooled, it contracts like any other liquid, but it differs in that when its temperature reaches 4°C (39.2°F), contraction ceases, and expansion begins. This freak expansion continues until 0°C (32°F) is reached, at which temperature the water freezes into the solid form. On freezing, it also expands, by about one-tenth of its volume. This is why ice is a lighter substance than water, and why ice therefore floats on water. This also explains why water at a lower level ceases to be cooled by means of convection currents once the temperature has dropped below 4°C. Water at the bottom of a pond will therefore remain at temperatures above freezing point, while that at the surface (in ice form) may be many degrees below it. Life at the bottom of ponds and lakes can remain dormant but unfrozen because of this. It is because of its peculiarity, and because it combines some of the disadvantages of mercury and alcohol, that water is not a suitable liquid for use in thermometer tubes.

Notes

1 Most substances contract when they freeze. Water and iron are two notable exceptions in that they expand on freezing.

2 A substance in the *solid state* has a definite size, *i.e.* volume, at a given temperature, and can maintain a fixed shape.

3 A substance in the *liquid state* has a definite size (volume) at a given temperature, but no fixed shape. This lack of shape results in a liquid adopting so far as is possible the shape of any solid vessel in which it is contained. One metal—mercury—conforms to these definitions at ordinary temperatures and is therefore in the liquid state at temperatures at which other metals are in the solid state. A characteristic of a liquid is that, when it is completely at rest, its surface is horizontal and level.

4 A substance in the *gaseous state* has no definite size (volume), and no fixed shape. In the gaseous state, a substance always tends to spread throughout the available space in any vessel which contains it, in addition to taking the shape of its container. Most gases cannot be seen, but some can be sensed by means of smell. Air is a mixture of gases. Steam—or water vapour—is also a gas. The cloud visible just beyond the spout of a kettle of boiling water is not steam. It consists of tiny drops of water which have condensed from steam.

5 *Heat* is not a substance, as was once supposed, but a form of energy. The actual *amount* of heat contained by a substance at a given temperature depends upon the quantity of that substance. A given quantity of a particular substance will always contain the same amount of heat at the same temperature—assuming that other conditions, *e.g.* atmospheric pressure, remain the same.

6 The temperature of a particular body is its degree of hotness. This may be measured by several arbitrary scales, *e.g.* Fahrenheit and centigrade scales, in the same way as length may be measured by several arbitrary scales. Temperature has nothing to do with the size of a body or the *quantity* of heat which it contains. A bathful of boiling water would contain far more heat energy than a bucketful of boiling water, but the temperature, *i.e.* the degree of hotness, would be the same.

7 The molecules of a substance, even in the solid state, are considered to be in continual motion. The heat of a sub-

stance has been defined as the energy which is inherent in the random movement of these molecules. As the substance gains heat, the molecules move faster and therefore require a greater space in which to move—this being apparent as expansion. Loss of heat has, in general, the opposite effect, and the result is apparent as contraction. The greater freedom of movement of molecules of liquids and gases accounts for their greater rate of expansion.

CODE

1 Demonstrate that air expands when heated and contracts when cooled.

(a) Squeeze an 'empty' plastic carton—of the kind supplied with liquid soap—and fix on the cap. Stand the carton in hot water. Observe how the carton regains its original shape because of the expansion of the heated air within it. Remove the carton from the hot water, and observe how the walls collapse inwards as the air inside cools and contracts.

(b) Stretch a balloon over the neck of a medicine bottle, and stand the bottle in hot water. Observe how the balloon becomes partly inflated owing to the expansion of the air inside the bottle. Remove the bottle from the water, and observe how the balloon becomes deflated as the air contracts.

(c) Partly inflate a balloon so that it just passes loosely through the opening of a dried-milk tin containing hot water. Now hold the balloon by the neck, and immerse in the hot water. Observe that the expanding air inside the balloon inflates it to the point where it is difficult to remove it from the tin.

(d) Dent a table-tennis ball, without cracking it. Place it in very hot water, and observe that it resumes its normal shape because of the expansion of the air inside it. (Keep the ball for Lesson 15.)

2 Demonstrate that some liquids expand when heated and contract when cooled.

(*a*) Set up one of the 3 pieces of apparatus shown in Diagram
1. Ensure that some of the inky water is in the tube,
and that there is no air left in the bottle. If you use
apparatus A, apply heat. If you use B or C, stand the
bottle in hot water. Observe how the inky water expands up the tube. Now remove the bottle or flask
from the heat, and observe how the liquid contracts
down the tube.

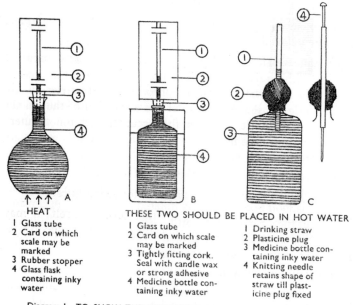

HEAT   THESE TWO SHOULD BE PLACED IN HOT WATER

1 Glass tube	1 Glass tube	1 Drinking straw
2 Card on which scale may be marked	2 Card on which scale may be marked	2 Plasticine plug
3 Rubber stopper	3 Tightly fitting cork. Seal with candle wax or strong adhesive	3 Medicine bottle containing inky water
4 Glass flask containing inky water	4 Medicine bottle containing inky water	4 Knitting needle retains shape of straw till plasticine plug fixed

Diagram 1   TO SHOW THE EXPANSION OF A LIQUID, e.g. inky water

Notes 1 If using a one-hole rubber stopper, moisten stopper before twisting it on to tube.
2 In A a large test-tube could replace the glass flask.
3 In B and C make sure that joints are airtight.
4 Before heating, make sure that there is some liquid in the tube and no air at all in the container.

(*b*) Observe on an ordinary thermometer (or an air thermometer, if made), how the level of the liquid in the glass
tube varies from day to day as the temperature varies.

To make an air thermometer, see Diagram 2.

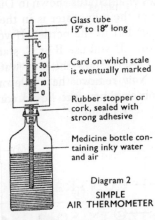

Glass tube
15″ to 18″ long

°C
40
30
20
10
0

Card on which scale
is eventually marked

Rubber stopper or
cork, sealed with
strong adhesive

Medicine bottle con-
taining inky water
and air

Diagram 2
SIMPLE
AIR THERMOMETER

(i) Half fill the bottle with tinted water, and fit the tube through the stopper.

(ii) Draw liquid up the tube until it just shows above the stopper, and then fit stopper into bottle. It must be airtight.

(iii) Fix blank card on tube.

(iv) Place bottle and an ordinary thermometer in hot water. As the water cools, mark the scale on the card to tally with the readings on the ordinary thermometer.

NOTEBOOK WORK

Answers should be along the following lines.

1 A substance may change to another form of itself; it may change to another kind of substance; it may change in size.

2 (*a*) Expanding means increasing in size.

(*b*) Contracting means decreasing in size.

3 Gases and many liquids begin to expand as soon as they begin to gain heat.

4 Expanding steam can cause a boiler to burst.

5 We can use gases to force things to move because they expand a lot when heated.

6 The two liquids usually used in thermometers are mercury and alcohol.

7 It is unwise to pump up tyres too much in hot weather because they may burst, owing to the expansion of air inside them.

Answers to Puzzles

1 The bubbles are due to the heat from the hands causing the air in the flask to expand.

2 The thermometer shows the wrong temperature for ice.

3 A dent can be taken out of a table-tennis ball by putting it into very hot water. (It is liable to melt if placed in an oven, and to burn if held over a flame.)

(14) EXPANDING AND CONTRACTING

CHANGE OF SIZE IN SOLIDS

DEMONSTRATION MATERIAL

Equipment to show that a metal expands when heated and contracts when cooled: length of wire, candles, etc, as illustrated in the Pupils' Book

SAMPLE LINK QUESTIONS

1 What are the three main ways in which a substance may be changed by a change in temperature? (*Change to another form; change to another kind of substance; change in size*)

2 When a substance is increasing in size, what do we say it is doing? (*Expanding*)

3 When a substance is decreasing in size, what do we say it is doing? (*Contracting*)

4 In which is a change of size more obvious—in liquids or in gases? (*In gases*)

5 What can cause the lid to rattle on a kettle of boiling water? (*Expanding steam*)

6 If a gas expands in a sealed container, what may it do to the container? (*Burst it*)

7 What may cause a balloon to burst if it goes near a fire? (*Expanding air inside the balloon*)

8 Which two liquids are used chiefly in the glass tubes on thermometers? (*Mercury and alcohol*)

9 When the temperature of a substance rises, is it gaining heat or losing heat? (*Gaining heat*)

RELEVANT INFORMATION

The main points of this lesson are that

1 many solids expand as they gain heat, and contract as they lose heat;

2 change of size in solids is slight.

Change of size in solids is by no means as obvious as it is in gases or liquids. In general, metals in the solid state expand more than other solids, but even in these the rate of expansion is inconsiderable. For example, a length of steel which is 300 feet long when the temperature is 0°C will be only about one inch longer when the temperature is 20°C. Even so, it is often necessary to make allowances for expansion in solids, particularly where comparatively long lengths or large masses are involved.

1 On railway lines, it was once customary to leave a small gap between lengths of rail to allow the rails to expand in hot weather without buckling. These gaps were responsible for the familiar clickety-clack sound. Modern tracks have much longer rails with tapered ends which overlap to allow for expansion.

2 On concrete roads, narrow gaps between one block of concrete and the next allow the concrete to expand without cracking. The gaps are filled with pitch which becomes soft and allows the expansion to take place.

3 Lengths of steam piping have bends or loops in them to allow the pipe to expand without being damaged.

4 Glass for window and picture frames is cut a little smaller than the frame.

5 Where long lengths of metal are used for construction purposes, allowance may be made for expansion by leaving a gap at one end, and mounting that end on rollers so that there is a reduction in friction. On some bridges, for example, one end is fixed, and the other end mounted on rollers. On some other bridges both ends are mounted on rollers. Still others

may have provision for expansion at one or more intermediate parts. The Forth Bridge (carrying the railway) has roller bearings at each end of the bridge, and in addition there are rocking posts at each end of the main centre span. This bridge is some 1½ miles long and has allowances for a total expansion of up to 6 feet. The Pupils' Book shows an expansion device used on modern concrete road bridges, where a gap filled with pitch would be unsatisfactory as the pitch would gradually ooze downwards, leaving the edges of the gap exposed to weathering. The two bands of toothed plates made from rust-proof metals enable the surface of the road to be kept uniform at all temperatures.

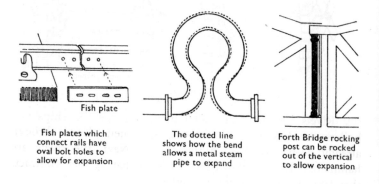

Fish plate

Fish plates which connect rails have oval bolt holes to allow for expansion

The dotted line shows how the bend allows a metal steam pipe to expand

Forth Bridge rocking post can be rocked out of the vertical to allow expansion

Expansion of Solids can be used to Advantage

A glass stopper, fitting tightly in the neck of a bottle, may be loosened by holding the neck of the bottle under a stream of hot water until it has expanded slightly.

A metal screw-cap, fitting tightly to the neck of a bottle or jar, may be loosened by heating the cap itself, *e.g.* with a lighted match or by holding it under a stream of hot water, so as to make the cap expand.

A rusty screw may be loosened by heating a poker and applying it to the screw-head. Heat conducted by the screw causes it to expand slightly and to contract when cooled, the expansion and contraction of the screw tending to loosen it.

Contraction of Solids can be used to Advantage

The metal tyres on the wheels of locomotives and railway trucks are often shrunk on to the wheels. The tyre is made slightly smaller than the wheel, and then heated so that it expands enough for it to be forced on to the wheel. On cooling, the tyre contracts and grips the wheel tightly.

Iron tie rods, the ends of which can still be seen on the walls of old property, were used by builders to support bulging walls. The rod was heated to make it expand, and then an end plate was screwed to the wall.

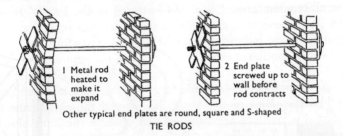

1 Metal rod heated to make it expand

2 End plate screwed up to wall before rod contracts

Other typical end plates are round, square and S-shaped

TIE RODS

Rivets for fastening metal plates together on ships and boilers are heated until red-hot, and then placed through already prepared holes in the plates. Next, the rivets are hammered flat and allowed to cool, so that as they contract, they force the plates tightly together.

Different solids expand at different rates. The following are listed in order of rate of expansion, beginning with the greatest: aluminium, brass, copper, concrete, cast iron, platinum, Pyrex glass. The alloy invar (from *invariable*) hardly expands at all when heated. It consists of steel with a 36% nickel content.

Although when water freezes, it expands considerably, ice itself obeys the general principle for solids, *i.e.* it contracts as its temperature falls, and any available water will flow into the resulting space. This is why a rim of water may sometimes be seen between the ice floating on the surface of a pond or bucket, and the sides. When this water freezes, the sheet of ice becomes once more continuous. With a rise in temperature towards melting point, the ice will expand and exert an enormous pressure. Burst pipes and cracks in rocks and concrete can be caused in this way.

The expansion of wood on drawers and doors in winter, is due not to a change of temperature, but to the absorption of water from a damp atmosphere.

CODE

Demonstrate that some solids expand when heated and contract when cooled, *e.g.* as illustrated in the Pupils' Book. In A, observe that as the wire is heated, the pointer moves slowly down, indicating that the wire is expanding; and that when the candles are removed, the end of the pointer moves up, indicating that the wire is contracting. In B, observe that the knife slowly descends, indicating that the wire is expanding. When the point of the blade has pierced the small cube of plasticine, remove the candles, and observe the knife slowly ascending, indicating that the wire is contracting. The knife should take the small cube of plasticine with it. The longer the wire, the more obvious the result.

NOTEBOOK WORK

Answers should be along the following lines.

1 Telegraph wires sag slightly more in hot weather because heat makes them expand.

2 Many solids, liquids and gases begin to contract as soon as they begin to lose heat.

3 The solid substances which generally expand or contract most are metals.

4 Gaps were left between lengths of railway line so that the line could expand without buckling.

5 When the rivets cool, they contract and pull the plates tightly together.

Answers to Puzzles

1 The hot water causes the tightly-fitting metal cap to expand slightly.

2 Heat from the red-hot poker causes the tightly-fitting screw to expand. As it cools, it contracts and is thus loosened.

3 When the iron tyre cools, it will contract and fit the wheel tightly.

4 As glass is a poor conductor of heat, the heat from the boiling water will be conducted slowly through the sides of the glass, so that the inside will expand before the outside, and the resulting stress may cause a fracture.

(15) AIR PRESSES AGAINST THINGS

IT PRESSES IN ALL DIRECTIONS

DEMONSTRATION MATERIAL

As many as possible of the following:

Shallow bowl of tinted water and a large bottle or jar; bottle (*e.g.* milk bottle) with a smooth rim, water, piece of thin card; sheet of newspaper and an old ruler; length of transparent plastic tubing; small paper or plastic bags; coins, *e.g.* pennies; rubber suckers; eye droppers; length of candle (about 3″) and a 2-lb jam jar; plastic liquid-soap container with cap; balloon and medicine bottle; table-tennis ball

SAMPLE LINK QUESTIONS

1 What are the three forms of never-alive things? (*Solid, liquid, gas*)

2 How does a gas differ from a solid and a liquid? (*A gas has neither size nor shape*)

3 What are draughts, breezes, winds, gales and hurricanes? (*Moving air*)

4 When air is heated, does it expand or contract? (*It expands*)

5 What does the air consist of? (*A mixture of gases*)
6 What are the three main things which force other things to move from place to place over the surface of the earth? (*Moving air, moving water, moving animals*)
7 The earth forces things to move towards it. What do we call this pull of the earth? (*Gravity*)
8 Towards which part of the earth are things pulled? (*Towards the centre*)

RELEVANT INFORMATION

The purpose of a lesson in Pupils' Book 1 was to show that air is something.

The main points of this lesson are that

1 air presses against things;
2 it presses in all directions;
3 removing the air from one part of a thing allows air pressing against other parts to push it in that direction.

Air is a mixture of gases, the chief ones being nitrogen (about 78%) and oxygen (about 21%). The three most important gases in the remaining 1% are carbon dioxide, argon, and water vapour, although the actual amount of water vapour varies considerably from one place to another. A gas has no definite size, *i.e.* volume, and no fixed shape. Thus, in the gaseous state, a substance always tends to spread throughout the available space in any vessel which contains it, in addition to taking the shape of its container.

Air has weight. The weight of something is a measurement of the force with which it and the earth pull one another. The earth pulls each molecule of air, and is in turn pulled by it. (It is the earth which pulls—not gravity. Gravity is merely the term applied to the pull of the earth.)

The pull of the earth is such that a cubic foot of the molecules of air weighs about $1\frac{1}{4}$ ozs. We live at the bottom of an ocean of air which is several hundred miles deep, and in this ocean, each cubic foot of air is forced by gravity to press down on the air beneath it with the result that there is a total weight of some 5,000 million million tons of air pressing against the earth's surface. This is equal to 14.7 lbs per square inch at sea level. The total weight of the column of air pressing down on the top of an average child's head is between 500 and 600 lbs—nearly a quarter of a ton. Bigger heads have to withstand more. However, as air is a mixture of gases and can flow freely in any direction, the pressure is applied in all directions—not only downwards, but sideways and upwards as well. A somewhat similar effect may be observed if you press your bare foot on wet sand, when the sand will be forced not only downwards, but also sideways and upwards between the toes. The equal pressing of the air in all directions is responsible for a soap bubble being round; if air pressed more against some parts than others, the bubble would not be round. It is distorted in shape while it is being blown, owing to the unequal pressure of air on the inner surface.

Removing the air from one particular place creates temporarily an area of reduced pressure, and as the surrounding air has no shape to stop it flowing, it immediately flows in from all directions. In a similar way, if you dip a cup into water and remove a cupful, the surrounding water immediately flows in from all directions to fill up the space as rapidly as it is formed. Because of this, when the air pressing against one part of something is removed, the air pressing against other parts tends to push it in that direction. This is what happens when you drink liquid through a straw. You remove the air from inside the straw, and the air pressing against the surface of the liquid forces some of it up the straw ahead of it. Similarly, in a modern vacuum cleaner, a fan turned by an electric motor forces air out through one end of the cleaner. More air flows in at the other end (moving from an area of high pressure to an area of low pressure), and takes dust and other particles with it. A vacuum cleaner does not have a vacuum inside it, of course.

Liquid is drawn into an eye-dropper by first squeezing the bulb to force some of the air out. When the bulb is released, the air outside forces liquid into the space vacated by the air. A fountain pen filler operates on the same principle.

A rubber sucker does not suck. When it is squashed flat against a surface, air is forced out from the inner part of the sucker, and when it is released, the surrounding air tries to return. If however there is an airtight seal between the rim of the sucker and the surface, the air pressing against the outer part of the sucker forces it against the surface.

Lids are placed on jam jars while the contents are hot. As the air and any other gases trapped in the top of the jar cool, they contract, so reducing their effective pressure on the underside of the lid. The air pressure against the top of the lid is comparatively greater, and this makes the lid difficult to remove. When the lid is pierced, air rushes in through the hole so that the pressure on both sides becomes equal, and the lid can then be easily removed.

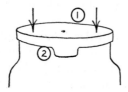

I Air pressing against this side with a total weight of about $14\frac{1}{2}$ lbs per square inch

2 Ideally, no air pressing against the underside

'PIERCE WITH A PIN AND PUSH OFF'

Sometimes at moderately high altitudes, an ear will 'pop' or go slightly deaf. This is due to the reduction in the amount of air pressing against the outer surface of the eardrum while that pressing against the inner surface remains the same and pushes the eardrum out a little. The amount of air pressing against the inner surface can usually be adjusted by yawning and swallowing.

CODE

1 Demonstrate that air presses against things.

   (a) Fill a bottle or jar with coloured water. Cover the neck temporarily with a sheet of card, and invert so that the neck is below the surface of water in a shallow bowl or dish. Remove the card, and observe that the coloured water does not run out of the jar or bottle owing to the pressure of air on the surface of the water in the bowl.

Note. This is illustrated in the Pupils' Book as a puzzle. A similar arrangement is used for providing water in birdcages.

(b) Spread a sheet of newspaper flat on a table. Smooth paper well out to remove as much air as possible from beneath it. Slide an old ruler between the paper and the table so that part is covered by the paper, and part projects over the edge of the table. Strike the projecting part of the ruler sharply, and observe that the paper is hardly lifted owing to the pressure of air on its surface. The paper may tear, or the ruler may snap.

2 Experiment to show that air presses against things in all directions. Use a bottle of water and a piece of thin card as shown in the Pupils' Book. It is not necessary to fill the bottle with water so long as the rim is sufficiently moist to provide an airtight seal, *i.e.* so that air cannot enter. It is, of course, advisable to test this first to ensure that the rim has no cracks or chips which would prevent an airtight seal.

3 Demonstrate that if the air which is pressing against one part of something is removed, the air pressing against other parts will push it in that direction.

(a) Insert the end of some plastic tubing well into a large bottle or jar and invert in a bowl of water as shown in the diagram. Suck air out through the other end of the plastic tube, and observe how water is forced to rise in the bottle owing to the pressure of air on the surface of the water in the bowl. This illustrates what happens when milk is drunk through a straw.

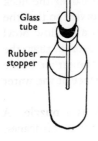

Glass tube

Rubber stopper

For comparison, prevent air from moving, and observe the result. Obtain a one-holed rubber stopper, fitted with a glass tube, and insert this so that it fits tightly in the neck of a bottle containing some milk and the tube reaches into the milk. A pupil who is invited to

drink this milk will be unable to do so, because air
will be unable to enter the bottle.

(b) Experiment with rubber 'suckers' on various surfaces.

(i) Press one on to a rough surface, or over the crack
where a cupboard door meets the framework.

(ii) Press one with a dry rim on to a glass surface.

(iii) Press one with a moistened rim on to a similar
surface.

Observe that (i) will not remain in position at all because
there is no airtight seal; that (ii) falls off next because the seal is
imperfect, and that (iii) remains until the water providing the
seal has evaporated.

(iv) Moisten two suckers and press together.

Observe how difficult it is to pull them apart. (This is
similar to the famous Magdeburg hemisphere experiment.)
Observe also that the air presses in all directions, *i.e.* the
suckers can be turned in any direction.

Note. A rubber plunger, of the kind used for evacuating a
blocked waste pipe, has a large rubber hemisphere which may
be used to pick up a chair or a stool. Pupils will find it difficult
to remove one of these.

(c) Demonstrate how to siphon water out of an aquarium.

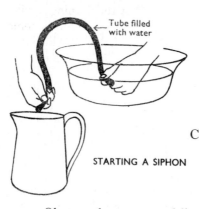

Tube filled
with water

STARTING A SIPHON

Fill a bowl with water, and
put an empty jug at a lower
level. Completely submerge
a length of plastic or rubber
tubing in the water until air
bubbles cease to come out
of the ends, *i.e.* until the
tube is full of water.

Close both ends with fingers.
Retain one below water
surface; lift out other end,
and place over jug. Open
both ends simultaneously.

Observe that as water falls out of the tube into the jug,
the air pressing on the surface of the water in the bowl
pushes more up the tube. This in turn falls into the jug;

and a continuous stream of water is forced uphill and over the edge of the bowl, whence it falls into the jug.

Notes (i) This demonstration is more effective if coloured water and transparent plastic tubing are used.

(ii) Water will continue to flow through the tube as long as the exit is lower than the surface of the water in the bowl. Once the level in the bowl falls to the level of the exit end of the tube, the flow will cease.

(iii) The stream of water entering the tube will take small light particles with it, so that a siphon can be used to remove sediment as well as water from an aquarium.

(*d*) Experiment to find what proportion of the air is oxygen. Pin an oblong of thin card to the bottom of a length of candle (about 3"), as shown in the diagram. Stand this in a shallow bowl of water, and light the candle. Invert a 2-lb jam jar over the lighted candle so that the rim holds the card down.

Observe that as the oxygen is used by the burning candle, air pressing on the surface of the water forces some into the jar to replace that part of the air which has been removed. As a jam jar is 5" high, the water level will rise about 1" before the candle goes out, showing that the oxygen used up constituted one-fifth of the original air. This measurement is, of course, approximate, as allowance should be made for the shaping of the jar and for the space occupied by the candle.

(*e*) Use the balloon and medicine bottle employed in Lesson 13. Stand the bottle in boiling water for some time. The neck of the balloon will act as a valve, allowing some of the expanding air to escape.

Remove the bottle and allow to cool. As the air inside the bottle contracts, the air pressing against the outer surface of the balloon will force it in through the bottle neck. It is unlikely that the balloon will be easily pulled out.

(f) Use the table-tennis ball employed in Lesson 13.

Leave the ball in boiling water for some time, until the air expanding inside it makes it noticeably larger. Remove and allow to cool.

Observe that as the air inside cools and contracts, the air pressing against the outer surface causes the ball to collapse. (If it doesn't, bounce it.)

NOTEBOOK WORK

Answers should be along the following lines.

1 Air presses against things because the earth pulls it.

2 Air presses in all directions.

3 (a) When you take away the air from one part of something, the air pressing against other parts will be able to push it in that direction.

(b) When you drink liquid through a straw, you suck air out of the straw; then the air pressing down on the surface of the liquid pushes some of it up the straw.

Answers to Puzzles

1 The air pressing on the surface of the water in the bowl prevents the water from coming out of the jar.

2 As the plunger is withdrawn, the air pressing on the surface of the water in the bowl pushes some into the syringe.

3 Air is first forced out of the eye-dropper. When the bulb is released, air pressing on the surface of the water forces some into the eye-dropper.

4 The hot water causes the air in the plastic container to expand and some escapes. When the top is closed and the container removed, the remaining air cools and contracts. As there is now less air in the container than at the start, the outside air is able to push the sides inwards.

(16) SQUEEZING AIR

MAKING AIR PRESS MORE

DEMONSTRATION MATERIAL

Balloons; cycle pump; bottle or flask fitted with one-hole rubber stopper and length of glass tubing (*see* C O D E); Cartesian diver, *e.g.* wine bottle (clear glass) with tightly-fitting cork, an eye-dropper and water

SAMPLE LINK QUESTIONS

1 What is air a mixture of? (*Gases*)
2 How does a gas differ from a solid or a liquid? (*A gas has neither size nor shape*)
3 What forces air to press against things? (*The pull of the earth (gravity)*)
4 In which directions does the air press? (*In all directions*)
5 If air pressed more against one part of a soap bubble than against others, how would its shape be altered? (*It would be distorted*)
6 If you take away the air pressing against one part of something, what is the air pressing against other parts able to do? (*Push it in that direction*)
7 What happens when you drink liquid through a straw? (*First you suck air out of the straw. Then air pressing against the surface of the liquid is able to push some of it up through the straw*)
8 Why is a rubber sucker wrongly named? (*It does not suck*)

9 What is happening when you press a rubber sucker against a flat surface and it stays fixed there? (*Air is forced out between the sucker and the surface. Then air pressing against other parts forces it against the surface*)

RELEVANT INFORMATION

The main points of this lesson are that

1 compressed air presses against things with more force than the air about us;

2 two ways of compressing air inside a container are by (*a*) forcing more air in, (*b*) squeezing the air already in.

The more air there is (*i.e.* the more molecules there are) pressing against a surface, the greater is the pressure against that surface. The number of molecules of air pressing against a unit area of surface can be increased by pressing them closer together, *i.e.* by compressing the air. Air is a mixture of gases, and gases—unlike liquids and solids—are easily compressed. Whether the compressing of air is accomplished by forcing more air into a closed container, or by reducing the actual volume of the container so that the air already in it is compressed, the result is the same—the number of molecules of air pressing against a unit area of surface becomes greater than that of the outside atmosphere.

A deflated tyre is a good example of a container of fixed size with the enclosed air at normal atmospheric pressure. When the tyre is pumped up, the quantity of air inside is increased

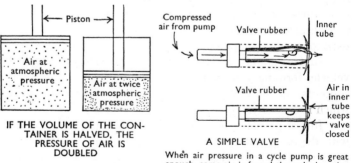

IF THE VOLUME OF THE CONTAINER IS HALVED, THE PRESSURE OF AIR IS DOUBLED

A SIMPLE VALVE

When air pressure in a cycle pump is great enough, some air is forced through the valve and into the inner tube and its pressure against the inside walls becomes greater than the pressure of the atmospheric air against the outside walls. Pressure can be measured in terms of lbs per square inch by using a pressure gauge.

To compress air by reducing the volume of the container, some form of piston may be used, or a liquid may be introduced into the container so that the volume left for the air is less. A bicycle pump or the pump used for blowing up footballs is a simple example of a compression pump in which a piston is used to reduce the volume of the container.

Compression pumps are used to force additional air into containers in which compressed air is stored, and they are often driven by some kind of engine, *e.g.* in connexion with a road drill. The container for the compressed air is often a large cylinder on the underside of the engine. Leading from this container is the high-pressure tubing through which compressed air flows to the pneumatic drill.

Uses of Compressed Air

The uses of compressed air in industry are virtually limitless. A few of the many are for sandblasting; spraying insecticides, paints and enamels; operating hoists, lifts, tube-train doors and air-brake systems; cleaning parts of vehicles, and drying damp surfaces; pumping water and sewage; transferring liquids and fine solids such as grain and sand from one place to another; pressure cooking; glass-blowing; operating pneumatic tools; ventilating various out-of-the-way places; iron lungs; salvaging sunken ships; diving bells, underwater caissons, and the cylinders of air carried by skin divers. It is also used for stuffing sausages.

In a hovercraft, air is forced down through the base of the vehicle, forming a cushion of compressed air which raises and supports the hovercraft, and also provides a surface of air which reduces friction.

Just as pressure increases with depth in air, so it increases with depth in water, and in diving bells and caissons, compressed air is used to keep out water from the working space. A caisson is a large bottomless container which is sunk in the water and then filled with compressed air to drive out the water so that men can work on underwater construction, *e.g.* the building of supports for bridges.

CODE

Demonstrate that compressed air presses against things with more force than the air about us:

1 By forcing more air into an enclosed space. Blow up a balloon and observe how the rubber is stretched.

2 By squeezing the air already present in an enclosed space.

(*a*) Use a cycle pump as a popgun. Place a tiny pellet of paper or plasticine in the outlet end. Press the handle in sharply, and observe how the pellet is ejected by the compressed air inside the pump pressing against it.

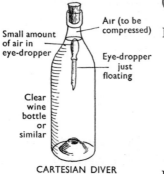

Air (to be compressed)

Small amount of air in eye-dropper

Eye-dropper just floating

Clear wine bottle or similar

CARTESIAN DIVER

(*b*) Set up a simple Cartesian diver model, as in diagram. First adjust the level of water in the eye-dropper so that it just floats below the surface of water in a bowl. Transfer the eye-dropper to a large bottle of water which has a small air space at the top and a tightly-fitting cork.

Pressure on the cork will compress the small amount of air at the top of the bottle. This will increase the pressure on the surface of the water, and force a little more water into the eye-dropper. (Water, like other liquids, is almost incompressible.) The extra weight in the eye-dropper will cause it to sink. Releasing the pressure on the cork will allow the 'diver' to rise.

NOTEBOOK WORK

Answers should be along the following lines.

1 The two main ways of compressing air are by forcing more air in, and by squeezing the air already in.

2 When you blow up a balloon, you force more air in.

3 A tyre feels harder when you put more air into it because the air is squeezed more and it presses harder against the inside surface.

4 If you compress compressed air, it presses against things with more force still.

Solutions to Puzzles

1 Pressure is increased in the blowpipe by forcing more air in, and in the popgun by squeezing the air already in.

2 (*a*) The tin may be picked up by inserting the body of the balloon into the opening of the tin, and inflating until the sides of the balloon are forced against the sides of the tin.

(*b*) The books may be raised by placing the balloon underneath them and inflating.

(*c*) The whistle may be blown by inflating the balloon and inserting the mouth of the whistle into the neck of the balloon.

(17) MAKING IT DIFFICULT FOR THINGS TO SLIP

INCREASING FRICTION

DEMONSTRATION MATERIAL

String and scissors—or a model which stops and starts according to command (See page 164); pupil's gloves; smooth sloping board, sandpaper, and suitable load (*e.g.* flat-bottomed tin filled with sand) *or* board, two rough bricks and a tin lid; bottle stopper or cap with roughened edge

SAMPLE LINK QUESTIONS

1 Which is the easier surface to slide over—rough or smooth? (*A smooth surface*)

2 What name do we give to the resistance to movement between surfaces? (*Friction*)

3 What does friction cause? (*Wear and heat*)

4 Because of friction, what do we need to start things moving, and to keep them moving? (*Power*)

5 Name two different kinds of bearings that are used to reduce friction? (*Ball bearings, roller bearings*)

6 When substances such as oil and grease are used to reduce friction, what do we call them? (*Lubricants*)

7 What reduces friction underneath a hovercraft? (*A layer of compressed air*)

RELEVANT INFORMATION

The main points of a lesson on friction in Pupils' Book 3 were that

1 the resistance to movement between any two surfaces is called friction;

2 it is because of friction that we need power to start things moving and to keep them moving;

3 friction causes (*a*) wear and (*b*) heat.

The main points of a lesson on reducing friction in Pupils' Book 3 were that

1 when friction is reduced, less power is needed to keep things moving;

2 four ways of reducing friction are (*a*) making a surface smooth, (*b*) using a lubricant, (*c*) using ball bearings or roller bearings, (*d*) using a surface of air.

The main points of this lesson are that

1 sometimes a surface is so smooth that sliding takes place too easily;

2 two ways of increasing friction between solid surfaces so that sliding becomes more difficult are by (*a*) pressing the surfaces together more firmly; (*b*) making one or both of the surfaces rougher.

The Meaning of Friction

There is a natural resistance to the movement of one surface upon another. This resistance results partly from the molecular attraction between surfaces in contact, and partly from the nature and condition of the surfaces. The resistance itself is in the nature of a force and is termed friction.

The resistance to movement applies to both stationary and moving substances. If a nail is driven into a piece of wood, friction (caused by the pressure of the wood against the nail) prevents the nail from sliding out. Similarly, if a box is at rest on a sloping board, the force of friction between the surfaces of box and board prevents the box from sliding down. Friction between surfaces which are not in motion across one another is known as *static friction*. If the board is tilted to an angle at which gravity can overcome static friction, the box will slide down the board, and the resistance between the surface of the sliding box and the surface of board is known as the *friction of motion*. The force required to overcome static friction is always greater than that required to overcome the friction of motion. That is to say, more power is required to start a thing moving, than to keep it moving. Reducing friction makes movement easier and therefore reduces the power that is required. It also reduces the amount of wear and heat.

Reducing Friction too Much

Rolling friction is less than sliding friction. In an ideal situation, each point of contact between a rolling object and the surface over which it rolls is one of momentary rest. This means that in theory there is no friction of movement between the two surfaces. However, the static friction at this point of contact must be sufficient to ensure this momentary position of rest. If the static friction at the point of contact is too small, then sliding (by slipping or skidding) will take place at that point. Thus a reduction of friction is not always to our advantage. On an icy road or on a patch of oil, for example, friction may be so reduced that wheels are unable to obtain a grip, and slide instead of rolling. Similarly, on icy surfaces and smooth polished floors, friction is reduced, and feet tend to slide and slip. If a banana skin is trodden on, the soft material from the skin fills in the tiny depressions in the solid surface of the shoe (or pavement), and thus acts as a lubricant to make a smoother surface and reduce friction. Slipping on a bar of wet soap, on spilt food, or treading on unseen marbles are further examples of friction being reduced to our disadvantage.

When friction is reduced so much that a surface is too smooth for our liking, we say it is slippery. In such cases, it may be necessary to increase friction to obtain the required control of movement.

Increasing Friction to Make Sliding More Difficult

There are two main ways of doing this.

1 *By pressing two surfaces together more firmly.* When two solid surfaces are in contact, the frictional resistance between them is proportional to the force with which the surfaces are pressed together (proportional to the load). Because of increased friction, a load of two bricks would require more power to force it to slide than would a load of one brick.

Pressure is used to prevent sliding when climbing a rope, when using an elastic band or a strap to fasten things together, or to prevent the hand from slipping when unscrewing a cap or stopper. Increasing pressure on a bicycle brake is another example of pressing two surfaces more firmly together to increase friction, thereby making it more difficult for the wheel rim to slide over the brake blocks.

2 *By making one or both of the surfaces rougher.* The rougher the surfaces in contact, the harder it is to force something to slide. A surface may be made rougher in order to provide suitable conditions for rolling, *i.e.* static friction may be increased at the point of contact so as to prevent sliding. The tread on a rubber tyre makes it less likely for a wheel to skid. In icy conditions, chains are put round vehicle wheels to provide them with an even rougher surface. Grit is used to provide a rougher surface on the road itself.

There are many everyday examples of providing rougher surfaces to increase friction so that sliding is reduced, *e.g.* using a towel to grip a tightly-fitting bottle stopper, or fitting the wooden handles of cricket bats with rubber grips.

Friction allows us to chalk on a blackboard. The friction between the surface of the board and a piece of chalk causes tiny particles of chalk to be worn away and deposited on the board. Sometimes part of the blackboard is worn too smooth, *i.e.* the frictional resistance is reduced so much that the chalk slides or skids across the smooth patch and there is insufficient wearing of the chalk for enough particles to be deposited on it. Coating the blackboard with a renovating paint provides a rougher surface, and gives the necessary increase in friction.

If there were no friction at all, movement would be extremely difficult to control. Walking and running would not be possible, because feet would just slide backwards. Wheeled vehicles would not move, because the wheels would simply spin —in fact they would never have been invented. Nails would slide out of wood, and things would slip out of our grasp. We should not have matches to strike or petrol lighters to ignite, because there would be no friction to cause heat.

Lack of friction is of course an advantage in the airless regions of outer space, where a space vehicle can continue at a set speed without the continued use of power to maintain it.

CODE

1 Observe examples of a reduction in friction being disadvantageous, *e.g.* wheels skidding on an icy or muddy surface, feet slipping on a highly-polished floor.
2 Demonstrate that forcing two solid surfaces together makes sliding more difficult.
   (*a*) Place hands together lightly and slide over one another quickly. Then press hands together hard, and observe that sliding is more difficult.
   (*b*) Pull a length of string or cord between someone's fingers. Observe that as they increase the pressure of their fingers, it becomes harder to pull the string.
   (*c*) Thread a length of string through the handles of a pair of scissors as suggested in the Pupils' Book. When the string is held slack (with one hand higher than the other), the scissors will slide down it. When the string is pulled taut, the scissors will stop, because the string is forced against the sides of the handles, thus increasing the friction between string and handles. A

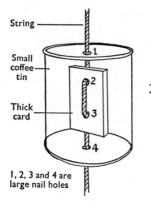

String

Small coffee tin

Thick card

1
2
3
4

1, 2, 3 and 4 are large nail holes

more mysterious model can be made as shown in the diagram, using a tin so that the bend in the string is hidden.

3 Observe examples of solid surfaces being pressed together to make sliding more difficult, *e.g.* the use of elastic bands for holding things together, or children trying to unscrew tightly-fitting bottle stoppers and caps and then passing them to an adult whose more powerful grip exerts more pressure and prevents the hand from slipping.

4 Demonstrate that making a surface rougher makes sliding more difficult.

(*a*) Rub the bare hands together quickly. Then, exerting the same pressure, rub gloved hands together.

(*b*) Fasten a length of sandpaper along half of a smooth board, as in top diagram opposite.

Place a suitable load, *e.g.* a brick or a flat-bottomed tin filled with sand, on the smooth surface, and tilt the board to the angle at which the load just slides down. Support the board at that angle.

Place the same load on the sandpaper, and observe that, because friction is increased by the rougher surface, the load does not slide.

5 Observe examples of rough surfaces being used to make sliding more difficult: the tread on tyres, chains on vehicle wheels in icy weather, sand and grit on icy roads, rough tiles instead of smooth tiles round the edge of a swimming bath, ridged edges round screw tops, use of coarse cloth when unscrewing stoppers and caps, rubber grips on handles of bats and rackets.

6 Experiment to show that friction may be increased by providing a rougher surface, or by pressing two surfaces more tightly together.

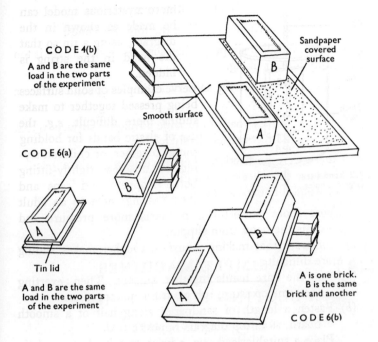

CODE 4(b)

A and B are the same load in the two parts of the experiment

Sandpaper covered surface

B

Smooth surface

A

CODE 6(a)

B

A

Tin lid

A and B are the same load in the two parts of the experiment

B

A

A is one brick. B is the same brick and another

CODE 6(b)

(*a*) Place a smooth tin lid on a board, and in the lid place a brick. Tilt the board to the angle at which the brick on its tin lid begins to slide.

Keeping the board tilted at the same angle, remove the tin lid, and place the brick at the top of the slope. Observe that the brick no longer slides, because its own surface is rougher than that of the tin lid, *i.e. providing a rougher surface increases friction.*

(*b*) Tilt the board slowly to the angle at which the brick will now slide. Keeping the board tilted at the same angle, replace the brick at the top of the slope, and put a second brick on top of it. Observe that the bottom brick no longer slides because of the increased pressure provided by the top brick, *i.e. pressing two surfaces more tightly together increases friction.*

NOTEBOOK WORK

Answers should be along the following lines.

1 A surface is called slippery when something slides over it too easily for our liking.

2 Rubber is better for the soles of P.T. shoes because it has a rougher surface.

3 Grit is put on icy roads to provide a rougher surface so that wheels and feet are less likely to slip.

4 If there were no friction wheeled vehicles would not move, because the wheels would just spin. Nails would slide out of wood. Things would slip out of our grasp.

18 SIMPLE MACHINES

A SLOPING SURFACE HELPS

DEMONSTRATION MATERIAL

As many as possible of the following: material for demonstrating how a ramp makes work easier, (a sloping board, a suitable load, such as a roller skate or a tin filled with sand, paper clip and elastic band, or a spring balance); bowl of water; pencils and right-angled triangles of exercise book paper; any appliances incorporating the use of the wedge (*e.g.* knife, scissors, saw, toy boat with pointed prow, nail); any appliances incorporating the use of a screw (*e.g.* wood screws, nut and bolt, corkscrew, gimlet, clamp, screw press)

SAMPLE LINK QUESTIONS

1 When something is used to make work easier, what do we call it? (*A machine*)

2 What can a machine help us to obtain? (*More force*)

3 What kind of simple machine does a spoon become when it is used to force the lid off a tin? (*A lever*)

4 In which two simple machines is a wheel used? (*A pulley, and a wheel and axle*)

5 What does a pulley have round its wheel to prevent a rope from slipping off? (*A groove*)

6 Which part of a wheel and axle helps to obtain more force? (*The wheel*)

7 Which force have you to overcome when you lift something up? (*Gravity*)

RELEVANT INFORMATION

The main purpose of a lesson on simple machines in Pupils' Book 3 was to show that

1 when something is used to make work easier, we call it a machine;

2 three of the simplest forms in which materials are used as machines are (*a*) a lever, (*b*) a pulley, (*c*) a wheel and axle;

3 machines can be used to obtain more force.

The main purpose of this lesson is to show that there are three main ways in which a sloping surface may be used as a simple machine—

1 as a ramp 2 on a wedge 3 on a screw.

When an object is being used to enable work to be done more easily than would be possible without it, it is being used as a machine. A machine enables existing and available energy to be utilised in the way and direction required, but it neither creates energy nor adds to it. When a heavy load has to be raised to a certain height, for example, the use of a ramp will enable the work to be done with the application of less force, but the force will be applied over a greater distance.

An object used as a machine need not necessarily have been made for that purpose. A plank of wood, for example, is not a machine to begin with, but if it is rested on a step and used as a ramp, then it is being used as a simple machine. The ability of human beings to utilise various materials as machines has helped immeasurably to widen the gap between their progress and that of other animals.

The purposes for which a machine may be used are:

1 to change the effectiveness of the force which is applied to it;
2 to change the direction of the force;
3 to change the speed of the force;
4 to make the force effective some distance from where it is applied.

There are six different ways in which objects may be used as simple machines.

1 As a lever   2 As a pulley   3 As a wheel and axle

A pulley-wheel and a wheel and axle are really rotating levers.

4 As a ramp   5 As a wedge   6 As a screw

Ramps, wedges and screws all involve the use of sloping surfaces (inclined planes).

The most complicated machinery is only a combination of a number of these six simple machines.

Using a Sloping Surface as a Ramp

A ramp is perhaps the most elementary example of a sloping surface used to make work easier. Simply, it is a flat surface with one end higher than the other. A ramp helps to overcome the force of gravity. It enables a load to be raised to a certain height with the application of less force than would be required to lift it straight up. The work is easier, but the actual amount done remains the same, as the force has to be applied over a greater distance.

The ancient Egyptians probably used giant ramps in constructing the pyramids. Modern examples include sloping planks on building sites which enable wheelbarrows to be raised easily from ground to floor-level, and ramps at the end of railway platforms for luggage trucks. There are ramps in many places for motor cars. Mountain roads are typical examples of long ramps, and so are mountain railways. A staircase is a steep ramp divided into steps to give a firm footing. An escalator is a moving ramp, and so is a sloping conveyor belt used on a dock for raising luggage to the opening in a ship's side.

The illustrations in the Pupils' Book show ramps being used to advantage for sliding, rolling and wheeling.

Using Sloping Surfaces on Wedges

When a wedge is moved, its sloping surface enables more force to be obtained for prising other surfaces apart. Some wedges have a single sloping surface, as on a woodworker's chisel; but many have a double slope, as on an axe.

Wedges are used to cut through things. Razors, knives, spears, swords, joiner's planes, choppers, chisels, axes, arrow-heads, scissors and other sharp instruments all involve the use of the sloping surface of the wedge. On a saw, each tooth is a tiny wedge. The wedge-shaped prow of a boat cuts easily through the water. The speed of a boat or ship depends to a large extent upon the wedge shape of its bows. In piercing tools, such as nails, needles, pins and pickaxes the principle of the wedge is also employed, using a point instead of an edge.

Wedges are also used for raising heavy weights. The procedure is similar to that employed with a ramp, except that instead of the load being forced up a sloping surface, the sloping surface is forced under the load. In dry dock, for example, a ship may be raised a little by forcing wedges under the keel.

Wedge shapes have been developed on the parts of many living things—on beaks and claws, for example, and also on certain plants, *e.g.* on the root tips of herbs, trees and shrubs, and on the leaves of bulbous herbs whose leaves have to pierce the soil above them as they grow from the bulb.

Using a Sloping Surface on a Screw

The most ingenious form of inclined plane is found on a screw. It may be described simply as a sloping surface winding spirally round a cone (as on a joiner's screw) or round a cylinder (as on a bolt). These are *external* screws. A similar surface on the interior of a cylindrical hole (as in a nut) is known as an *internal* screw. On a corkscrew, the sloping surface is on its own. Screws enable considerable force to be obtained, or considerable resistance to be overcome. A corkscrew, a wood screw, a gimlet, a wood bit and a cuphook are all familiar appliances on which this type of sloping surface is used as a machine for boring holes. A clamp, a screw press, a screw vice and a nut and bolt are familiar appliances for obtaining considerable force for pressing things tightly together. The screw jack, for raising a car, is a very good example of a screw making it easier to overcome the force of gravity.

The principle of the screw has been adapted in various ways for the purpose of forcing things to move. Screw conveyers, worm gears and screw propellers are examples. Probably the earliest type of screw conveyer was the famous screw pump supposedly invented by the Greek scientist Archimedes in the third century B.C., and known as the Archimedean screw. Rotation of the screw enabled water to be raised from one level to another for irrigation purposes. A worm gear enables a high gear ratio to be obtained by using a screw on the end of a shaft instead of a small gearwheel. Screw propellers on ships and aircraft force the vehicles to move through water or air.

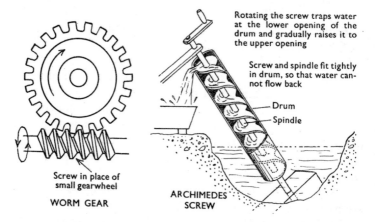

Rotating the screw traps water at the lower opening of the drum and gradually raises it to the upper opening

Screw and spindle fit tightly in drum, so that water cannot flow back

Drum

Spindle

Screw in place of small gearwheel

WORM GEAR

ARCHIMEDES SCREW

Very often the wheel-and-axle principle is employed in conjunction with a screw, to obtain more force for turning the screw.

On the old type of meat mincer there are two screws. One —turned by a wing nut—holds the mincer in position. The other serves as a screw conveyer, forcing the meat through the

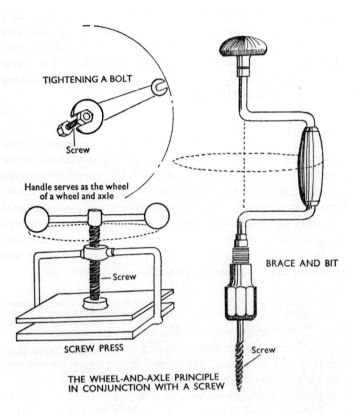

TIGHTENING A BOLT

Screw

Handle serves as the wheel
of a wheel and axle

Screw

SCREW PRESS

THE WHEEL-AND-AXLE PRINCIPLE
IN CONJUNCTION WITH A SCREW

BRACE AND BIT

Screw

holes of the fixed cutter plate to be minced by the revolving cutter plate. The screw conveyer is forced to turn by a handle working on the wheel-and-axle principle.

Sloping surfaces in the forms of ramps, wedges and screws are part of our everyday life. Without the ability to use them as simple machines, human beings would be at a considerable disadvantage.

CODE

1 Experiment to find how a ramp can make it easier to force a heavy load to a greater height.

(a) With a paper clip and elastic band drag a load up a vertical surface. Observe or measure the extent to which the band is stretched.

(b) Place the load at the bottom of a sloping board, and drag up the board. Observe or measure the shorter extent to which the band is stretched while the load is sliding.

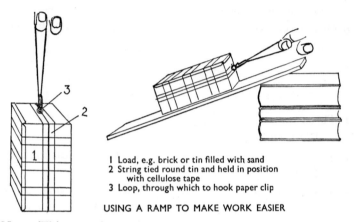

1 Load, e.g. brick or tin filled with sand
2 String tied round tin and held in position with cellulose tape
3 Loop, through which to hook paper clip

USING A RAMP TO MAKE WORK EASIER

Note. This experiment is similar to the one suggested in the Pupils' Book using a roller skate, and may be undertaken as an alternative or in addition. For more accurate measurements, use a spring balance reading up to 8 lbs instead of an elastic band.

2 Experiment to find how a wedge makes it easier to cut through water.

Force the flat of the hand or the flat side of a ruler through water. Repeat using the edge of the hand, or the edge of the ruler. Observe which is easier.

3 Demonstrate that a screw is a spiral ramp.

Crayon a broad line diagonally from corner to corner of a sheet of paper, and cut along it. Observe that the line now looks like a ramp or inclined plane.

Place the shortest edge of one of the right-angled triangles along a pencil (colour line outwards), and wind the paper round the pencil. Observe that the straight colour line (ramp or inclined plane) has become a spiral slope or screw. Release paper and you have a helter-skelter.

4 Demonstrate that a screw enables considerable force to be obtained.

If a strong bar and a car jack are available, place the bar on the jack, and have a number of boys try to hold it down while a small-built girl winds it up.

5 Observe wedge shapes on various appliances, *e.g.* knives, axes, toy boats, scissors, nails.

6 Observe screws on various appliances, *e.g.* nut and bolt, screw press, clamp, gimlet.

NOTEBOOK WORK

Answers should be along the following lines.

1 Three ways of using sloping surfaces as simple machines, are as ramps, on wedges and on screws.

2 The sloping surface of a ramp helps us to overcome the force of gravity.

3 A wedge has one sloping surface, or two or more sloping surfaces which meet at an edge or a point. Wedge shapes are used on tools to cut through solids, and on vehicles to cut through water and through air.

4 On a screw the sloping surface is in spiral form.

5 The main uses of screws are for boring and for forcing things tightly together.

19 FORCING VEHICLES THROUGH WATER AND THROUGH AIR

PUSHING AND SCREWING

DEMONSTRATION MATERIAL

Nut and bolt; thin card, wood bit, marble or ball bearing; toy boat with screw propeller, bowl of water, ink; any toy vehicles with screw propellers; sheets of exercise paper; sheet of card

SAMPLE LINK QUESTIONS

1 What are the three main ways of forcing things to move from place to place on land? (*Carrying, sliding, rolling*)
2 What do humans make vehicles for? (*To transport things from place to place*)
3 Was the power to move the first vehicles across water obtained from animals or from the wind? (*From animals*)
4 What did early ships have so that the wind could force them to move? (*Sails*)
5 Why can we not always obtain power from the wind for forcing things to move? (*The wind does not always blow*)
6 What does a machine make easier? (*Work*)
7 What can we use a machine to obtain? (*More force*)
8 What are the three ways in which we can use a sloping surface as a machine? (*As a ramp, on a wedge and on a screw*)
9 What force does the sloping surface of a ramp help us to overcome? (*The force of gravity*)
10 In what form is the sloping surface of a screw? (*In the form of a spiral*)

RELEVANT INFORMATION

The main purpose of a lesson in Pupils' Book 3 was to show that the power to force vehicles to move across water was originally obtained from (*a*) the muscles of human beings and other animals, (*b*) moving air (wind).

The main purpose of this lesson is to show that the two main ways of forcing a vehicle to move through water or air are (*a*) by pushing, (*b*) by screwing.

Living animals force themselves to move from place to place by pushing in some way. An animal which swims pushes against the water. A flying bird, insect or bat pushes against the air. On land, an animal walking, hopping or running pushes against the land. The first vehicles which humans made were forced to move from place to place by pushing or pulling. In either pushing or pulling a vehicle, something else has to be pushed against, *e.g.* the ground over which the vehicle is forced to move.

A vehicle is any conveyance which makes it easier for us to transport things from one place to another. This of course depends on

1 the vehicle being suitable to the particular medium where its use is required, *i.e.* water, land or air;

2 sufficient power being available to force it to move.

Transport across water usually requires less effort than transport over land—apart from the fact that no road or track has to be made—and it allows the transport of large loads which would be impossible on land. Water has long been used as a medium, and in prehistoric times rafts and boats were probably poled in shallow waters and paddled in deeper waters. With a pole, the vehicle was forced to move by pushing against the solid bed beneath the water; with a paddle, it was forced to move by pushing against the water itself. The use of oars for rowing also involved pushing against the water. One of the main differences between an oar and a paddle, is that the oar is supported at a fixed point on the side of the vehicle itself.

When sails are used, the vehicle is forced to move by the wind pushing against them.

In the nineteenth century steam power began to replace wind power, and the transition from sail to paddle-wheels, and from paddle-wheels to screw propellers began to take place. The *Charlotte Dundas*, a small canal boat built in 1801, was a steam-powered vessel with a paddle-wheel at the stern. The success of this small steamboat inspired Robert Fulton in 1807 to construct the *Clermont* which was to become very popular in the U.S.A. as a passenger boat. The *Clermont* differed from the *Charlotte Dundas* in having two paddle-wheels, one at each side. Both stern-wheelers and side-wheelers became popular as riverboats, and from about 1820 to 1870 they dominated the general economy of agriculture and commerce along the banks of the Mississippi. Paddle-wheels were also added to sailing ships designed for long sea voyages.

1839 saw the introduction of the screw propeller, for in this year the steamship *Archimedes*, fitted with such a device, sailed round Britain, and by 1845 the Atlantic crossing from Liverpool to New York had been made by a screw-driven steamship, the *Great Britain*. Screw propellers enabled more force to be obtained, and proved to be more economical than paddle-wheels. This was shown in 1845, when two ships of the Royal Navy, lashed stern to stern, engaged in a tug-of-war to test the relative merits of the two types of propulsion. The screw-propelled ship was able to tow the paddle-steamer at a speed of $2\frac{1}{2}$ knots.

In spite of the apparent advantage of the screw propeller, considerable faith was still placed in both sails and paddle-wheels. The famous and uneconomical *Great Eastern* (maiden voyage 1860) had not only a four-bladed screw propeller, but two side paddle-wheels, and six masts for sails as well.

Although sails and paddle-wheels continued to be used, screw propellers were to become established as the dominant means for forcing vehicles to move through water. By 1862, twin screws were in use, and shortly after the turn of the century triple screws. During the last century, improvement has centred on the best way of forcing screw propellers to turn.

Following the development of the petrol engine, screw propellers eventually enabled humans to construct vehicles which could be forced to move through the air, thus realising a centuries-old dream. A ship's propeller pushes against the water and thus forces the ship forward. The propeller of an aeroplane acts on the same principle. It pushes against the air so that the aeroplane is forced to move forwards. On a ship, the action of the propeller can be reversed in order to make the ship go astern. The blades of a propeller are bent, something like those of an electric fan. On an aeroplane there may be two, three, four, or five of these blades.

Once an aeroplane is airborne, its wing(s) help it to keep up, just as the wings of a glider help to keep the glider up, but it is the speed of the turning propeller which forces it to move forward. The faster the propeller is forced to turn, the faster its vehicle moves. On an aeroplane, the propeller must turn rapidly enough to force the aeroplane to move at a speed which is above a certain minimum. Once the speed of the aeroplane drops below its necessary minimum, it begins to fall.

A helicopter does not have wings for support. Instead, it has a large propeller on top. Just as an aeroplane propeller pushes backwards against the air, thus forcing the vehicle forwards, a helicoplter propeller pushes downwards against the air, thus forcing the vehicle to move upwards. Controlling the speed of the propeller, and also altering the pitch of the blades allows it to rise, sink or hover. In order to make the helicopter move forward, backward or sideways, the pitch of each blade is altered as the rotating propeller brings it into the position where it is required to apply the most push. A single propeller would tend to make the helicopter twist in the opposite direction to which the propeller is turning. This is offset by the use of a second propeller rotating so as to stabilise the vehicle. An autogyro, forerunner of the helicopter, differed in that its forward movement was achieved by the use of a separate propeller.

CODE

1 Collect pictures illustrating different ways of forcing vehicles to move through water and through air, *e.g.* using (*a*) a pole (punt, gondola); (*b*) paddles (canoe, kayak, coracle); (*c*) oars alone (rowing boat, skiff); (*d*) oars and sails (Roman and Greek war galleys, Viking ships); (*e*) sails alone (galleon, clipper, yacht); (*f*) sails and paddle-wheels (early steamships equipped for sea voyages); (*g*) paddle-wheels alone (Mississippi riverboat); (*h*) screw propellers for forcing through water (modern ships, motorboats, submarines); (*i*) screw propellers for forcing through air (aeroplane, helicopter).

2 Observe that as a screw turns in one direction, it moves forward; and as it turns in the opposite direction, it moves backwards, *e.g.* using a nut and bolt, hold the nut and turn the bolt.

3 Demonstrate how a turning screw can force something to move backwards.

Construct a cardboard channel, slightly wider than the diameter of a wood bit or corkscrew. Place the screw in the channel and a ball bearing or a small marble near the pointed end of the bit.

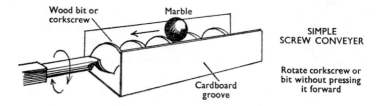

Wood bit or corkscrew

Marble

SIMPLE
SCREW CONVEYER

Rotate corkscrew or bit without pressing it forward

Cardboard groove

Observe that by turning the screw towards the right, the ball bearing or marble is forced to move backwards along it. This is the principle of the Archimedes screw and the screw propeller.

4 Demonstrate how a ship's propeller forces the ship forward by pushing against the water.

Place a toy boat, with its propeller spinning, in a bowl of water. Drop a blob of ink into the water behind the propeller, and observe how it is pushed away from the propeller.

5 Observe how a cooling fan illustrates the principle of a screw propeller forcing a stream of air to move, *e.g.* an electric fan, or the fan in front of a car engine.

6 Demonstrate how an increase in air pressure on the underside of a moving wing forces it upwards.

Hold a sheet of paper or a sheet of card by one edge so that it hangs vertically. Pull it quickly through the air and observe that the trailing edge rises so that the moving sheet becomes horizontal. This is largely due to the air meeting the under-surface becoming compressed, thus making the upward pressure on the lower surface greater than the downward pressure on the upper surface. On an aircraft, this 'lift' is governed by the angle of the wing and its speed relative to the air.

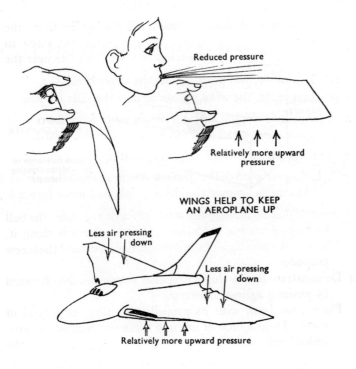

7 Demonstrate that if the upper surface of the wing is given a convex curve, the wing tends to rise when air is moving over it, owing to the pressure of air on the upper surface being less than the pressure of air on the lower surface.
Hold a sheet of paper by two corners so that it forms a curve. Blow over the upper surface, and observe that the trailing edge of the paper rises. In this instance, the air meeting the curved upper surface is bounced up a little, thus decreasing the amount of downward pressure relative to the upward pressure.

Note. An aeroplane requires an engine of sufficient power and sufficiently low weight to force its wings fast enough through the air to support the combined weight of itself, the engine, the propeller, and the load it is designed to carry.

NOTEBOOK WORK

Answers should be along the following lines.

1 (*a*) In a punt, you use a pole to push against the bed beneath the water.

  (*b*) In a canoe, you push against the water itself.

  (*c*) In a yacht, the wind pushes against the sails for you.

2 A propeller's sloping surfaces obtain more force for pushing against water or air and forcing the vehicle forward.

3 On an aeroplane, wings help to keep it up.

4 A helicopter's propeller pushes down against the air and makes the helicopter rise, hover, sink, and move forwards, backwards or sideways.

20 USING HEAT TO MAKE GASES EXPAND

POWER FROM MOVING GASES

DEMONSTRATION MATERIAL

Any of the following, which are detailed on pages 187-8:

1 simple demonstration model to show how a piston can turn a wheel
2 commercially manufactured model of a piston and cylinder steam engine
3 demonstration model of a steam turbine, and a butane burner or other source of heat

SAMPLE LINK QUESTIONS

1 What are the three main things which force others to move from place to place? (*Moving animals, moving liquids (water), moving gases (wind)*)
2 From what did human beings obtain power to turn the very first wheels? (*Animals*)
3 What was the first moving liquid from which power was obtained? (*Water*)
4 What was the first moving gas from which power was obtained? (*Air (wind)*)
5 What are two examples of a moving solid providing power to turn a lightweight wheel? (*An unwinding spring (as in a watch), a falling weight (as in a cuckoo clock)*)
6 What are the two main ways of forcing a vehicle to move through water and through air? (*Pushing and screwing*)
7 Which was first used to force a steamship to move—a paddle-wheel or a screw propeller? (*A paddle-wheel*)
8 Which parts of a screw propeller obtain more force for pushing against water or air? (*The sloping surfaces*)
9 From which moving gases could the *Great Eastern* obtain power? (*Wind and steam*)
10 What makes a gas expand? (*Gaining heat*)

RELEVANT INFORMATION

The main purpose of two lessons in Pupils' Book 3 was to show that power to force the wheels of early machines and vehicles to turn could be obtained from

1 the muscles of human beings and other animals;
2 moving solids (an unwinding spring and a falling weight);
3 moving liquids (water);
4 moving gases (wind).

The main purpose of this lesson is to show that

1 power to force wheels and screw propellers to turn can be obtained from moving steam;
2 steam is a gas which can be forced to move by using heat;
3 the two main kinds of steam engines are (a) the piston and cylinder engine, (b) the turbine engine.

We obtain the power to force things to move by using and adapting energy in some way. Anything which is in itself moving has energy, that is to say it has the ability to do work. Up to the time of the industrial revolution, the muscular energy of human beings and other animals, and the energy of moving air and water were the principal sources of power. Since then, ways have been found for forcing gases to move, so that their energy can be utilised. These ways invariably entail using heat to make gases expand, and they have enabled civilisation to progress materially. Associated with this progress have been the invention and development of different engines for utilising heat.

An engine is generally defined as a device for converting some form of energy into mechanical energy. Heat itself is a form of energy, and most engines of today are 'heat engines'; that is to say they convert heat energy into mechanical energy.

Heat began to be a major source of power with the invention of engines which put steam to practical use. Savery's engine of 1703, and the Newcomen and Cawley rocking beam engine of 1705 began the steam age. In both of these, steam was introduced so that it could be condensed to provide a partial vacuum so that air pressure could do the required work. Newcomen's engine incorporated a simple piston and cylinder, but, like Savery's, was wasteful, inefficient and dangerous. Subsequently an instrument-maker—James Watt—improved on the Newcomen engine by admitting and condensing steam alternately at opposite ends of the cylinder, so that air pressure forced the piston to move both ways. Eventually he invented steam engines in which the steam itself did the work of pushing the piston. Indeed he invented every important part found in the modern piston and cylinder engine.

When water changes into steam it expands about 1,700 times, *i.e.* 1 gallon of water produces about 1,700 gallons of steam, so that making the steam itself do the actual work is the best way of using it in an engine. Nowadays the steam engine is comparatively simple and easy to maintain, and is one of the main types of power machines. There are two main kinds:

(*a*) the piston and cylinder engine in which the steam pushes a piston,

(*b*) the turbine engine in which steam is made to turn a wheel.

Principle of a Simple Piston and Cylinder Steam Engine

Steam from the boiler enters the cylinder through the first steam port, and pushes the piston forward, as shown in the left-hand diagram. As the piston reaches the forward position, the slide valve, moving in the opposite direction, opens a second steam port and closes the first to incoming steam. (Right-hand diagram.) This allows steam to move against the other side of the piston, and push it back.

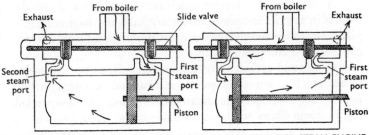

THE WORKING OF A SLIDE VALVE IN A PISTON AND CYLINDER STEAM ENGINE

As the piston is pushed back, the steam responsible for pushing it forward is forced out into an exhaust.

As the piston reaches the rear position, the slide valve, moving in the opposite direction opens the first steam port. Steam once again pushes the piston forward, and at the same time the used steam in front of the piston is forced out through an exhaust. Thus the to-and-fro movement continues.

The piston is attached to a crankshaft or a flywheel by means of a connecting rod. Thus the to-and-fro motion of the piston is converted into a circular motion. When the flywheel is turning, its momentum carries the piston over its 'dead points', *i.e.* the points at which, momentarily, no work is done by the piston. Thus the continuous momentum of the flywheel also ensures a smooth running movement for the engine. The slide valve is also attached to the flywheel by means of a connecting rod, so that, indirectly, the piston is responsible for the opening and closing of the steam ports.

Principle of a Simple Turbine Engine

In a simple turbine engine, the piston and cylinder is replaced by an enclosed wheel. The wheel has strong steel blades against which a jet of steam is directed to force it to revolve. This revolving wheel can then, by means of a shaft, be made to force the wheels of machinery to turn, or, as in a ship, the shaft can be made to turn a screw propeller. Compound turbines have a succession of steel-bladed wheels mounted on the same shaft. This is known as a rotor.

A turbine engine is more efficient than a piston and cylinder engine in that its movement is rotary from the beginning. As piston, cylinder and flywheel are not required, a turbine engine can be more compact.

Piston and cylinder engines are generally more economical where small amounts of power are needed, whereas turbine engines are more economical where large amounts are needed, *e.g.* in ocean liners or plants for generating electricity.

Uses of Steam Engines

The early steam engines of Savery and Newcomen were first used to work pumps for raising water, *e.g.* out of flooded mine workings. They also raised water to a height so that it could fall on to overshot waterwheels, for at that time most factories relied on power from waterwheels, and in flat areas where water did not naturally fall from a height these new engines were a boon. Later in the eighteenth century they were also used to force the wheels of machines to turn.

During the nineteenth century, steam was harnessed to force vehicles to move. Piston and cylinder engines were used to force paddle-wheels to turn, and subsequently to turn the first screw propellers. On sea-going ships, the steady development of engines of increasing power brought a transition from sail to steam. First came sailing ships with auxiliary steam engines; then steamships with auxiliary sail, and finally steamships. In 1897 a small experimental vessel which was equipped with a turbine and called the *Turbinia*, gave a startling demonstration of speed during a naval review at Cowes.

On land, steam carriages were constructed both for roads and for rails, led by Trevithick who was responsible for the first steam coaches and the first steam railway. By 1825 a steam-powered railway engine, designed and driven by George Stephenson, pulled both goods and passengers on the Stockton and Darlington railway. At the outset, steam locomotives consisted basically of two piston and cylinder engines which rolled on their flywheels. Turbine engines were later adapted for use in certain locomotives.

Steam-powered road coaches—puffing devils—inspired much opposition and little public confidence, and in 1865 the Red Flag Act restricted their speed to 4 m.p.h. in the country, and 2 m.p.h. in towns, and required a man carrying a red flag to walk 60 yards ahead of the vehicle. Steam-powered land vehicles were therefore confined to the railways, and road vehicles in Britain remained horse-drawn. Steam cars were, however, being made in America up to 1939.

By the end of the nineteenth century attempts were also

being made to use steam engines to force vehicles through the air, but such intended aircraft were never successful.

Obtaining Heat to Boil Water to Make Steam

Wood was the first fuel used for steam boilers. On the banks of the Mississippi, for example, large tracts of timber were cut down to provide fuel for the paddle-steamers. Coal is obviously a better fuel, and the development of the steam engine increased the coal-mining industry considerably. Before the control of atomic energy was established, coal was a chief fuel in those electric power stations whose dynamo wheels were forced to turn by steam-driven turbines.

In early piston and cylinder steamships, when steam engines were not very efficient, carrying a sufficient supply of fuel for a journey was a problem. In 1838, when the *Sirius*—the first ship to cross the Atlantic on steam power alone—set out from Liverpool, there was coal in every available space on board, yet when she steamed into New York, planking, spars, and even furniture were having to be burned to keep the steam pressure up. However, as steam engines were made more efficient, less heat was wasted and therefore less fuel required. During the early twentieth century, oil began to supersede coal as a fuel in most of the big steamships, *e.g.* for producing the steam to drive the turbines of the *Queen Elizabeth* and the *Queen Mary*. Oil is more expensive than coal, but it is cleaner to use.

Today atomic energy is increasingly used. The heat produced by a controlled nuclear reaction is considerably more from a much smaller weight of fuel. For example, an ounce of uranium can yield the same amount of energy as more than 80 tons of coal, so that a relatively small weight of fuel is sufficient to provide the power to last a sea-going vehicle several years.

Some Technical Information

Force. A force tends to alter the uniform motion or rest of a body. Force is measured in terms of the weight which would exert an equal force, *e.g.* in lbs.

Work. Work in the scientific sense is done when a force alters the uniform motion or rest of a body. More simply, work is done when something is forced to move, or when something which is already moving is forced to stop, or to change its speed or direction. Work is measured in the terms of the force applied and the distance moved. For example, if a 2-lb weight is moved through a distance of 3 feet, then the work done is expressed as 6 ft lbs.

Energy. Energy is the ability to do work, and is measured in the same terms as work.

Power. Power is the *rate* at which work can be done. It is a measure of the total capabilities of a force, or the maximum capabilities which it cannot exceed. It is measured in terms of the work which can be done in a given time, *e.g.* in terms of foot pounds per minute. Thus both a child and an adult have the energy to force a 2-lb weight through a distance of 3 ft. They can both do 6 ft lbs of work. The adult however can do the work in a shorter time; the adult is more powerful. One horsepower is the equivalent of 33,000 ft lbs of work per minute.

CODE

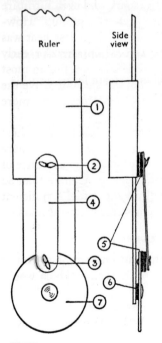

Ruler

Side view

1 Demonstrate with a simple model how, by means of a connecting rod, a piston is made to turn a wheel.

1 Matchbox cover

2 and 3 Paper fasteners

4 Cardboard connecting rod, at least $1\frac{1}{2}$ times diameter of flywheel

5 Pairs of cardboard washers to lift rod over drawing-pin head

6 Cardboard washer

7 Cardboard flywheel, attached (through washer) to ruler with drawing pin

Roll on non-slippery surface

MODEL TO SHOW ACTION OF FLY-WHEEL, CONNECTING ROD AND PISTON

2 Demonstrate with a commercially manufactured model of a piston and cylinder steam engine how heat boils water to make steam to drive the piston to turn a flywheel.

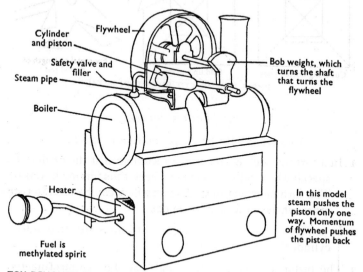

Cylinder and piston

Flywheel

Safety valve and filler

Steam pipe

Boiler

Bob weight, which turns the shaft that turns the flywheel

Heater

In this model steam pushes the piston only one way. Momentum of flywheel pushes the piston back

Fuel is methylated spirit

TOY DEMONSTRATION MODEL OF A PISTON AND CYLINDER STEAM ENGINE

3 Demonstrate with a simple model how steam forces a turbine wheel to turn.

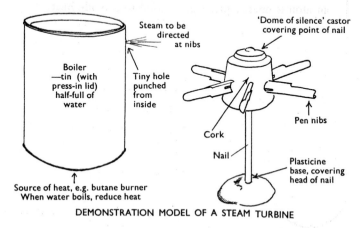

Steam to be directed at nibs

'Dome of silence' castor covering point of nail

Boiler —tin (with press-in lid) half-full of water

Tiny hole punched from inside

Pen nibs

Cork

Nail

Plasticine base, covering head of nail

Source of heat, e.g. butane burner When water boils, reduce heat

DEMONSTRATION MODEL OF A STEAM TURBINE

188

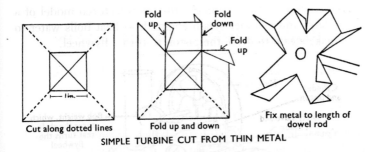

Fold up Fold down Fold up

O

Fix metal to length of dowel rod

Cut along dotted lines   Fold up and down

SIMPLE TURBINE CUT FROM THIN METAL

NOTEBOOK WORK

Answers should be along the following lines.

1 In a turbine engine, steam is directed against the blades of a special wheel called a turbine wheel, thus forcing it to turn. The turbine wheel turns a shaft which can be used to turn other wheels or a screw propeller.

2 In a piston and cylinder engine, steam is directed into a cylinder where it pushes a piston.

3 The piston pushes a connecting rod. The connecting rod turns a flywheel.

4 Wood was the first fuel used for obtaining heat to boil water to make steam. Coal or oil were used as fuels later. Today an atomic energy pile can be used to provide heat.

ENGINES IN WHICH FUELS ARE BURNED

DEMONSTRATION MATERIAL

Petrol lighter; cycle pump; balloons; simple steam jet engine (See page 197) and heat, *e.g.* from butane burner

SAMPLE LINK QUESTIONS

1 What do humans make vehicles for? (*To transport things*)
2 What do you push against when you paddle or row a vehicle across water? (*Water*)
3 What are the three main ways in which a substance may be changed by a change in temperature? (*A change to another form*; *a change to another kind of substance*; *a change in size*)
4 When a substance is burning, what is it changing into? (*Other substances*)
5 Which gas do most things use when they burn? (*Oxygen*)
6 When a substance is burned specially to give heat or light, what do we call it? (*A fuel*)
7 How can we force steam to move? (*By using heat to make it expand*)
8 What are the two main kinds of steam engines that help us to obtain power from steam? (*A turbine engine, and a piston and cylinder engine*)
9 Which of these two steam engines was the first to be invented? (*The piston and cylinder engine*)
10 In a piston and cylinder steam engine, which part connects the piston to a pump or flywheel? (*The connecting rod*)

RELEVANT INFORMATION

The main points of this lesson are that
1 there are two main ways of obtaining power by using heat:
  (*a*) to use the expanding steam from boiling water,
  (*b*) to use the expanding gases from a burning fuel;

2 expanding gases from a burning fuel may be used

   (*a*) in petrol and diesel oil engines to push against a piston,

   (*b*) in rocket and jet engines to push against the engine itself.

    A steam engine is not the most efficient means for obtaining power by using heat. Steam is raised by burning a fuel outside the engine, which means some heat is lost. In petrol, diesel oil, jet or rocket engines, the fuel is inside the engine and so less heat is lost. A piston and cylinder steam engine and a turbine steam engine are both classed as *external* combustion engines, whereas petrol, diesel oil, jet and rocket engines are classed as *internal* combustion engines.

    Development of internal combustion engines has increased the efficiency by which heat is used to obtain power. In such engines, the 'push' is supplied by the gases produced by the burning fuel. The two commonest of these are the petrol engine and the diesel oil engine.

The Petrol Engine

    Mechanically, this is similar to the piston and cylinder steam engine, consisting of pistons, cylinders, connecting rods, a crankshaft and a flywheel. The fuel system consists of a fuel tank, a fuel pump, and a carburettor in which vapour from liquid petrol mixes with air. Petrol evaporates readily at normal temperatures (when we smell petrol, it is the vapour reaching our nostrils), and combines readily with oxygen. At higher temperatures, the combination results in rapid burning. From the carburettor, the mixture of petrol vapour and air passes into the cylinder. Here a spark provides the heat at which the vapour and oxygen from the air burn with sufficient rapidity to produce an explosion. The heat from this causes the remainder of the air to expand, together with the gases produced during burning, and these force the piston along the cylinder.

    The piston pushes a connecting rod which turns the crankshaft, using the wheel-and-axle principle. Usually connecting rods from a number of pistons turn the same crankshaft, their power strokes being timed to occur separately. The flywheel, fixed to and turned by the crankshaft, can thus keep turning with enough force to send the pistons up again. Once the shaft is turning, it can be utilised to turn a wheel or a screw propeller.

Most petrol engines have from two to sixteen cylinders—the average car engine has four, and aeroplane engines more than sixteen. On a radial aeroplane engine, the cylinders are arranged round a centre shaft, to save space and weight.

One advantage of the petrol engine is its compactness, as the gases produced by the burning fuel do the 'pushing'. Another advantage, particularly for an automobile, is that it can be used more or less immediately, without the initial build-up of pressure required in a steam engine. By 1885 Carl Benz had built his three-wheeled petrol engine car—the first of its kind. Two years later another German, Daimler, built a motor cycle; and in 1896 the British parliament altered the Red Flag Act to allow cars to travel up to 14 m.p.h. From this time on, petrol engines steadily replaced horses.

A *motor*, like an engine, is generally defined as a device for converting other forms of energy into mechanical energy. The term is generally applied to petrol engines as well as to electric motors.

The Diesel Oil Engine

The principle of this engine is similar to that of the petrol engine, except that oil is used as fuel. Also, the required temperature for burning is attained by compressing the air in the cylinder before the fuel oil is squirted in, whereas in a petrol engine, a mixture of petrol vapour and air is admitted to the cylinder and then its temperature is raised to ignition point by means of a spark from a spark plug. Fuel oil is cheaper than refined petrol, but this advantage is offset by the diesel's greater weight per horse power. Because of these two factors, diesel engines are most economically used in heavy, powerful vehicles.

The engine is named after Rudolph Diesel, the German who produced it in 1895. During World War I, it was developed considerably for use in German submarines, and afterwards increasingly in passenger ships. Nowadays, diesel engines are used in many ships, trains, haulage vehicles, tractors and buses. They also provide the power for many large machines, and for operating the dynamos in some electricity generating stations.

The Principle of Jet and Rocket Engines

In jet and rocket engines the expanding gases resulting from burning are used to push against the inside of the engine itself and so are directly responsible for forcing the vehicle to move. It is important to note that these vehicles are not forced to move by the expanding gases pushing against the air behind them as the gases emerge. What does happen is explained simply below and can be demonstrated with a balloon.

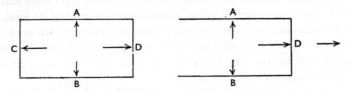

The expanding gases in the combustion chamber of the engine push in all directions on the inside of the chamber

If the chamber is completely sealed, the push against B is cancelled by the push against A. Likewise the push against D is cancelled by the push against C

If C is not there to be pushed against, i.e. if that end is open, then the push against D will not be cancelled out. As a result, the chamber will be forced to move in that direction

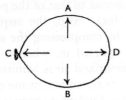 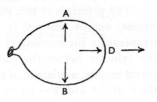

The air compressed inside a balloon exerts pressure equally in all directions on the inside of the balloon

If the neck is closed, the push against B is cancelled by the push against A. Likewise the push against D is cancelled by the push against C

If the neck of the balloon is opened, the push against D will no longer be cancelled out. As a result, the balloon will be forced to move in that direction

A JET OR ROCKET ENGINE IS FORCED TO MOVE IN THE SAME WAY AS AN INFLATED BALLOON WHOSE NECK IS RELEASED

Jet Engines

The modern jet engine resulted from the development of the gas turbine engine. In a gas turbine engine, a rotating compressor compresses air and forces it into combustion chambers. The expanding gases from the combustion chambers are directed against a turbine wheel, forcing it to turn. The shaft of this wheel turns the compressor, and can also be made to turn other wheels or a screw propeller. The various fuels which can be used include petrol, paraffin, fuel oil and powdered coal. Gas turbine engines are used in certain locomotives and are being developed for road vehicles.

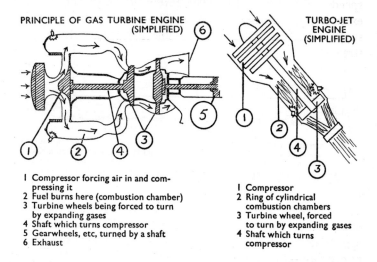

PRINCIPLE OF GAS TURBINE ENGINE (SIMPLIFIED)

TURBO-JET ENGINE (SIMPLIFIED)

1 Compressor forcing air in and compressing it
2 Fuel burns here (combustion chamber)
3 Turbine wheels being forced to turn by expanding gases
4 Shaft which turns compressor
5 Gearwheels, etc, turned by a shaft
6 Exhaust

1 Compressor
2 Ring of cylindrical combustion chambers
3 Turbine wheel, forced to turn by expanding gases
4 Shaft which turns compressor

The *turbo-jet* engine, used in aircraft, is designed so that some of the energy of the moving gases is used to push the vehicle forward while the rest is spent on turning the turbine wheel. The essential parts of this engine are (a) the compressor—a kind of fan which forces air back into the engine and compresses it; (b) the combustion chambers; (c) the turbine. The compressed air, together with a spray of fuel, is admitted to the closed ends of the combustion chambers where the fuel is burned, combining with the oxygen in the compressed air. The expanding gases produced force the engine and its vehicle forward. As the gases emerge from the open rear ends of the combustion chambers, they are directed against the blades of the turbine wheel; this turns the shaft which turns the compressor. The gases then escape from the rear end of the engine in a narrow jet.

There have been several developments from the turbo-jet engine. Their chief advantages are the relative cheapness of the fuel, and the considerable speeds at which they can force aircraft through the air.

The *turbo-prop*, jet-prop, or prop-jet engine is a development of the turbo-jet designed to fly aircraft economically at speeds under 500 m.p.h. The turbine is large, and its shaft extends right to the front where it turns a propeller which supplies the main thrust with some assistance from the jet stream.

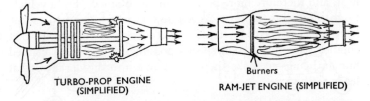

TURBO-PROP ENGINE
(SIMPLIFIED)

Burners

RAM-JET ENGINE (SIMPLIFIED)

The *ram-jet* differs in having neither turbine nor compressor. It relies on the forward speed of the vehicle to ram the air under pressure into the engine. The faster it flies, the more efficient it becomes. It cannot be used until the air is entering at speeds above 300 m.p.h. It therefore requires some other form of engine to take it up to the required speed.

Rocket Engines

The basic difference between a rocket engine and a jet engine is that the rocket uses oxygen carried by the vehicle itself, whereas the jet obtains its oxygen from the surrounding air. The oxygen supply may be compressed into a liquid form or be part of a chemical which gives off oxygen. The fuel which is to combine with the oxygen is carried in a separate chamber. This fuel and the oxygen are allowed to mix in a third chamber (the combustion chamber) in which burning takes place, releasing quantities of hot expanding gases which push the vehicle forward in the same way as a jet engine is pushed forward.

The principle of rocket propulsion is fairly simple and for centuries has been used in fireworks. However, it is only in comparatively recent times that two major achievements have enabled rocket propulsion to be used for vehicles.

1 The flight of a rocket vehicle can now be controlled.

2 New metal alloys have been developed, which can withstand the intense heat resulting from the burning of the fuel necessary to drive large rockets.

As a rocket vehicle carries its own supply of oxygen, it can be forced to move in regions far beyond the earth's atmosphere. Because the oxygen supply is in concentrated form, it can be used for burning as rapidly as required. This means that more heat, and therefore more power, can be obtained. For a vehicle to go into orbit, it must exceed 18,000 m.p.h., and to escape from the earth's pull, it must exceed 25,000 m.p.h. Rocket engines have made such speeds possible. They have enabled human beings to make their first move into the darkness that leads to the stars.

Note on Burning and Oxygen

When a substance is burning, it is undergoing chemical change, *i.e.* other chemical substances are being formed. In most cases of burning, oxygen is involved, as it combines with most existing elements—a process termed oxidation. The higher the temperature, the more rapid the oxidation; and when the energy released during the process becomes evident in the form of light as well as heat, the action is termed burning or combustion. If the speed of burning is sufficiently rapid, the result is an explosion, *i.e.* the sudden release of energy in a very short space of time.

CODE

1 Demonstrate with a petrol lighter how the petrol vapour is ignited in the cylinder of a piston and cylinder engine, *i.e.* the spark raises the temperature of the petrol vapour to the point at which it burns.

2 Demonstrate how compressing the air in a diesel engine cylinder raises its temperature. Close the end of a cycle

pump, and work the piston up and down several times. Observe how the end of the pump becomes warm (owing to heat energy released by air under pressure).

3 Demonstrate how a gas under pressure can force a vehicle to move by pushing against the inside of an engine.
(a) Blow up a balloon, pinch the neck, and then release.
(b) Boil water in a simple steam jet engine (illustrated below), and observe how the boiler is forced to turn.

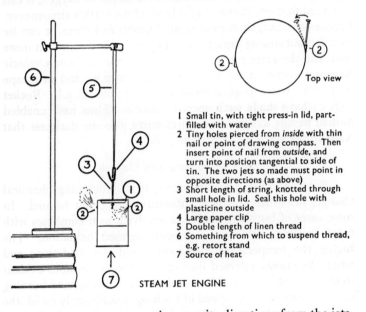

Top view

1 Small tin, with tight press-in lid, part-filled with water
2 Tiny holes pierced from *inside* with thin nail or point of drawing compass. Then insert point of nail from *outside*, and turn into position tangential to side of tin. The two jets so made must point in opposite directions (as above)
3 Short length of string, knotted through small hole in lid. Seal this hole with plasticine outside
4 Large paper clip
5 Double length of linen thread
6 Something from which to suspend thread, e.g. retort stand
7 Source of heat

STEAM JET ENGINE

As the steam emerges in opposite directions from the jets, the tin will be forced to turn. The heat should then be reduced to prevent speed becoming excessive. As the tin spins, the double length of thread will become twisted and will raise the tin from the source of heat. The water will then cease to boil, and the twisted thread will begin to unwind, thus turning the tin in the opposite direction. Once the tin is sufficiently low, the water will once again boil, and the tin will again turn as at first.

197

This model is adapted from the engine developed as a toy by Hero of Alexandria some 2,000 years ago.

NOTEBOOK WORK

Answers should be along the following lines.

1 In a petrol engine, vapour from petrol is made to burn very rapidly with oxygen gas from the air. During the burning other gases are produced and the heat causes these to expand. These expanding gases push a piston along a cylinder.

2 The two main ways of obtaining power from heat are to use the expanding steam from boiling water, and to use expanding gases from a burning fuel.

3 In jets and rockets the expanding gases push against the inside of the engine.

4 A rocket vehicle can travel in outer space because a supply of oxygen for its engine is carried by the rocket itself.

5 A firework is like a rocket engine.

22 ELECTRICITY IS CAUSED BY ELECTRONS

ELECTRIC CHARGES AND ELECTRIC CURRENTS

DEMONSTRATION MATERIAL

Materials for making an electric charge detector—plasticine, needles, paper; various cloths, *e.g.* wool, cotton, silk; plastic ball-pen, polythene; various materials to demonstrate the effects of electric charges, *e.g.* inflated balloon, nylon hair ribbon, acetate sheeting, bakelite, plastics, rubber, glass, sealing wax, jam jar, grains of common salt, sawdust, sand

SAMPLE LINK QUESTIONS

1 What is the tiniest possible bit of a substance which can exist on its own? (*Molecule*)
2 Every molecule consists of one or more particles. What are these called? (*Atoms*)
3 What does most of an atom consist of? (*Empty space*)
4 What is the centre of an atom called? (*The nucleus*)
5 What are the very tiny particles which revolve round the nucleus? (*Electrons*)
6 When two surfaces are rubbed together, what resistance is set up between them? (*Friction*)
7 What does friction cause? (*Wear and heat*)

RELEVANT INFORMATION

The main points of this lesson are that
1 electricity is caused by electrons;
2 an electric charge is due to a substance having too many or too few electrons, and can be caused by friction;
3 an electric current is due to a stream of electrons flowing, and can be caused by a battery or a dynamo.

The word *electricity* is derived from *elektron*—the Greek word for amber. Greeks, Romans and Phoenicians attributed mysterious powers to amber because of its ability to attract lightweight particles when rubbed. Electricity is now known to be caused by electrons—the minute particles that orbit round the nuclei of atoms and that were introduced in Lesson 2.

As an atom normally contains one proton in its nucleus for every electron revolving round it, a quantity of a substance will, in the normal state, have the same number of protons as electrons. Electrons repel one another. Protons repel one another. An electron and a proton, on the other hand, attract one another. Electrons are said to be negatively charged, and protons are said to be positively charged.

The force of attraction between a proton and an electron decreases with distance, so that in an atom the electrons in the outermost orbits are less attracted by the nucleus than are those in the innermost orbits. In addition, the outermost electrons are repelled by the inner electrons. Consequently the outermost electrons in atoms may, under certain circumstances, be forced from their orbits.

Electric Charges
Also known as Frictional or Static Electricity

Friction between the surfaces of two different substances commonly causes numbers of electrons from one to become attached to the other. When one substance loses electrons, it has more protons left than electrons, *i.e.* it is positively charged. On the other hand, the substance which has gained extra electrons will have a greater total of electrons than protons, *i.e.* it is negatively charged. Both substances are electrically charged. For example, if a piece of glass is rubbed with silk, the glass loses electrons to the silk. Both substances become electrically charged—glass positively, and the silk negatively. Similarly if a plastic ball-pen is rubbed with wool, the wool loses electrons to the plastic so that the wool becomes positively charged, and the plastic becomes negatively charged.

Where electrons have been lost from a particular area of a substance, others are subsequently gained from the surroundings. Similarly, where extra electrons have been gained by a particular area, they are subsequently lost to the surroundings. In both cases the electric charge is lost. A substance in which electrons flow easily (*i.e.* a good conductor) will tend to lose a charge rapidly from a charged area; on the other hand, a substance in which electrons do not flow easily (*i.e.* a poor conductor) will tend to lose a charge slowly from a charged area. The ability to retain a charge varies from substance to substance according to how readily the outermost electrons may be forced from their atomic orbits.

While a substance remains electrically charged, it tends to attract other substances, particularly poor conductors. This is due to the charged substance inducing an opposite charge, and to areas with opposite charges attracting one another. For example, if a negatively charged plastic pen is brought near to a small piece of paper, it tends to repel the electrons in the paper, and induce in the paper an area that is positively charged. Similarly, a positively charged object would attract electrons in the paper, and so induce an area that would be negatively charged. This is why a fountain pen rubbed on a sleeve will pick up tiny bits of paper or grains of salt, and why an inflated balloon rubbed on wool will cling to a wall or ceiling.

Just as objects with dissimilar charges attract one another, so objects with similar charges repel one another. If two inflated balloons are rubbed with wool and placed together on a table, they will roll away from one another, because they have similar charges. If dry hair is vigorously brushed, individual hairs become similarly charged, and stand out, repelling one another.

The more electrons a substance gains or loses, the more difficult it becomes for this unbalanced state to be maintained, and, given suitable conditions, the charge may be lost, *i.e.* there may be a sudden discharge. The suddenness of such a discharge may result in a spark or a flash, the most spectacular example of this being lightning. Within a cloud, electrically charged areas are produced by friction between drops of water or ice crystals tossed violently about by turbulent air currents. Lightning occurs when an accumulated charge becomes so great that it overcomes the resistance of the surrounding air. It may take place between cloud and cloud or between cloud and ground. St Elmo's fire, seen at the tips of flagpoles and the masts of ships at sea, is also due to electrical discharges; so too is the slight crackling noise which is sometimes heard when you comb dry hair or stroke the back of a dry cat.

Thunder is *not* caused by two clouds bumping together. The air through which the electrons flow becomes heated (because it is a poor conductor and therefore offers resistance). This causes it to expand explosively, *i.e.* it sets up a compression wave which ultimately causes the eardrums to vibrate. The compression wave has the same effect as the compression wave set up by a fast-flying aircraft 'breaking the sound barrier'.

Electric Currents

An electric current is a stream of electrons—roughly analogous to a stream of water. Whereas, however, a stream of water flows from a high level to a low level, a stream of electrons flows from a negatively charged area to a positively charged area. A discharge is a temporary flow. In order to obtain a continuous flow, an area which has surplus electrons and an area which is deficient in electrons must be maintained. Batteries and dynamos are used for this purpose.

A *battery* consists of one or more cells. In a cell, two dissimilar metal plates (or a metal plate and a carbon plate) are separated by chemicals which react with them. Chemical

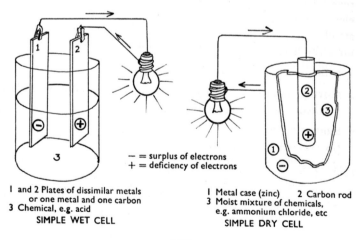

— = surplus of electrons
+ = deficiency of electrons

1 and 2 Plates of dissimilar metals
or one metal and one carbon
3 Chemical, e.g. acid
SIMPLE WET CELL

1 Metal case (zinc)   2 Carbon rod
3 Moist mixture of chemicals,
e.g. ammonium chloride, etc
SIMPLE DRY CELL

reaction causes a surplus of electrons on one plate, and a deficiency of electrons on the other. When these two plates are connected by a suitable conductor, *e.g.* a length of copper wire, the surplus electrons flow through it from the plate with a surplus (the negatively charged plate) to the plate with a deficiency (the positively charged plate). If the circuit is broken, *e.g.* if the wire is removed, the chemical reaction stops because the surplus electrons are no longer able to escape.

A *dynamo*, simply defined, is a device in which a coil of metal wire is made to move in relation to the magnetic field from a magnet (or vice versa). Three main ways of doing this are by

(*a*) rotating the coil rapidly between two different magnetic poles,

(*b*) rotating the coil rapidly round the poles of a magnet, or rotating the magnet within the coil,

(*c*) moving the magnet rapidly in and out of the coil.

The movement of the magnet relative to the coil, or of the coil relative to the magnet, causes 'loose' electrons in the atoms of the wire to flow from one atom to another, and an electric current is induced in the coil.

Obviously some form of mechanical energy is required to force either the magnet or the coil to move, so that a dynamo is really an instrument for converting mechanical energy into electrical energy. A magnet or a coil of wire may be turned by attaching it to a shaft which is turned by a wheel. Power to force the wheel to turn may be obtained from

1 animals, as in the case of a cycle dynamo;

2 moving water, as in a hydro-electric power station where the wheel is a turbine wheel;

3 moving gases, *e.g.*

(*a*) steam forcing a turbine wheel to turn,

(*b*) gases in a petrol or diesel oil engine turning the crank-shaft which turns the dynamo wheel by means of a belt,

(*c*) moving air initially forcing a windwheel to turn. This turns the dynamo wheel by means of gears and shafts.

Notes

1 As an electric current is a stream of electrons, electricity cannot be stored. In a car battery (an accumulator), a current from a dynamo driven by the engine passes through the cells of the battery in the opposite direction from that taken by the current obtained from the battery. This reverses the chemical reaction which produces current in the battery and returns the chemicals to their original state. Charging a battery does not 'fill it with electricity'. It merely reverses a chemical reaction so that it can take place again.

2 Electricity is generated at a great number of places throughout the United Kingdom. The various power stations are linked together by overhead lines. These constitute the grid. If a district is using more electricity than its own dynamos can provide, it can obtain additional current from dynamos generating it in another district.

CODE

Demonstrate that electric charges are caused by friction, and that electrically charged objects attract other things.

1 Rub an inflated balloon with wool. See if it will cling to a wall or attract dry hair and tiny bits of paper.

2 Rub a nylon hair ribbon with wool. The ribbon will cling to the skin.

3 Rub a piece of stiff acetate sheet with wool and hold it above dry hair. This should make it stand on end.

4 Rub a plastic ball-pen or fountain pen on wool. It should attract tiny bits of paper, sawdust, grains of sand or salt.

5 Rub a plastic ball-pen on wool. It may be used to
 (*a*) make a postage stamp stand on edge. First hold the stamp upright on a table and then position the pen about $\frac{1}{2}''$ above it.
 (*b*) attract small floating plastic objects, *e.g.* plastic boats, ball-pen tops, or even matches.

6 Suspend a lightweight length of wood, *e.g.* a pencil, horizontally by a thread (which can be stuck on with cellulose tape). Rub a plastic ball-pen or other object on cloth, and make the suspended pencil spin by attraction.

7 Similarly suspend a plastic ball-pen and try to attract it with various charged objects.

Notes

(*a*) If a plastic ball-pen is suspended and rubbed so that it becomes charged, it will be attracted to other objects, including metals (in which the pen will induce positive charges). Because of this, it will also be attracted towards a magnet, and while this is an interesting trick, care should be taken to avoid giving the impression that the magnetism of an ordinary magnet can force plastic to move.

(*b*) If a second plastic ball-pen is charged, it can be used to make the first pen spin by repulsion. (Like charges repel.)

8 Experiment with the simple electric charge detector illustrated in the Pupils' Book. This is sensitive to charges which are not normally easy to detect. It can be used to show that charges are retained by quite a number of materials, including bakelite, glass, rubber, plastics, sealing wax and various cloths. Given suitable conditions, it may even twitch in response to the slight charge on a finger or pencil rubbed on cotton. By its lack of response to metals, it can be used to show that these do not readily retain electric charges.

9 Make a charge detector and mark it with a horizontal arrow. Invert a jam jar over the detector. The arrow can be made to point to any particular section of the glass by rubbing that section with wool or silk. A plastic ball-pen rubbed with wool should make the detector revolve, even though the wall of the jar intervenes.

Notes

1 Electrons flow better through moist air than through dry air, which is why any experiments to show that a substance is retaining an electric charge are more effective when both substance and surrounding air are dry.

2 Nylon and plastics, *e.g.* polythene, perspex, and the plastic materials used for ball-pens, are outstanding for experiments to show electric charges. Very thin polythene well rubbed with wool will often adhere to a smooth wall or door for a long period. A plastic ball-pen rubbed with wool can be used to bend a trickle of water from a tap. It is because plastic materials retain charges so very well that they readily attract dust.

NOTEBOOK WORK

Answers should be along the following lines.

1 A substance with too many or too few electrons is said to be electrically charged.

2 An electric current is a stream of electrons flowing from one place to another.

3 Two things which are used to cause electric currents are batteries and dynamos.

4 An inflated balloon can be fixed to a wall without glue, by first rubbing it on wool to give it an electric charge.

ELECTRIC CURRENTS AND CIRCUITS

CONDUCTING AND INSULATING

DEMONSTRATION MATERIAL

1 Batteries, *e.g.* 3-volt, $4\frac{1}{2}$-volt, 6-volt
2 Torch bulbs and bulb holders; lengths of plastic-covered
   1-amp bell wire; paper clips (or spring clips); small screwdriver
3 A switch that shows clearly how a circuit may be made and
   broken
4 Various good conductors and poor conductors, *e.g.* various
   metals, plastic, wood, string, paper, sealing wax, cotton
   wool, rubber, wool, glass, piece of coke, pencil 'lead'
5 Materials for making weak current detectors: empty matchboxes (large), small pocket compasses, sticky tape; plastic-
   covered 1-amp bell wire in lengths of at least 6 yards
6 Materials for causing weak electric currents, *e.g.* salt, bicarbonate of soda or iodine dissolved in water; vinegar,
   lemon juice, copper coins, magnesium ribbon, aluminium
   wrapping foil; zinc and carbon rods from old small-voltage
   batteries
7 Any demonstration models to show the use of simple circuits
   (See pages 214-5)

SAMPLE LINK QUESTIONS

1 What is electricity caused by? (*Electrons*)
2 What is an electron? (*One of the minute particles revolving
   round the nucleus of an atom*)
3 Which electrons are most easily forced from their orbits?
   (*The outermost ones*)
4 When two substances are rubbed together, what may happen
   to the outermost electrons in some of the atoms of one of
   them? (*They may be lost to the other substance*)
5 When a substance has too many or too few electrons, what is
   it said to be? (*Electrically charged*)

6 If a substance has gained some extra electrons, what normally happens to them eventually? (*They are lost to the surroundings*)

7 If there is a sudden movement of enough electrons, what may we see the result as? (*A spark or a flash*)

8 What is a flash of lightning caused by? (*Millions of extra electrons escaping from a cloud*)

9 When a whole stream of electrons is flowing from one place to another what do we call it? (*An electric current*)

10 What are two things we can use to force a stream of electrons to move? (*A battery and a dynamo*)

RELEVANT INFORMATION

The main points of this lesson are that

1 anything through which a stream of electrons is flowing is conducting electricity;

2 some things conduct it better than others.

An electric current may be considered as the flowing of electrons from an area with a surplus of electrons (negatively charged area) towards an area deficient in electrons (positively charged area). When such a flow of electrons occurs in a substance, that substance is conducting electricity.

When a stream of electrons enters one end of a conductor, a corresponding stream emerges at the other almost instantaneously (*e.g.* at 20,000 miles per second if the conductor is copper wire). However, the speed of individual electrons *through* the conductor is relatively slow—probably not more than an inch per second. As they proceed, some will bypass atoms, and others will replace orbiting electrons, forcing these on instead, so that although there is a general movement throughout the conductor, the electrons which emerge are not necessarily the same as those which entered.

The ability to conduct varies from substance to substance according to atomic structure. In the atoms of some substances, the outer electrons are so loosely held that they are virtually free to drift haphazardly from atom to atom even when a current is not flowing. A substance which loses its outer electrons easily will present an easy passage for a stream of electrons

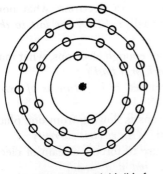

A copper atom, with 'shells' of 2, 8, 18 and 1 electrons, easily loses the outermost electron

moving in one direction only. It will be a good conductor of electricity, and it will also lose a charge rapidly from a charged area. On the other hand, a substance which does not lose the outer electrons from its atoms easily will not present an easy passage for the movement of electrons. It will be a poor conductor of electricity, and it will not lose a charge rapidly from a charged area.

Note. Conventionally, an electric current is said to flow from positive to negative, whereas the flow of electrons is from negative to positive. This confusion dates back to the days before there was a proper understanding of what an electric current is, and just for convenience it was said that electricity flowed from positive to negative. It would perhaps be advisable to consider positive and negative as terms assigned to opposite forces of attraction, rather than to consider them as indicative of plus and minus quantities.

Conducting and Insulating

The ability of a substance to conduct is usually judged on its conduction of currents normally generated by man-made agencies. In this respect, carbon and most metals are classed as good conductors. Silver and copper are about the best, but copper's relative cheapness makes it more economical to use. Aluminium is not quite so good a conductor as copper but is lighter in weight. It can also be made into wires with a steel core which makes it as strong as copper, and cheaper. A lightning conductor usually consists of a sharply pointed metal rod, which is attached to the highest part of a building and connected to a thick metal cable which leads to a copper plate buried in the ground. The cable itself may be copper, but iron can also be used and is cheaper. When lightning occurs, the discharge is naturally towards any high object such as a building or tree—the nearest points on the surface of the earth. This is why it is inadvisable to stand on a hill or under a tree during a storm. Where the highest object is a metal conductor leading directly to earth, the discharge is naturally to that, as it provides the easiest path along which electrons can flow.

Glass, porcelain, cloth, ebonite, plastics, rubber, mica and dry air are very poor conductors and may be used to prevent a stream of electrons flowing in an unwanted direction, *e.g.* to prevent two conducting wires touching and forming a circuit. When poor conductors are utilised in this way, they are termed insulators. Rubber has long been used for insulating domestic wiring, but plastic is better and does not perish like rubber. Porcelain, bakelite and rubber are typical substances used for insulating purposes in electric plugs. Porcelain and sometimes glass are used as insulators to support telegraph wires and overhead electric cables so as to prevent current leaking down to earth during wet weather. Mica is used for insulation in electric irons and toasters.

Some very poor conductors, *e.g.* air, are sometimes described as non-conductors, but in fact there is no known substance through which electrons will not flow, given suitable circumstances. A very powerful current is more likely than a weak current to force its way through a substance. Lightning, for example, is powerful enough to overcome the poor conductivity of air. The presence of other substances may also affect conduction. For example, the presence of moisture in the air improves conduction, which is why experiments with electrostatics are best undertaken in a dry atmosphere. Pure water is considered to be a poor conductor, but the presence of other substances in the water increases its ability to conduct. Human skin is not a particularly good conductor, but the presence of moisture increases its conductivity considerably. This is why it is dangerous to handle electrical appliances, *e.g.* switches and plugs, with wet hands.

The earth is not a particularly good conductor. Much of it consists of poor conducting material, but it serves as a kind of giant clearing-house, to and from which loose electrons constantly come and go. This is why an electric appliance is safer if it is connected to the earth by means of a very good conductor. This is customarily in the form of a separate wire—the earth wire. In the event of any metal parts on an appliance becoming 'live', the current is more likely to be conducted to the earth through the earth wire, than through any human being touching the appliance.

Circuits and Switches

When an electric current is being used, it is not actually being 'burned' or consumed in any way. It is merely flowing through a conductor and being made to do some kind of work on the way, just as a stream of water flowing from a high to a low level can be made to do some kind of work en route without the water itself being consumed, *e.g.* turn a waterwheel.

If a current is being generated by a battery or dynamo, the conducting material must obviously connect the area which is being negatively charged with the area which is being positively charged, so that the current is led back to the battery or dynamo which is forcing it to flow. The current is then completing a circuit. This is why every electrical appliance must be connected to at least two wires; the current flows to the appliance along one wire, and returns from the appliance along the other. When a third wire is used, this is for safety purposes, and should connect any outer metal parts of the appliance directly or indirectly to the earth. If a circuit is severed in some way, then the electrons can no longer circulate, *i.e.* the current ceases to flow. A switch is a convenient way of opening or closing a gap in a circuit, so that a current can be allowed to flow through an electrical appliance as and when required. A circuit need not consist of wire. In a pocket torch, for example, the metal case of the torch is the chief part of the circuit.

CODE

1 Experiment to show that a current must complete a circuit in order to flow from a battery or dynamo.

Screw a torch bulb into a bulb holder. Connect a single wire from one terminal of a battery to the bulb holder. Observe that the bulb does not light.

Connect a second wire from the bulb holder to the battery's other terminal. Observe that the bulb lights, because the current completes a circuit.

If a simple switch is available, wire that into the circuit to show how a gap may be opened and closed in a circuit.

2 Experiment to show that some things are good conductors of electricity and others are not.

Construct the apparatus for testing shown in the Pupils' Book, and try bridging the gap with various things, including metals and those that were found, in the previous lesson, to retain electric charges. Interesting things to try are cotton wool soaked in salt water, a piece of coke and a pencil 'lead'. (The last, of course, is not lead but graphite —a form of carbon.)

Observe that the poor conductors are those which were found, in the previous lesson, to retain an electric charge, *e.g.* polythene, nylon, plastic, wool, sealing wax, glass, rubber.

Observe that the good conductors include those which were found in the previous lesson to lose their charges quickly, *e.g.* common metals such as iron, steel, copper, brass, aluminium.

Note. Some substances on which it was difficult to detect a charge will also be shown to be poor conductors, *e.g.* wood and cork. These may be grouped as 'in-betweeners'—not poor enough to retain an easily detectable charge, and not good enough to conduct the current necessary to light a torch bulb.

3 Experiment to show that weak currents can be obtained from chemicals—as in the cell of a battery.

Construct the current detector shown in the Pupils' Book. In it use any of the following as liquids: (*a*) water, in which has been dissolved salt, or bicarbonate of soda or iodine; (*b*) vinegar or lemon juice. And use any of the following as 'plates': (*a*) different metals, *e.g.* bright copper coin, magnesium ribbon, aluminium wrapping foil (*e.g.* milk top), perforated zinc; (*b*) carbon rod, *e.g.* from an old battery.

Connect the wires from the detector to any two different 'plates'. Ensure that the wire in the coil is parallel with the compass needle. Dip the two plates in the selected liquid, and observe whether or not the compass needle moves—as it will if a current flows through the wire.

Notes.

(*a*) As this detector is better than a torch bulb for indicating when a current is flowing, it may be used in place of the torch bulb in experiment No. 2.

(*b*) If a strong bar magnet is available, it may be possible to show that a magnet can force a stream of electrons to flow in a wire—which is basically what happens in a dynamo. Connect a coil of wire to the detector as shown in the diagram, and jerk the magnet quickly in and out of the coil. The strength of the current depends on the number of turns in the coil and the strength and speed of the moving magnet.

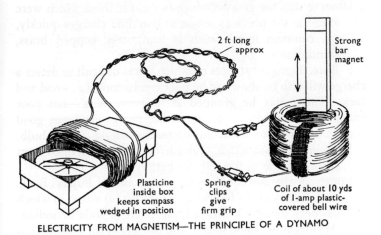

2 ft long approx

Strong bar magnet

Plasticine inside box keeps compass wedged in position

Spring clips give firm grip

Coil of about 10 yds of 1-amp plastic-covered bell wire

ELECTRICITY FROM MAGNETISM—THE PRINCIPLE OF A DYNAMO

4 Demonstrate the use of simple circuits in a model, *e.g.* with a toy set of traffic signals, or with a question and answer game. (See illustrations on pages 214 and 215.)

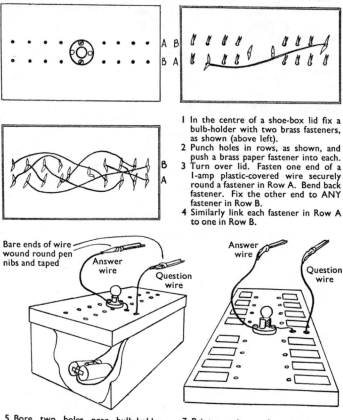

1 In the centre of a shoe-box lid fix a bulb-holder with two brass fasteners, as shown (above left).
2 Punch holes in rows, as shown, and push a brass paper fastener into each.
3 Turn over lid. Fasten one end of a 1-amp plastic-covered wire securely round a fastener in Row A. Bend back fastener. Fix the other end to ANY fastener in Row B.
4 Similarly link each fastener in Row A to one in Row B.

5 Bore two holes near bulb-holder. Through one, thread the question wire and attach it to a battery terminal.
6 Through the other, thread a wire and connect bulb-holder to other battery terminal. Connect answer wire to other terminal of bulb-holder.

7 Print questions and answers, each on a separate label.
8 Fix a question beside each paper fastener on the left-hand side. Find which fastener on the right is linked to each on the left, and place answers accordingly.

For a 3-volt battery, use a 2.5-volt bulb. For a 4½-volt battery, use a 3.5-volt bulb

When the question and answer wires touch the fasteners beside a question and its right answer, the circuit is completed and the bulb lights

A dress-box gives room for two longer rows of questions and two of answers

QUESTION AND ANSWER GAME

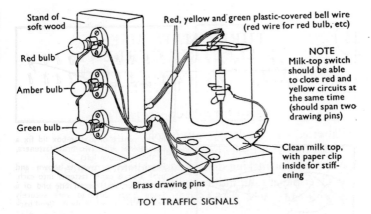

Stand of soft wood

Red bulb

Amber bulb

Green bulb

Red, yellow and green plastic-covered bell wire
(red wire for red bulb, etc)

NOTE
Milk-top switch
should be able
to close red and
yellow circuits at
the same time
(should span two
drawing pins)

Clean milk top,
with paper clip
inside for stiff-
ening

Brass drawing pins

TOY TRAFFIC SIGNALS

NOTEBOOK WORK

Answers should be along the following lines.

1 A substance is said to be conducting electricity when a stream of electrons is flowing through it.

2 An insulator is a very poor conductor being used to prevent electricity from being conducted.

3 We can stop a current completing a circuit by making a gap in the circuit.

4 A switch is used to open or close such a gap.

5 You should never experiment with the electrical supply at home, because it is strong enough to force its way through you.

THREE MAIN USES
FOR ELECTRIC CURRENTS

HEAT, LIGHT AND POWER

DEMONSTRATION MATERIAL

1 Batteries, *e.g.* 3-volt, 4½-volt, 6-volt
2 Metal foil with tissue paper attached
3 Materials for making doll's house radiators: matchbox trays, silver paper (aluminium foil), electric-iron heating element (at least the wire from one), short lengths of plastic-covered 1-amp bell wire
4 Materials for making electro-magnets: 4-inch nails, insulating tape (or cellulose tape), plastic-covered 1-amp bell wire in 6-yard lengths
5 Paper clips, needles, plasticine
6 Demonstration model to show how electricity can force a wheel to turn (See page 222)

SAMPLE LINK QUESTIONS

1 What does an electric current consist of? (*A stream of electrons*)
2 What do we call a substance through which a stream of electrons will not flow easily? (*A poor conductor*)
3 When a poor conductor is used specially to prevent electricity being conducted, what do we call it? (*An insulator*)
4 Why are electric wires made of metals such as copper and aluminium? (*They are good conductors of electricity*)
5 When a current flows from a battery or dynamo and then back again, what is it completing? (*A circuit*)
6 What does a gap in a circuit prevent electrons from doing? (*Flowing*)
7 What do we use to open and close such a gap? (*A switch*)
8 Why should you never experiment with electricity supply at home? (*It is too strong to be safe*)

9 When something is hot enough to burn or hot enough to glow, what does it give out as well as heat? (*Light*)

10 What do we need in order to force wheels and screw propellers to turn? (*Power*)

RELEVANT INFORMATION

The chief purpose of this lesson is to show that the three main uses for electric currents are to provide (*a*) heat, (*b*) light, (*c*) power.

All substances, including those classed as very good conductors, will resist a flow of electrons to some extent. This resistance depends on three main factors:

1 How easily the atoms of the substance lose electrons. The poorer the conductor, the greater the resistance.

2 The total length of the substance through which the stream of electrons has to flow. The greater the length, the greater the resistance.

3 The cross-sectional area. The narrower the path, the more difficult it is for a stream of electrons to force its way through, *i.e.* the narrower the path, the greater the resistance.

When a current is flowing through a substance, the resistance results in the generation of heat. The greater the resistance, the greater the heat.

Obtaining Heat

In heating appliances, the current is allowed to flow through a conductor which resists the flow of electrons sufficiently to give out the required heat. In domestic appliances, such as electric radiators, toasters, grills and kettles, this conductor (the element) is usually made of nichrome. Nichrome is an alloy of nickel, chromium and iron which is able to reach a high temperature without burning or melting. Its resistance may be increased (and therefore more heat obtained) by increasing its length. This is often done by coiling the wire.

Generation of heat by a current can be disadvantageous. For example, when heating appliances are connected to an electric light socket, or too many appliances are connected to the same power plug, the amount of current flowing through the circuit may cause the wire to become overheated. This is why a fuse is included at an accessible part of a circuit. A fuse wire is thin and is made of a metal that has a low melting point, so that if the circuit becomes hot due to overloading, the fuse wire melts and breaks the circuit.

Obtaining Light

In an incandescent lamp, such as an electric bulb, the conductor must resist the flowing electrons to such an extent that it becomes hot enough to glow brightly. In a light bulb, for example, the conductor (filament) is made of tungsten. Tungsten can be drawn out into a very narrow wire. The narrower it is, the greater its resistance; and in a light bulb, it becomes hot enough to glow at white heat. In order to prevent burning, the oxygen is removed, *i.e.* the air is exhausted or replaced with a gas such as argon or nitrogen, which does not react chemically with the tungsten.

In *neon gas* lamps and *sodium vapour* lamps, a gas is made to glow when a stream of electrons passes through it. Such lamps are more economical than lamps containing a wire, as less energy is dissipated in the form of heat.

In a *fluorescent* lamp, even less energy is wasted as heat. The gas in this type of lamp emits ultra-violet rays when electrons pass through it. The inner surface of the glass container of the lamp is coated with a phosphorescent sulphide which glows when the ultra-violet rays strike it. (See *fluorescence*, Lesson 6.)

Increasing the voltage increases the effects of resistance, *i.e.* increases heat. This is due to an increased voltage allowing an increase in current.

Obtaining Power

There are two main ways of obtaining power to force things to move.

1 *By means of electro-magnetism.* When a stream of electrons flows through a coil of wire, it sets up a magnetic field, so that

the coil can be used to attract things made of iron or steel. (In the current detector illustrated in Lesson 23, the magnetic field set up by a current flowing through the coil is responsible for moving the compass needle.) If the coil surrounds an iron core, the latter becomes a relatively strong magnet while the current is flowing, and this too can be used to attract things made of iron or steel. Electro-magnetism is used in appliances such as electric door-bells, morse keys, and the industrial electric magnets used in scrap-metal works.

2 *By means of an electric motor.* An electric motor is similar in structure to a dynamo, but its purpose is the reverse of that of a dynamo in that it is an instrument for converting electrical energy into mechanical energy. In a dynamo, a stream of electrons can be induced to flow through a coil of wire by rotating the coil between the north-seeking and south-seeking poles of a magnet. In this case, the coil has to be turned mechanically. In an electric motor, a stream of electrons flows through a coil, setting up magnetic forces between it and two opposite magnetic poles. These magnetic forces cause the coil to rotate. The coil, wound round a shaft (the armature shaft), forces this to rotate, and the shaft can then be used to force wheels to turn.

Electric motors are used to turn shafts and wheels in a wide variety of machines and vehicles. They provide power to operate machinery in factories and homes. As wires can be led over long distances to convenient connecting plugs, and as the motors are compact and light in weight, they obviate the need for the intricate systems of belts, shafts and pulleys which would be necessary to connect machines to a central unit if another source of power, *e.g.* wind, water or steam, were used.

In electric vehicles, the current for the motors is supplied by large batteries—as in many milk delivery vans—or generated by dynamos. Some electrically driven ships have their propellers turned by motors which receive their current from large batteries, but in most kinds the current for the motors is generated by dynamos. In a diesel-electric system, a diesel engine forces a dynamo shaft to turn. In a turbo-electric system, steam is used to turn turbine wheels which force the dynamo shaft to turn. Today the steam can be obtained from water heated by atomic energy.

Although the three main uses for electric currents are to provide heat, light and power, there are other subsidiary uses, such as electro-plating and the manufacture of chemicals by electrolysis.

Some Technical Information

1 A volt is a unit of electrical pressure. The force with which a stream of electrons can be pushed through a circuit is known as the electromotive force (e.m.f.) and is measured in volts. The greater the resistance in a substance, the greater the voltage required to force a stream of electrons through it.

2 An ampere (amp) is a unit of current. The amount of current flowing, *i.e.* the number of electrons passing a given point in a given time, is measured in amps. 1 amp = about 6 million million million electrons per second. This is the current which a 1-amp wire will allow to flow through it without danger of overheating. Doubling the voltage doubles the current, provided the resistance remains the same.

3 A watt is a unit of power. Electricity is not actually consumed or burned; it is made to do work. The rate at which work is done (*e.g.* the amount in one hour) is measured in watts. Watts = amps × volts. A 200-volt supply which is able to force a current of 5 amps through a radiator will do 1,000 watts' worth of work in 1 hour. 1,000 watts = 1 kilowatt. 746 watts = 1 horse power.

4 An ohm is a unit of resistance. The total resistance of a conductor is measured in ohms. A pressure of 1 volt, forcing electrons through a resistance of 1 ohm, gives a current of 1 amp, and can do 1 watt's worth of work in 1 hour.

CODE

1 Experiment to show that resistance in a conductor results in heat.

(*a*) Cut this shape from the foil-and-tissue-paper wrapping of a packet of chocolate or cigarettes. The narrow part should be less than one-sixteenth of an inch wide. Place the ends of the foil in contact with the terminals of a battery—the higher the voltage, the better. The tissue paper at the narrow part should burn, and the foil there may melt and break.

(b) Construct the doll's house radiator shown in the Pupils' Book. The short strip of nichrome element should become hot enough to glow if used with a 6-volt battery. A complete electric-iron element should provide enough nichrome wire for more than 40 little radiators. If an old element is not available, a new one can be bought very cheaply. (Note the mica plates which serve as insulators.)

Connect to battery for short periods only, as they use current rapidly.

2 Experiment to show how an electric current can be used to obtain power to force things to move.

(a) Construct the simple electro-magnet shown in the Pupils' Book. When connected to a 3-, 4½-, or 6-volt battery, this will pick up pen nibs, drawing pins, paper clips, etc.

Notes (i) Before coiling the wire, several layers of insulating tape (or cellulose tape) should be wound round each end of the nail. These serve as end stops.

(ii) The three layers of the coil should be built up, if possible, from one continuous length of wire, and there should be about 12 inches of free wire at the beginning and at the end. When the coil is complete, fix the wire firmly in position with tape at each end.

(b) Demonstrate with the electro-magnet how electricity can be used to force a wheel to turn, as shown in diagrams. Connect to battery for short periods only, as it uses current rapidly.

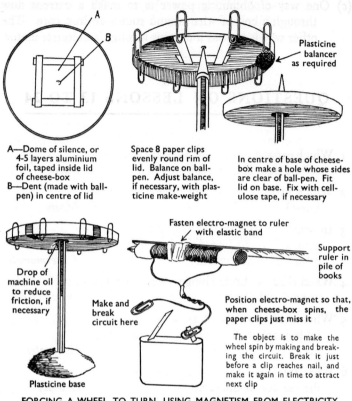

A—Dome of silence, or 4-5 layers aluminium foil, taped inside lid of cheese-box
B—Dent (made with ball-pen) in centre of lid

Space 8 paper clips evenly round rim of lid. Balance on ball-pen. Adjust balance, if necessary, with plasticine make-weight

In centre of base of cheese-box make a hole whose sides are clear of ball-pen. Fit lid on base. Fix with cellulose tape, if necessary

Plasticine balancer as required

Fasten electro-magnet to ruler with elastic band

Support ruler in pile of books

Drop of machine oil to reduce friction, if necessary

Make and break circuit here

Position electro-magnet so that, when cheese-box spins, the paper clips just miss it

The object is to make the wheel spin by making and breaking the circuit. Break it just before a clip reaches nail, and make it again in time to attract next clip

Plasticine base

FORCING A WHEEL TO TURN, USING MAGNETISM FROM ELECTRICITY
(The principle of an electric motor)

NOTEBOOK WORK

Answers should be along the following lines.

(a) In an electric heating appliance, a current passes through a conductor which resists the current enough to become very hot.

(b) In an electric lamp, a current passes through a conductor with such a high resistance that it becomes hot enough to glow very brightly.

(c) One way of obtaining power is to make a current flow through a coil of wire wound round an iron core. The other way is to pass a current through an electric motor.

QUESTIONS ON LESSONS 13 TO 24

1 Which expand most when they are heated—solids, liquids or gases? *Gases*

2 Which expanding gas can force a boiler to burst? *Steam*

3 In which instrument is the expansion or contraction of a liquid used to show a rise or fall in temperature? *A thermometer*

4 When is a steel bridge longer—on a hot day or on a cold day? *On a hot day*

5 What would you use to get a dent out of a table-tennis ball—an oven, hot water or a fire? *Hot water*

6 What forces air to press against things on the surface of the earth? *Gravity*

7 In which direction does air press? *All directions*

8 Which presses with more force—compressed air or the air about you? *Compressed air*

9 Is it easier to slide over a rough surface or over a smooth surface? *A smooth surface*

10 When a surface is so smooth that things slide over it too easily for our liking, what do we say the surface is? *Slippery*

11 What does the tread on a rubber tyre make the tyre less likely to do? *Skid*

12 What does a machine make easier? *Work*

13 What can a machine help us to obtain? *More force*

14 What force does the sloping surface of a *The force of* ramp help us to overcome? *gravity*

15 The sloping surface on a chisel is used as a simple machine. What do we call this kind of simple machine? *A wedge*

16 When a sloping surface is used in the form of a spiral, what do we call it? *A screw*

17 What do you push against, when you paddle a canoe or row a boat? *Water*

18 When a vehicle is forced to move through air or through water by screwing, which *Screw* part does the screwing? *propeller*

19 Which air vehicles have propellers but no wings? *Helicopters*

20 Which were used on the first steamboats— *Paddle-* paddle-wheels or screw propellers? *wheels*

21 Some paddle-steamers had a paddle-wheel at the rear; if a paddle-steamer had two paddle-wheels, where were they fitted on the vehicle? *At each side*

22 Which could be used to force the *Great Eastern* to move—steam power, wind power, or both? *Both*

23 In which kind of steam engine is steam directed against the blades of a special *A turbine* wheel? *engine*

24 In which kind of steam engine is steam used *A piston and* to push a piston? *cylinder engine*

25 Which of these two kinds of steam engines *The piston and* was the first to be invented? *cylinder engine*

26 Which of these two kinds of steam engines *The piston and* was used on Stephenson's *Rocket*? *cylinder engine*

27 What was first used as fuel for boiling water to make steam for a steam engine? *Wood*

28 Which is used to keep a hovercraft clear of land or water—steam or compressed air? *Compressed air*

29 What does the vapour which is burned in a diesel engine come from? *Oil*

30 Which are used in petrol and diesel oil engines—pistons and cylinders, or turbine wheels? *Pistons and cylinders*

31 Jet vehicles and rocket vehicles are forced to move by expanding gases pushing against the inside of something; what is that something? *The engine*

32 Which gas is needed for burning in jet engines, rocket engines, petrol engines and diesel oil engines? *Oxygen*

33 Which of these engines is best suited for journeys into space? *Rocket engine*

34 What is electricity caused by? *Electrons*

35 When a substance has lost or gained electrons, what kind of charge has it? *An electric charge*

36 When a stream of electrons flows through a wire, what do we call it? *An electric current*

37 What would you fit to a tall building specially to conduct an electric current from cloud to earth? *A lightning conductor*

38 Which of these is the best conductor of an electric current—wood, rubber, copper, plastic, air? *Copper*

39 When a poor conductor is used specially to prevent an electric current from being conducted, what do we call it? *An insulator*

40 When an electric current flows from a battery or dynamo, and then back to the battery or dynamo, what does it complete? *A circuit*

41 What do we use to open or close a gap in a circuit? *A switch*

42 When a stream of electrons flows through a conductor, what causes the conductor to become hotter? *Resistance*

43 Which of these three—heat, light and power—do we obtain from conductors with a high resistance? *Heat and light*

44 Name two things that we use to obtain power from an electric current? *Electric motor and electro-magnet*

45 What do we call the shaft which is forced to turn in an electric motor? *The armature shaft*

46 What is wound round an iron core to conduct the electricity which makes the iron core into an electro-magnet? *A coil of wire*

47 If you wanted to increase the friction between two surfaces, would you make them rougher or smoother? *Rougher*

48 If a metal screw cap were fitting too tightly to a bottle neck, which would be more likely to loosen it—hot water or cold water? *Hot water*

49 If a rubber sucker is pressed on to a smooth wet surface, is it the pressure of the air, suction, or the water that forces it to stay there? *Pressure of the air*

50 When you blow up a balloon, what causes it to expand—heat, expanding air, or compressed air? *Compressed air*

SOME INSECTS WHICH BEGIN LIFE IN FRESH WATER

DRAGONFLIES AND CADDIS FLIES

DEMONSTRATION MATERIAL

Any living, mounted or preserved specimens of (*a*) dragonfly larvae and adults, (*b*) caddis fly larvae (in cases) and adults

SAMPLE LINK QUESTIONS

1 What are animals with six legs called? (*Insects*)
2 What are the four stages in the life of a beetle? (*Egg, larva, pupa, adult*)
3 What are the three stages in the life of a bug? (*Egg, larva, adult*)
4 Which is the only stage of life in which an insect grows bigger? (*The larval stage*)
5 In which stage can an insect have wings? (*The adult stage*)
6 How many wings has an adult moth or butterfly? (*Four*)
7 How many wings has an adult true fly, such as a housefly, bluebottle or midge? (*Two*)
8 How many feelers has an insect? (*Two*)
9 Where do insects live, apart from on land? (*In fresh water (not in the sea)*)
10 What special parts do some animals have to take oxygen from water? (*Gills*)

RELEVANT INFORMATION

In Pupils' Book 1, animals with six legs were introduced as insects.

In Pupils' Book 2, the development of insects from the egg to the adult (imago) stage was shown to follow one of two main courses:

   1 Egg, larva, adult   2 Egg, larva, pupa, adult

Also in Pupils' Book 2 there were separate lessons on moths and butterflies and on true (two-winged) flies. In Pupils' Book 3 there were separate lessons on beetles and on bugs.

Insects in General

The following is a brief summary of the more detailed information given in Teacher's Book 1, pages 45-9, and Teacher's Book 2, pages 61-9.

Habitat. Land and fresh water. Sea water does not suit them.

Body structure. Three main parts: (*a*) *head*, with mouth parts, eyes and one pair of feelers (antennae); (*b*) *thorax*, with three pairs of legs in the adult stage, and sometimes in the larval and pupal stages; also, for most species, one or two pairs of wings, which are present in the adult stage only; (*c*) *abdomen*, containing organs of respiration, reproduction, digestion and excretion.

Respiration. Land-dwelling insects take in air through holes in the body (spiracles). This enters a fine network of passages, through the walls of which an exchange of gases takes place. Many aquatic insects take their oxygen from the air at the surface; others have modifications to enable them to take oxygen from the water.

Food. This varies from species to species, practically all known living or dead animal and plant parts being suitable food for some species. Food is taken in by complicated mouth parts which are either (*a*) sucking mouth parts, or (*b*) biting and chewing mouth parts, as on dragonflies and caddis flies. Mouth parts may vary in structure between larva and adult of same species.

Growth. This takes place in the larval stage only. Some insects, *e.g.* dragonflies, have a three-stage life of egg, larva (nymph), adult. Others, *e.g.* caddis flies, have a four-stage life of egg, larva, pupa, adult.

Reproduction. Almost all insects have young by means of eggs, which are usually deposited close to, on, or even inside the food on which the larvae will feed. Some, *e.g.* greenfly, can retain the eggs in the body until the young hatch out. Virgin birth (parthenogenesis) is found in certain insects, *e.g.* stick insects.

Those insects which spend the whole or part of their lives

in fresh water may be looked upon as being land animals which have taken to water at some stage in their particular evolution.

Dragonflies (Odonata)

There are more than forty British species, divided into two main groups—*anisoptera* and *zygoptera*, the latter being generally termed damselflies.

Eggs may be laid above or below the water surface, either singly or in batches, and may be inserted into the stems or leaves of aquatic herbs, according to species.

When the *larva* emerges from the egg, its legs are enclosed by its skin, but within a few minutes this skin is moulted, and the legs are then free. On the head of the larva are two short thread-like feelers and two large compound eyes. Oxygen is absorbed from the water by means of gills situated at the tail end. On an anisopterid larva these gills are internal and concealed from view, but on a zygopterid larva they are external and appear as three long conspicuous filaments. The water which the anisopterid larva uses for respiration may be expelled with such force that the larva is propelled forwards. This simple form of jet propulsion is used to help the insect to escape from enemies.

Dragonfly larvae are beasts of prey, feeding on other small living animals such as other insect larvae, crustaceans and small worms. Some species hide in the mud and wait for prey; others stalk it, walking slowly over aquatic plants. To assist in catching prey, the lower lip is developed into a special organ which can be extended and retracted at will. This organ—the mask—is unique amongst insects. In its normal position it is

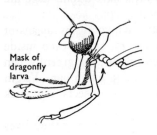

Mask of dragonfly larva

folded back under the head and then forward again, so that the front part covers the mouth. When the larva is suitably close to its prey, it shoots out the mask and seizes it with a pair of pincers at the mask's tip. The mask is then withdrawn, bringing the victim to the biting and chewing mouth parts.

During its life in water, the larva moults its skin several times, growing bigger after each moult. With each successive moult after about the sixth, the outline of the wings developing beneath the skin becomes more apparent. When ready for the final moult which will reveal the adult insect, the larva crawls out of the water, often up a stem or leaf that projects above the surface. Shortly after leaving the water, the skin splits just behind the head, and the adult carefully extricates itself through this slit, leaving the skin complete, even to the covering over the eyes. Within a short while the wings and abdomen fill out to their full size, and the adult flies away.

The anisopterid larva has a plump squat body, whereas the zygopterid larva has a narrow slender body with the three gill filaments prominent at the tail end.

The *adult*, like the larva, is a beast of prey. On the head, the two feelers are very short. There are small eyes on top of the head, in addition to the large compound eyes, but the unique mask of the larva is no longer present. In this stage the six legs are of little or no use for walking. They serve mainly for clinging when the insect is at rest and for clutching the living prey on which the insect feeds. Adults are sometimes found preying on the insects which are always in the vicinity of grazing cows and horses. They are also seen on occasions flying joined together in tandem, in which case they are in the process of mating. They live for a month or so, and none survives the winter.

The anisoptera are the larger variety with two dissimilar pairs of wings which remain outstretched when the insect is at rest. In the air they are probably the fastest of all insects, darting to and fro over their native water and preying on other insects which they catch during flight. The zygoptera have slender bodies and two similar pairs of wings which are folded over the back when the insect is at rest. They are not so rapid in the air as the anisoptera, and flutter with a moth-like flight from plant to plant, feeding on those suitably small animals which are found on or near them.

The life history of the anisoptera lasts two years or more; that of the zygoptera lasts about a year.

Caddis Flies (Trichoptera)

There are more than 180 British species, and these are grouped into seven families.

Eggs are laid in spring and summer. They vary in shape from species to species and are equipped with thread-like growths which help them to become attached to objects in the water. These eggs are generally dropped in a jelly-like mass into the water, where they float about until they become attached.

When a caddis fly *larva* first hatches out of the egg, it obtains oxygen by absorption through the skin, but after the first few moults most species develop gills along the body. Movements of the body force water over these gills, so that the insect may be said to breathe. (An animal is said to breathe when it assists respiration by forcing air or water over or into any parts developed specially for the absorption of oxygen.) The head of the larva is equipped with strong biting and chewing mouth parts. The larvae of most species feed on plant parts—particularly algae—but those of some species are carnivorous.

The larva (which is sometimes misleadingly called a caddis worm) has six active legs. The first three segments of the body are protected by a tough skin, but the remainder of the body is soft, and the larvae of most species construct special cases to protect this soft part. A case is bound together with silken threads spun from silk glands in the head, similar to those of a moth or butterfly larva. The materials for the cases vary from species to species—bits of dead stems, dead leaves, sand, gravel, and small snail shells (often still occupied by living molluscs). Some species attach their cases to objects in the water, but others prefer to move about carrying their cases with them, and some are even able to swim. When alarmed, a larva withdraws completely into the protective camouflage of its case. Undulating movements of the body force streams of water to flow through the case and over the gills.

At the tail end of the body two strong hooks grip the inside of the case—so firmly that if an attempt is made to pull a larva out of its case head first, it is more than likely that the body will be torn in two. The best way to encourage the insect to vacate the case is to prod it gently from the tail end. The larval period lasts up to a year, during which, as the insect grows, the case is extended by adding more material to the front end. When a larva is ready for the pupal stage, it spins a sieve of silk at each end of its case, and if this is not already attached, it fastens it to some stationary object in the water. Those few species which construct no case for the larval stage, spin a complete cocoon of silk for the pupal stage. The silken sieve at each end of the case keeps out other animals but allows water to filter through for respiration purposes. Inside the closed case the larva sheds its final skin and becomes a pupa.

The *pupal* stage is mainly one of rest. It generally lasts for a few weeks, but may be extended over the winter. The pupa has gill filaments like the larva, and also biting mouth parts. Shortly before the end of pupation, it chews its way out of its case, swims to the surface and emerges from its skin as an adult caddis fly.

Adult caddis flies are somewhat moth-like in appearance and fly chiefly at night. The fore wings are comparatively long and narrow, and the hind wings comparatively short and broad. They are covered with short bristles instead of the powdery colourful scales found on moths and butterflies and are generally sombre in hue with brown, fawn and grey predominating. These wings are folded along the body when the insect is at rest. The antennae (feelers) are long, and many-jointed.

Oxygen is obtained from the air by means of airholes in the sides of the body. Chewing mouth parts are present, but these are often reduced and useless. In general, little or no food is taken by the adults, although they are known to imbibe dewdrops and flower nectar. In fact the adult stage is concerned primarily with reproduction and is unlikely to last as much as three weeks.

CODE

Collect specimens of dragonfly larvae and caddis fly larvae for observation purposes. Where their presence is suspected in

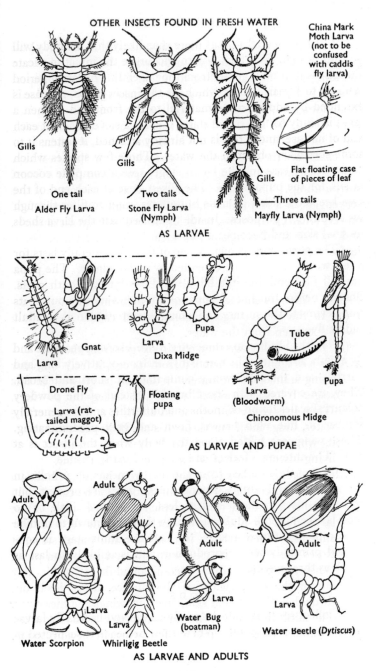

OTHER INSECTS FOUND IN FRESH WATER

China Mark Moth Larva (not to be confused with caddis fly larva)

Gills

One tail
Alder Fly Larva

Gills

Two tails
Stone Fly Larva (Nymph)

Gills

Flat floating case of pieces of leaf

Three tails
Mayfly Larva (Nymph)

AS LARVAE

Pupa

Larva

Gnat

Pupa

Larva
Dixa Midge

Tube

Larva
(Bloodworm)

Pupa

Drone Fly

Larva (rat-tailed maggot)

Floating pupa

Chironomous Midge

AS LARVAE AND PUPAE

Adult

Adult

Adult

Adult

Larva

Larva

Larva

Larva

Water Bug (boatman)

Water Scorpion   Whirligig Beetle

Water Beetle (Dytiscus)

AS LARVAE AND ADULTS

233

a particular area of water, they may usually be captured by removing a clump of plants from the water, together with surrounding mud, and spreading it out on a sheet of newspaper. Alternatively, the whole clump may be taken away and placed in an aquarium, containing water, for more leisurely examination. Caddis fly larvae of different species are found in running water and in still water. Those in the still water of ponds, lakes and canals are the most amenable to captivity, and are best kept in an aquarium containing water and plants from their original surroundings. They have been reported as surviving as active scavengers in a tropical aquarium. Dragonfly larvae will feed on very small earthworms, tadpoles, other small aquatic animals, and even on small scraps of raw meat if these are waved about in front of the head.

NOTEBOOK WORK

Answers should be along the following lines.
1 (a) In the larval stage dragonflies and caddis flies obtain oxygen from the water.
   (b) In the adult stage they obtain oxygen from the air.
2 After a dragonfly has hatched from its egg, it feeds on other living animals in the water. It does all its growing in this stage. It looks like a small adult, with six legs but no wings. When it is ready to become an adult, it crawls out of the water, drags itself out through a slit in its old skin, opens its wings and flies away. Adult dragonflies feed on other living insects, most of which are caught in the air.
   After a caddis fly larva has hatched from its egg, it builds a case to protect the soft parts of its body. The case is held together by silken threads which the larva spins. Most larvae feed on plant parts, but some kinds feed on tiny animals. When a larva is ready for the pupal stage, it closes the ends of its case with silk and rests as a pupa. When a pupa is ready to become an adult, it bites its way out of the case, swims to the surface, drags itself out through a slit in its old skin, opens its wings and flies away. The adult lives only a few days and hardly feeds at all.
3 Dragonflies and caddis flies have four wings in the adult stage.

THE SIMPLEST LIVING THINGS

CELLS

DEMONSTRATION MATERIAL

1 If available, a microscope or micro-projector, and any mounted specimen to show cells (See page 239)
2 Pieces of blue glass or cellophane
3 Any small portions of organic material suitable for burning, *e.g.* cork, string, wood, fruit skin, leaf, paper, sugar, wool, cotton, linen, bread

SAMPLE LINK QUESTIONS

1 What are the three kinds of things in the world? (*Alive, dead, never alive*)
2 What are the two kinds of living things? (*Animals and plants*)
3 What are the two kinds of dead things? (*Animal and plant*)
4 What are the three forms in which we find never-alive things? (*Solid, liquid and gas*)
5 What is the tiniest possible bit of a never-alive substance which can exist on its own? (*Molecule*)
6 Every molecule consists of one or more particles. What are these called? (*Atoms*)
7 What is the centre of an atom called? (*The nucleus*)
8 What are the tiniest living things you know?

RELEVANT INFORMATION

The main points of this lesson are that
1 cells are the simplest of all living things;
2 every living animal or plant consists of one or more of them.

In the biological sense, a cell is the simplest possible example of a complete living unit. The simplest of all living things consist of one cell only. Single-celled plants include bacteria and a number of algae. Single-celled animals (protozoa) include the amoeba, the foraminifera, radiolaria and infusoria. Mostly they live in sea water or fresh water.

Almost all living things large enough to be visible to the

naked eye are made up of millions of cells. In one mature leaf from an apple tree, for example, there are some 50 million cells. In a single-celled plant or animal, one cell has to perform all the functions necessary for its continued existence, *e.g.* absorbing oxygen and food. In most of the multi-celled animals and plants, on the other hand, there is a high degree of specialisation, with the different functions being attended to by cells developed specially for that purpose. In a mammal, there are breathing cells, digesting cells, reproductive cells, brain cells, bone cells, muscle cells and so on. A group of specialist cells doing the same job form a *tissue*. A group of tissues with a special function form an *organ*. The vein in a leaf is a tissue, and the leaf itself is an organ.

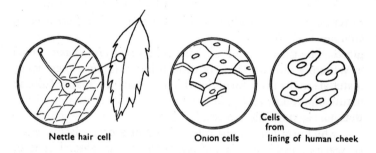

Nettle hair cell   Onion cells   Cells from lining of human cheek

Size and Shape of Cells

In general, single-celled plants and animals are too small to be seen with the naked eye, although different kinds are of different sizes. The smallest bacteria may be only 1/25,000 of an inch across, whereas the amoeba measures about 1/100 of an inch across and may just be visible to the naked eye as a minute greyish speck, smaller than this fullstop.

In multi-cellular plants and animals, the cells vary in size or shape according to their particular function. For example, the cell from the liver of a human being is roughly 1/1,000 of an inch across and about the same length. A nerve cell, on the other hand, may be less than 1/1,000 of an inch across, but up to three feet long. There are many different shapes of cells. Some retain a more or less fixed shape which is typical of their kind, whereas other kinds can alter in shape and even in size for particular reasons. An amoeba can alter in shape in order to move from place to place or to wrap itself round a particle of food. Muscle cells are able to contract, thus shortening the length of the muscle tissue, and enabling it to move the bones to which it is attached.

Certain kinds of cells, *e.g.* nerve and muscle cells, grow longer as the tissue grows longer. Most kinds of cells, however, do not grow beyond a maximum size, so that for most tissues, an increase in size is brought about by an increase in the actual number of cells.

Cell Parts

Small though a cell may be, and simple though it may be in terms of plants and animals in general, it is nevertheless a complex body in which a multitude of delicate processes takes place. The general mass of a cell consists of *protoplasm*. This is a highly organised substance containing many kinds of materials and minute structures. It is believed that the living nature of a cell is due to the organisation of its materials, rather than to any one vital element.

The outer part of the cell consists of a protoplasmic *wall*. In general, plant cells are more definite than animal cells in having this wall stiffened by cellulose, which provides rigidity. Within an ordinary cell the protoplasm consists of two fundamental parts—the denser and smaller *nucleus* enveloped in *cytoplasm*. The components of the nucleus differ in nature, behaviour and function from the components of the cytoplasm. Those of the nucleus play a primary role in heredity and in controlling development. Those of the cytoplasm are more concerned with the processes of absorption of oxygen and food, growth to maturity of the cell itself, and secretion of waste material. Even so, the components of both nucleus and cytoplasm are in intimate co-operation. Some kinds of components are found in the cells of nearly all plants and animals; others occur mainly or exclusively in plants, others mainly or exclusively in animals, and others occur only in certain groups of plants or certain groups of animals.

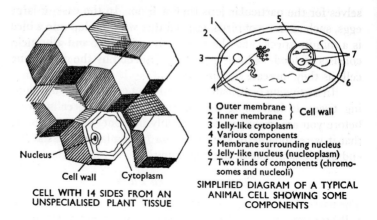

Nucleus

Cell wall   Cytoplasm

**CELL WITH 14 SIDES FROM AN
UNSPECIALISED PLANT TISSUE**

1 Outer membrane ⎫ Cell wall
2 Inner membrane ⎭
3 Jelly-like cytoplasm
4 Various components
5 Membrane surrounding nucleus
6 Jelly-like nucleus (nucleoplasm)
7 Two kinds of components (chromosomes and nucleoli)

**SIMPLIFIED DIAGRAM OF A TYPICAL
ANIMAL CELL SHOWING SOME
COMPONENTS**

Reproduction of Cells

Simply, a cell reproduces by dividing so that one cell becomes two. During an ideal division of a cell, there is an accurate division and distribution of the components, so that each of the two resulting daughter cells is a small replica of the parent cell. Mostly the cells formed by such a division grow to the original size of their parent cell before they in turn divide. Single-celled animals and plants are virtually immortal, as relatively few of them die a natural death, but they are prevented from unrestricted multiplication because many are consumed as food by larger animals.

In multi-celled animals and plants, individual cells do die—indeed certain tissues consist principally of dead cells. On many animals and plants, for example, the outer protective skin consists of dead cells. The skin of a human and the bark of a tree consist of dead cells. An individual human hair consists of a great number of cells. Those at the root of the hair are alive, but most of the rest are dead.

Every many-celled animal or plant starts life as a single cell. The single cell absorbs oxygen and food and divides into two individual cells. These two absorb oxygen and food and grow, and divide in turn, over and over again. During the process, the cells change in various ways so as to adapt themselves for the particular jobs they will do. In the case of large eggs, such as those of birds, the cell that will develop into a bird is a minute speck, and the rest of the egg (yolk and albumen) consists of food. This is gradually absorbed by the developing cells as they increase in number.

In a growing organism the number of cells in each developing tissue is increasing all the time. The children who sit before you are growing imperceptibly in front of your eyes, so that it is reasonable to state that you have a larger class at the end of a lesson than at the beginning!

Composition of Cell Parts

The parts of a cell consist of molecules of never-alive substances.

1 Protoplasm is built up from water (its chief constituent), carbohydrates, protein, fats and mineral salts.
2 Water is a compound substance consisting of hydrogen and oxygen.
3 The carbohydrates comprise starch, sugars, gums and dextrines, together with cellulose—all compound substances made up from carbon, hydrogen and oxygen.
4 Protein is built up from the action of nitrogen and other elements on carbohydrates.
5 Fats are built up from a combination of carbohydrates and protein.

Living things are therefore all built up mainly from carbon, hydrogen and oxygen. When living or dead things are incompletely burned, they are reduced to carbon. The same applies to materials and articles manufactured from, or extracted as, organic parts of living or dead things. Examples include fat, starch, sugar, paper, cotton, linen, string, bread.

CODE

1 If a microscope or micro-projector is available, examine any examples of cells. For example, take one of the fleshy swollen leaves from an onion bulb, and peel off a little of the very thin paper-like skin from its surface. Spread this out in water on a slide, and lower a cover slip over it. Observe the shape of the cells and the nucleus in each.

Staining the cells first with a mixture of iodine and water will make the nuclei more apparent.

2 Red blood cells can sometimes be seen, without a microscope, by looking steadily at a clear patch of sky for about a minute. Tiny dots will be 'seen' moving about—apparently in the sky. These are caused by the red blood cells moving through tiny capillary tubes in the back of the eye and casting shadows on the retina. Better results can be obtained by looking at the sky through blue glass or cellophane.

3 Experiment to show that dead things (and therefore living things) are made from never-alive substances. Take a small portion of dead or living material, *e.g.* wood, cork, feather, leaf, potato, apple, orange skin, wool, cotton, and heat to the temperature at which burning occurs. Observe that a black substance is left. In each case this will be carbon.

NOTEBOOK WORK

Answers should be along the following lines.

1 Every living thing consists of very tiny parts called cells.

2 The very simplest living things consist of one cell only.

3 Brain tissue consists of brain cells.

4 The bark of a tree consists of dead cells.

5 The parts of a cell consist of molecules of never-alive substances.

HERBS, TREES AND SHRUBS WHICH HAVE FLOWERS

THE FOUR MAIN FLOWER PARTS

DEMONSTRATION MATERIAL

As many as possible of the following:

1 Flowers with all four floral organs—sepals, petals, stamens, pistils
2 Flowers not possessing separate sepals and petals, *e.g.* daffodil, tulip, bluebell
3 Flowers lacking both sepals and petals, *e.g.* grass flowers
4 Magnifying glasses

SAMPLE LINK QUESTIONS

1 What are the three ways in which plants may have young? (*By a new plant growing from part of the parent*; *by means of spores*; *by means of seeds*)
2 What do we call trees and shrubs which have young by means of cones and seeds? (*Conifers*)
3 Which herbs have young by means of spores, instead of by means of flowers, fruits and seeds? (*Clubmosses, horsetails and ferns*)
4 From what part on a stem does a flower grow? (*A bud*)
5 Some flowers grow alone on the stem. How do other flowers grow? (*In clusters*)
6 In some flower clusters, each flower grows from the stem on a short branch stem. What do we call this branch stem? (*A stalk*)
7 On a spike and on a catkin, do the tiny stalkless flowers grow from the end of the stem, or from the sides of the stem? (*From the sides of the stem*)
8 Is a daisy head a single flower or a cluster of flowers? (*A cluster of flowers*)

RELEVANT INFORMATION

The main points of a lesson in Pupils' Book 2 were that

1 flowers can be grown only by plants with roots, stems and leaves, *i.e.* on most, but not all, of the herbs, trees and shrubs;

2 flowers are arranged on a stem in one of two main ways.

   (*a*) On some plants each flower grows separately some distance from the others;

   (*b*) On other plants they grow together in clusters.

The main points of a lesson in Pupils' Book 3 were that

1 in some flower clusters, the individual flowers grow at the end of short branch stems known as stalks;

2 in other flower clusters, the individual flowers are without stalks, and are borne directly on the stem itself.

The main points of this lesson are that

1 there are four main flower parts—sepals, petals, stamens and pistils;

2 the flowers of some kinds of plants have all four parts. The flowers of other kinds do not.

The main purpose for the existence of any living species is the propagation of its own kind. There are three main ways in which plants may reproduce themselves: (*a*) by the development of a new individual from a section of the parent, *e.g.* as in cuttings, (*b*) by means of spores, (*c*) by means of seeds.

Present-day herbs, trees and shrubs are classed according to the methods by which they reproduce themselves.

1 Herbs which can have young by means of spores, *i.e.* the clubmosses, horsetails and ferns

2 Trees and shrubs which can have young by means of cones and seeds, *i.e.* the conifers or cone-bearing plants (*gymnosperms*). Reproduction by means of seeds is more advanced than reproduction by means of spores.

3 Herbs, trees and shrubs which can have young by means of flowers, fruits and seeds (*angiosperms*). Reproduction by means of flowers, fruits and seeds is more advanced than reproduction by means of cones and seeds.

Plants that Have Young by means of Flowers, Fruits and Seeds

Herbs, trees and shrubs which can reproduce by means of flowers, fruits and seeds are the most highly evolved of the plants with roots, stems and leaves. Most herbs, trees and shrubs belong to this class.

Not all of them produce flowers every year. Biennial herbs, for example, build up a food store during the first year and produce flowers during the second. Trees and shrubs may live many years before they bear flowers; the oak, for example, may be sixty or seventy years old before it does so. Some plants flower infrequently—like the cacti, some of which may produce flowers only about every twelve years. Then again some individual plants manage to survive in conditions which are not entirely suited to their species, and in consequence are unable to produce flowers at all. The flowers of duckweeds, for example, are seldom seen in the British Isles.

Flowers develop from buds in the following ways.

1 *From a flower bud.* Either a single flower, *e.g.* daffodil and tulip, or a cluster of flowers, *e.g.* poplar, elm and dandelion, will develop according to the habit of the species.

2 *From a mixed bud,* a section of stem bearing both leaves and flower buds, *e.g.* horse chestnut, apple and cherry, will develop.

Information on solitary flowers and clusters of flowers, and the different ways in which they are arranged on stems, will be found in Teacher's Book 2, Lesson 25, and Teacher's Book 3, Lesson 26.

The Main Flower Parts

A flower is a section of stem specially modified for the production of seeds. It is the reproductive structure of those plants which have young by means of flowers, fruits and seeds, just as the cone is the reproductive structure of those which have young by means of cones and seeds.

In their origin and structure, some of the flower parts are similar to leaves, and others to twigs. The leaf-like appearance of sepals and petals is particularly noticeable. The flower itself consists of a receptacle to which are attached all or some of the four flower parts or floral organs—sepals, petals, stamens, pistils.

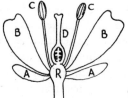

A Sepals (calyx)
B Petals (corolla)
C Stamens (male parts)
D Pistil (female part)
R Receptacle

DIAGRAMMATIC STRUCTURE
OF A FLOWER WITH ALL PARTS

Sepals are the outer leaf-like parts. They may be separate and free from one another or united along their edges. They are usually green, but on some flowers they have other colours. Their main function is to protect the other floral parts before the bud opens. They sometimes fall off before the bud opens, as they do on the poppy, but on other plants they either remain until the petals fall or persist during the development of the fruit.

Petals form an inner ring of leaf-like parts. They too may be separate and free from one another or united along their edges. They may be white—especially on flowers which are pollinated by the wind—or of some bright colour which attracts insects, where these animals are responsible for pollination. In a collection of flowers from different plants the most noticeable differences are those of shape, colour and arrangement of petals.

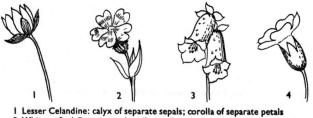

1 Lesser Celandine: calyx of separate sepals; corolla of separate petals
2 White *or* Red Campion: calyx of joined sepals; corolla of separate petals
3 Foxglove: calyx of separate sepals; corolla of joined petals
4 Cowslip: calyx of joined sepals; corolla of joined petals

On the flowers of most plants the petals are regular—each has the same general appearance as the others. On some plants the petals are irregular. For example, on flowers of the pea family one petal is much larger than the others.

Stamens are found within the ring of petals. A stamen is a male part, and on many plants each flower has a definite number of them. For example, on the hyacinth each flower has six stamens, and on plants of the pea family each flower has ten. On some plants, however, *e.g.* buttercup, poppy and rose, the number of stamens is indefinite and varies from one individual to another.

On some plants the stamens differ in length in the same flower. For example, the wallflower has four long stamens and two short stamens.

Stamens are attached directly to the receptacle on the flowers of plants such as buttercup and wallflower. In the flowers of some plants, however, they are attached to the sides of the corolla, or if there is no separate calyx and corolla, to the sides of the perianth.

In some flowers some or all of the stamens may be joined together. Bird's-foot trefoil, for example, has nine joined stamens and one free one. Bird's-foot trefoil belongs to the pea family, and in the flowers of this family joined stamens are not uncommon.

Pistils are the innermost of the floral organs. A pistil is a

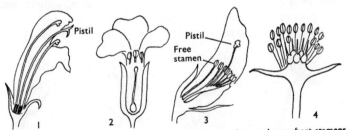

1 Cross-section of white deadnettle flower, which has two long and two short stamens. (One of each is shown)
2 Cross-section of thrum-eyed primrose flower, showing three of the six stamens joined to the sides of the corolla
3 Cross-section of bird's-foot trefoil, which has nine joined stamens and one free one
4 Receptacle of blackberry flower, showing stamens and more than one pistil

female part, and on many plants each flower has only one. There are some plants, however, *e.g.* buttercup and blackberry, whose flowers have more than one. Pistils are dealt with in more detail in the next lesson.

Family Groupings

Plants that have flowers, fruits and seeds (the angiosperms) are grouped into families according to the structure of their floral organs. This accounts for the fact that a family of plants often embraces a number of herbs, trees and shrubs that bear no general resemblance to one another.

The Daisy Family (*Compositae*)

The composite family are considered the most highly evolved of all plants. There are over 13,000 species, and they are the most widely distributed of all flowering plants. In the northern hemisphere they are mostly herbs, but in the southern some are shrubs.

The composite flower itself consists of a compact cluster of flowers crowded on to a flat or conical receptacle. They are known as florets, and may be tubular or strap-shaped. On a

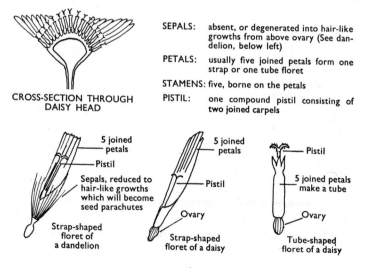

CROSS-SECTION THROUGH
DAISY HEAD

SEPALS: absent, or degenerated into hair-like growths from above ovary (See dandelion, below left)

PETALS: usually five joined petals form one strap or one tube floret

STAMENS: five, borne on the petals

PISTIL: one compound pistil consisting of two joined carpels

5 joined petals
Pistil
Sepals, reduced to hair-like growths which will become seed parachutes
Strap-shaped floret of a dandelion

5 joined petals
Pistil
Ovary
Strap-shaped floret of a daisy

Pistil
5 joined petals make a tube
Ovary
Tube-shaped floret of a daisy

dandelion all are strap-shaped. On a burdock all are tube-shaped. On a daisy both kinds are found—strap-shaped (ray florets) on the outside, and tube-shaped (disc florets) on the inside. On one daisy flower head there may be about 250 flowers.

On composite flower heads, the oldest flowers are on the outside, and the youngest on the inside. Before the whole head of flowers opens, the bud is surrounded by a group of specialised leaves, called bracts. These protect the whole cluster in the bud stage, in the same way as sepals protect individual flowers on other plants. Many of these flowers develop plumed fruits to facilitate wind dispersal.

Flowers without a Separate Calyx and Corolla

Not all flowers have all four floral organs. Those that do are generally termed *complete*; those that don't, *incomplete*.

The outer envelope of sepals and petals is termed the *perianth*. When a flower is incomplete in that it has no separate sepals and petals, the term *perianth* is retained for the outer envelope. It is applied, for example, to the collection of whorls on the bluebell, daffodil, tulip, crocus, gladiolus, freesia and lily.

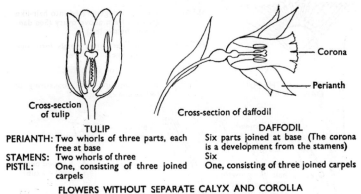

Cross-section of tulip

Cross-section of daffodil

TULIP	DAFFODIL
PERIANTH: Two whorls of three parts, each free at base	Six parts joined at base (The corona is a development from the stamens)
STAMENS: Two whorls of three	Six
PISTIL: One, consisting of three joined carpels	One, consisting of three joined carpels

FLOWERS WITHOUT SEPARATE CALYX AND COROLLA

Flowers that lack either stamens or pistils are discussed in the next lesson.

Flowers with neither Calyx nor Corolla

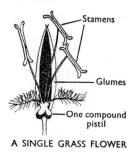

A SINGLE GRASS FLOWER

Such flowers are generally termed naked flowers. Prominent among them are the grasses (family name *Gramineae*), which are among the most widely distributed of all plant families from the equator to the poles. Grasses form the great natural pasture lands of the world, such as the Steppes of Russia, the Pampas of South America, the plains of North America, and the ranges or runs of Australia.

Included in the grass family are the cereals—wheat, rice, maize, rye, barley and oats. *Corn* is a term loosely applied to such cereals or to the seed after threshing. Each individual flower lacks both sepals and petals, and is enclosed by modified reduced leaves called *glumes*. These flowers grow in clusters known as spikelets. The spikelets themselves are clustered on the stem in one of two arrangements—either in spikes (as on wheat) or in panicles (as on oats).

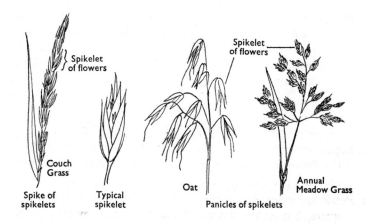

CODE

1 Observe the four main parts on any flower on which they are clearly defined.
2 Observe the positions of these four parts.
3 Observe the perianth on any flower without separate sepals and petals.
4 Observe the colour and count the number of the different parts on various flowers.
5 Observe whether sepals are free from one another or joined at their edges.
6 Observe whether the petals are free from one another, or joined at their edges.
7 Observe any flowers with more than one pistil, *e.g.* buttercup.
8 Collect different shapes and colours of the four floral parts, and fasten on to thin card with cellulose tape. The parts may be preserved in this way, if the cellulose tape completely seals them from the air.
9 *Systematic observations for children to make when examining flowers*
   (*a*) Observe whether each flower grows on its own on the plant, or if a number grow together in clusters. If the flowers grow in clusters, observe whether or not the individual flowers have stalks.
   (*b*) Observe, on an individual flower, how many of the floral organs it possesses. Record details as shown on page 250, where the illustrations represent *either* a specimen fixed into notebook with cellulose tape *or* a child's drawing.

NOTEBOOK WORK

Answers should be along the following lines.

1 Sepals are outer leaf-shaped flower parts, and they protect the flower before it opens. They are usually green, but on some plants they have other colours.
2 Petals are inner leaf-shaped parts. On some plants they are white, but on the flowers of other plants they may be of almost any colour.

OBSERVATIONS ON A FLOWER WITH ALL FOUR FLORAL ORGANS

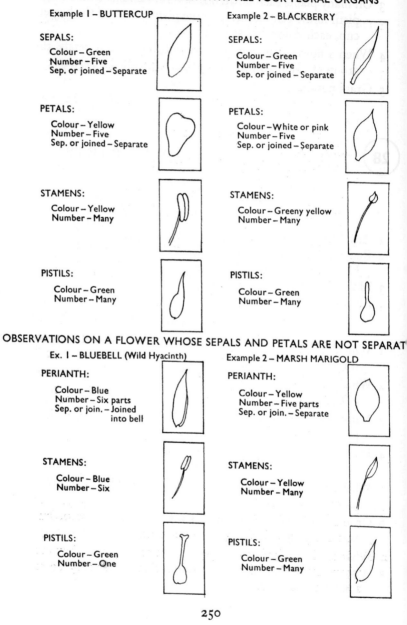

Example 1 – BUTTERCUP

SEPALS:

Colour – Green
Number – Five
Sep. or joined – Separate

PETALS:

Colour – Yellow
Number – Five
Sep. or joined – Separate

STAMENS:

Colour – Yellow
Number – Many

PISTILS:

Colour – Green
Number – Many

Example 2 – BLACKBERRY

SEPALS:

Colour – Green
Number – Five
Sep. or joined – Separate

PETALS:

Colour – White or pink
Number – Five
Sep. or joined – Separate

STAMENS:

Colour – Greeny yellow
Number – Many

PISTILS:

Colour – Green
Number – Many

OBSERVATIONS ON A FLOWER WHOSE SEPALS AND PETALS ARE NOT SEPARAT

Ex. 1 – BLUEBELL (Wild Hyacinth)

PERIANTH:

Colour – Blue
Number – Six parts
Sep. or join. – Joined
into bell

STAMENS:

Colour – Blue
Number – Six

PISTILS:

Colour – Green
Number – One

Example 2 – MARSH MARIGOLD

PERIANTH:

Colour – Yellow
Number – Five parts
Sep. or join. – Separate

STAMENS:

Colour – Yellow
Number – Many

PISTILS:

Colour – Green
Number – Many

3 On many plants each flower has several stamens with a single pistil in the centre, but on some plants, such as the buttercup, each flower has several pistils.

4 When a flower does not have separate sepals and petals, the group of coloured leaf-shaped parts is called a perianth.

5 Grass flowers have neither sepals nor petals.

28 THE ESSENTIAL FLOWER PARTS

STAMENS AND PISTILS

DEMONSTRATION MATERIAL

1 Any flower with large stamens and pistils, *e.g.* daffodil, tulip
2 Remains of a flower on which the pistil has swollen, *e.g.* bluebell, daffodil, tulip, sweet pea, ash, sycamore
3 Male and female catkins
4 Magnifying glasses

SAMPLE LINK QUESTIONS

1 Which of the four main flower parts protect the flower before it opens? (*Sepals*)

2 Which are usually the most attractive parts of a flower? (*The petals*)

3 Name some flowers that do not have separate sepals and petals. (*Tulip, daffodil, bluebell*)

4 If a flower does not have separate sepals and petals, what do we call the outer leaf-shaped parts? (*The perianth*)

5 What are the two kinds of parts in the middle of flowers? (*Stamens and pistils*)

6 On many plants each flower has a single pistil in its centre. Name a plant whose flowers have several pistils. (*Buttercup*)

7 What grow inside fruits? (*Seeds*)

8 What do fruits do for the seeds that develop inside them? (*Protect them*)

9 What are the three chief things that carry fruits and seeds away from the parent plant? (*Moving water, moving air, moving animals*)

10 From what part on a herb, tree or shrub does a fruit grow? (*A flower*)

RELEVANT INFORMATION

Points made in earlier Pupils' Books were that a fruit develops from part of a flower, and that its purpose is to protect the seeds which develop inside it.

The main points of this lesson are that

1 stamens produce pollen for the pollination of pistils;

2 pistils contain ovules which may be fertilised by pollen;

3 from pistils, as a result of fertilisation, develop fruits and seeds.

Sepals and petals are accessory parts, as they are not directly concerned with the production of seeds. Stamens and pistils are the essential parts, as they are directly involved in the production of seeds. This means that although a flower can lack both sepals and petals, it cannot lack both stamens and pistils.

A *stamen* is a male part. At its tip is an anther. In the flowers of most plants these anthers are borne on short stalks called *filaments*. Ripe anthers are regarded as folded modified leaves. They contain the pollen grains in which are formed the male productive cells or sperms.

A *pistil* is a female organ. Some flowers have one pistil. Others have more than one. The pistil consists of one or more

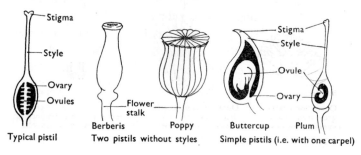

Typical pistil | Berberis   Poppy | Buttercup   Plum
Two pistils without styles | Simple pistils (i.e. with one carpel)

Stigma, Style, Ovary, Ovules — Flower stalk — Stigma, Style, Ovule, Ovary

carpels. *Carpel* is the term used to include an *ovary*, containing one or more *ovules*, together with the *stigma*, which is the receptive surface for pollen and which may or may not be raised on a stalk—known as a *style*. It is the ovules that develop into seeds after fertilisation.

If the pistil consists of just one carpel, it is termed simple. If it consists of more than one carpel, it is compound. A pea flower or a bean flower has a simple pistil consisting of one carpel. A buttercup flower has several simple pistils each consisting of one carpel.

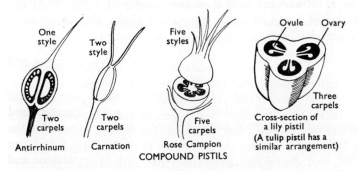

One style — Two carpels — Antirrhinum

Two style — Two carpels — Carnation

Five styles — Five carpels — Rose Campion

Ovule   Ovary — Three carpels — Cross-section of a lily pistil (A tulip pistil has a similar arrangement)

COMPOUND PISTILS

When two or more carpels are fused together to form a compound pistil, there may be one common style, as on an antirrhinum or a tulip, or there may be several styles, as on a meadow saxifrage, carnation or rose campion.

When ripe, the stigma may be sticky, or rough, or hairy in order to hold the pollen that comes from the anthers.

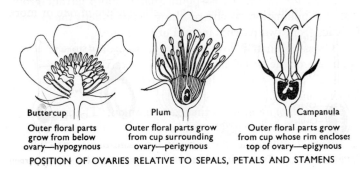

Buttercup
Outer floral parts grow from below ovary—hypogynous

Plum
Outer floral parts grow from cup surrounding ovary—perigynous

Campanula
Outer floral parts grow from cup whose rim encloses top of ovary—epigynous

POSITION OF OVARIES RELATIVE TO SEPALS, PETALS AND STAMENS

Some botanists have discarded the use of the word *pistil* on the grounds that it fails to discriminate between a simple structure consisting of one carpel and a compound structure consisting of fused carpels. In this lesson the general term *pistil* is retained, as it is unlikely that children will be able to distinguish whether pistils are simple or compound.

Pollination

In the plants which have young by means of flowers, fruits and seeds, pollination is the first step towards the formation of seeds. It consists simply of the transfer of pollen from the anther of a stamen to the stigma of a pistil. The structure of flowers is closely related to pollination methods.

Pollen grains are produced within pollen sacs inside the anther. These pollen sacs (usually four in number) open when the anther reaches maturity and expose the pollen grains. The flowers of many plants are *self-pollinated*, the stigma receiving its pollen from an anther in the same flower, or possibly from a flower on the same plant. It is usual in flowers which are self-pollinated for the anthers and stigma to ripen at about the same time, and often their stamens hold their anthers at a higher level than the stigma on the pistil. Consequently when the pollen is released by the ripened anther, it simply falls on to the stigma below. Wheat, oats, barley and cotton are examples of plants that reproduce satisfactorily by self-pollination.

A more common method of pollination is *cross-pollination*. In cross-pollination, a stigma receives its pollen from a flower on a *separate* plant. Cross-pollination is more advantageous than self-pollination, as any resulting plants inherit the charac-teristics from two parents instead of from one.

Cross-pollinated flowers depend, according to the plant, upon one of the three natural agents for carrying things from place to place—moving liquid (water), moving gas (wind), moving animals.

Pollination by water is the least common. The majority of plants with flowers, fruits and seeds are land plants. Those which are found in water are accepted as land plants which have reverted to aquatic habits. Many of these are only incompletely aquatic, with either floating or aerial leaves, and with flowers which are raised above the surface, where they may be pollinated by wind or insects. Even amongst those which have attained submerged habits, there is a general tendency for flowers to be produced above the surface of the water. Nevertheless, some have reverted so successfully to an aquatic existence that their flowers are produced and pollinated under water. The common hornwort (*Ceratophyllum*), and the vallisneria or tape grass which is commonly used for decorative purposes in an aquarium, are examples. On both of these herbs, however, reproduction by means of flowers, fruits and seeds is rare; usually new plants develop from part of the stem of the parent.

Pollination by wind is the simplest method. It is common among many of the British trees, including oak, poplar and hazel, and also among many of the grasses and sedges. Plants which are solely wind-pollinated need neither perfume nor brightly-coloured petals. Where petals are present, they may be small and inconspicuous—often whitish. Plants such as those of the grass family have flowers with no petals at all. Where the wind is depended on for cross-pollination, a considerable amount of pollen has to be produced to allow for wastage; in addition, anthers may hang well out of flowers to allow easier access to air currents. Many wind-pollinated plants flower early in the year, to avoid obstruction to the pollen by the leaves of plants.

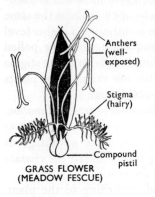

Anthers (well-exposed)

Stigma (hairy)

Compound pistil

GRASS FLOWER
(MEADOW FESCUE)

Pollination by animals is the most efficient method. Animals that fly are the best agents. Insects rank high in this category—in particular, bees, wasps, two-winged flies, moths, butterflies and beetles. Birds are occasionally responsible, *e.g.* the nectar-seeking humming-birds which pollinate certain species of tropical flowers. Other kinds of animals may assist in pollination, but their contribution is relatively small.

Various devices have been developed by plants to attract animals—particularly insects. Some flowers have glands that secrete the sweet sugary solution, known as nectar, which serves as food for certain insects. This is the bait. Bright, showy colouring on petals and other flower parts advertises it. On clusters of flowers where each individual flower is tiny, the complete cluster is usually conspicuous. Many of the early spring flowers, which attract small early insects, have white or yellow flowers. Bees, moths and butterflies are amongst the most common flower-visitors, however, and they are believed to have some preference for pink or blue flowers.

Some flowers have a special nectar guide to direct insects, so that contact with anthers and stigmas is guaranteed. The scents of oils secreted by flowers is a further enticement to insects. Flowers that do not open until dusk, when their petals are not likely to be easily seen, may give off a stronger scent in order to attract insects which may not see their petals in the faint light. The evening primrose, for example, has pale petals but a heavy scent.

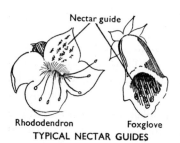

Nectar guide

Rhododendron   Foxglove
TYPICAL NECTAR GUIDES

Where cross-pollination is desirable, various precautions have been developed by plants to reduce the possibility of self-pollination. These include:

1 Anthers and stigma in the same flower so placed that the pollen cannot fall upon the stigma;

2 Anthers and stigma in the same flower ripening at different times;

3 Stigmas being sterile to pollen from flowers on the same plant;

4 Stamens and pistils appearing in separate flowers.

These arrangements *reduce* the possibility of *self-pollination*, but some species have developed methods to *increase* the possibility of *cross-pollination*.

Fertilisation

Fertilisation results from the union of two special cells (gametes). One of these is the male cell (or sperm). The other is a female cell (or ovum). The single cell which results from the fusion is known as a zygote, and by process of cell multiplication it subsequently develops into the embryo plant.

Pollen affects an ovary in two ways. It provides the male cell which fertilises the female cell in the ovule, and it stimulates the ovary into enlarging into a fruit.

The sequence of events following the deposition of a pollen grain upon a receptive stigma is outlined very simply below, and two examples are illustrated diagrammatically.

1 The pollen grain absorbs water and dissolved materials from the stigma and then germinates.

2 As a result of germination, a pollen tube is produced. It penetrates the stigma and grows down the inside of the style. Each pollen grain normally produces one tube which contains two male cells.

3 The pollen tube reaches and penetrates the ovary wall. Its tip enters the ovule (usually through a tiny pore known as a micropyle). Fertilisation now takes place. One of the two male cells fuses with the female cell (ovum) in the ovule. The resulting single cell (the zygote) eventually develops by cell multiplication into the embryo of the seed.

The second of the two male cells from the pollen tube fuses with another cell in the ovule. The result of this subsidiary fusion is the production of the food storage tissue of the seed (known as the endosperm).

4 (a) The fertilised ovule enlarges into a seed (as a result of the growth of the embryo plant, and the food storage tissue).

(b) The ovary itself enlarges to become a fruit.

It is normal for more than one pollen grain to be deposited on a stigma. Although they may all germinate and produce pollen tubes, only one will penetrate an ovule and fertilise it. If, as in the majority of plants, the ovary contains a number of ovules, then an equal number of pollen tubes will be necessary to fertilise them all.

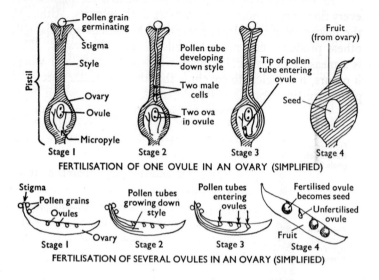

FERTILISATION OF ONE OVULE IN AN OVARY (SIMPLIFIED)

FERTILISATION OF SEVERAL OVULES IN AN OVARY (SIMPLIFIED)

Notes

(a) The time taken from pollination to fertilisation varies from plant to plant—from a few hours up to about a year—but is not necessarily proportional to the distance which the pollen tube has to grow to reach the ovule.

(b) Usually an ovule cannot be fertilised by pollen from another kind of flower. A daisy ovule, for example, cannot be fertilised by the pollen from a buttercup.

(c) The maturing of ovaries into fruits and of ovules into seeds requires a considerable amount of food, and often inhibits the growth of the rest of the plant. Some gardeners continually pick the flowers of annual plants such as sweet peas, and remove rose-heads whose petals are dropping, so that the plant's food reserves are not exhausted by the development of fruits and seeds.

Male and Female Flowers

As both stamens and pistils are essential for pollination, every flower must possess at least one of these parts. Although the flowers of many plants possess both stamens and pistil(s), others produce stamens and pistils in separate flowers. This is a measure of protection against self-pollination, and where it occurs, it is logical to conclude that that particular species of plant depends upon cross-pollination. Flowers which have stamens but no pistils are termed male (or staminate) flowers, and flowers which have pistils but no stamens are termed female (or pistillate) flowers.

Flowers with stamens only (male flowers)

Flowers with pistils only (female flowers)

Greater Reedmace

MALE AND FEMALE FLOWERS ON SAME CLUSTER

In some species, *e.g.* reedmace, sycamore, hazel and oak, separate male and female flowers are borne on the *same* plant. They may appear together in the same cluster as on a reedmace spike, or in separate clusters on the same plant as on the hazel.

Other species have separate male and female flowers on *separate* plants—male plants and female plants. The production of male and female flowers on separate plants is a guarantee against self-pollination. Examples include the willows and many varieties of holly—which explains why some holly trees never have berries.

Catkins are well-known examples of clusters of flowers, all of which are of the same sex.

The stamens and petals drop off most flowers almost immediately after fertilisation, and the ovary begins to enlarge. The sepals, if present, may also drop off, but on some plants they remain as withered remnants at one end of the fruit, *e.g.* orange and tomato.

The complete structure developed from the ovary is termed the fruit. A fruit is a matured ovary, and a seed is a matured ovule which develops completely enclosed inside the fruit.

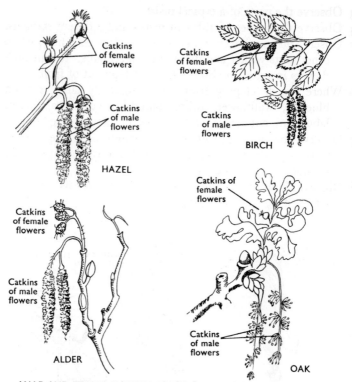

MALE AND FEMALE FLOWERS IN SEPARATE CLUSTERS ON SAME PLANT

Some of the plant parts referred to as fruits are not fruits at all in the botanical sense. The fleshy part of the strawberry, for example, is a swollen flower receptacle; the tiny pips are the real fruits, each containing a seed. Detailed information on the different kinds of fruits is appended to Lesson 4 in Teacher's Book 2.

CODE

1 Observe the parts of various stamens.

2 Gently touch any ripened anthers with a finger tip to obtain some pollen. Observe the colour of this. It is not always yellow; on a tulip stamen, for instance, it is brown.

3 Observe the parts of a typical pistil.

4 Observe the shapes of different pistils and different stamens.

5 Observe on any flowers retained in the classroom how, when other parts wither and die, the pistil remains. Retain such flowers in water to observe the development of fruits.

6 Where the developing fruits are sufficiently large, *e.g.* on bluebell, wallflower, tulip, daffodil, sweet pea, lupin, laburnum, cut across, and observe any developing seeds.

7 Observe the development of fruits where once the flowers were, *e.g.* on trees such as horse chestnut, apple, ash, sycamore, lime, laburnum.

8 Observe how, on some fruits, withered sepals are still attached, *e.g.* tomato, orange, grapefruit.

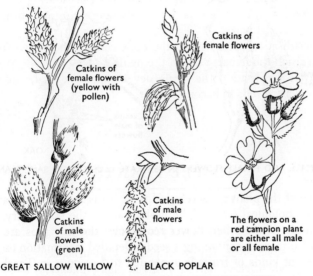

Catkins of female flowers

Catkins of female flowers (yellow with pollen)

Catkins of male flowers

Catkins of male flowers (green)

Catkins of male flowers

The flowers on a red campion plant are either all male or all female

GREAT SALLOW WILLOW   BLACK POPLAR

MALE AND FEMALE FLOWERS ON SEPARATE PLANTS

9 Observe any examples of separate male and female flowers

  (*a*) together on the same cluster, as on a reedmace spike,

  (*b*) in separate clusters on the same plant, as on hazel, oak, birch and alder catkins,

  (*c*) in separate clusters on separate plants, as on willow catkins.

10 Observe different insects that visit flowers for their nectar, *e.g.* bees, wasps, butterflies, moths, two-winged flies.

NOTEBOOK WORK

Answers should be along the following lines.

1 A stamen is a male part. At its top is an anther, in which grains of pollen are developed.
2 A pistil is a female part containing one or more sections called ovaries. Inside the ovaries are ovules.
3 On some plants the ovules are fertilised by pollen from stamens on the same flower. This results from self-pollination. On other plants, the ovules need to be fertilised by pollen from a flower on a separate plant of the same kind. This results from cross-pollination.
4 Flowers attract insects by means of scent and brightly coloured parts.
5 Fertilisation occurs when the male cells in the pollen tubes reach the female cells in the ovule.
6 After fertilisation the ovule develops into a seed, and the ovary swells to become a fruit.

SIMPLE PLANTS—1

ALGAE AND MOSSES

DEMONSTRATION MATERIAL

1 Terrestrial algae, (*a*) green powdery pleurococcus on damp wood, brick or bark, (*b*) thread alga (vaucheria) in soil in plant pot
2 Freshwater algae, (*a*) floating pond scum, (*b*) algae attached to stones or to the sides of an aquarium
3 Marine algae—any specimen of seaweed
4 Terrestrial moss, preferably with spore capsules
5 Freshwater moss, (*a*) great water moss (willow moss), alive or preserved, (*b*) sphagnum moss, alive or dead

1 What are the two main kinds of living things? (*Animals and plants*)
2 Where do we find plants growing, besides on land? (*In fresh water and in sea water*)
3 What are the three different kinds of plants with roots, stems and leaves? (*Herbs, trees and shrubs*)
4 Which plants have no true roots, stems or leaves? (*Simple plants*)
5 What are the three main ways in which plants have young? (*By young plants growing from part of the parent; by means of spores; by means of seeds*)
6 What are the three kinds of herbs which have young by means of spores? (*Clubmosses, horsetails and ferns*)
7 What do we call the trees and shrubs which have young by means of cones and seeds? (*Conifers*)
8 Can any simple plants have young by means of seeds? (*No*)
9 Are seaweeds herbs, trees, shrubs or simple plants? (*Simple plants*)
10 What do the very simplest of all living animals and plants consist of? (*One cell only*)

RELEVANT INFORMATION

The main aims of this and the following lesson are to introduce the four main kinds of simple plants, and to examine some of the main differences between them.

Simple Plants in General

Simple plants have no true roots, stems or leaves. They are predominantly aquatic, and even those adapted to land still need plenty of moisture. Bacteria and many algae are unicellular, but frequently form masses which make them easily visible. None has flowers, fruits or seeds. Reproduction is either by means of a new plant growing from part of the parent, or—in the more advanced species—by means of spores. Spores may be unicellular or multicellular but are not generally as well equipped as seeds to withstand adverse conditions. Owing to their microscopic size, enormous numbers may be produced by a single parent. In some species these are formed on the body of the plant itself; in others they are raised from the plant in special cases. As they are very light, they are easily dispersed by wind, water or animals.

Algae

There are probably more than 20,000 species of these, and they include some of the simplest and most primitive members of the plant kingdom. Most are aquatic, and the commonest are the seaweeds. Some live in fresh water, and a few on land. Of the aquatic species, some are floating plants, but most have some means of anchorage, such as a holdfast, which may look like a tangle of roots or like a sucker. Like the more highly evolved herbs, trees and shrubs, an alga contains chlorophyll and obtains food by means of photosynthesis. Frequently the green of the chlorophyll is masked by another pigment, as in brown seaweed. Growth and structure varies, the simplest being unicellular. More advanced species consist

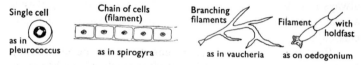

of chains of cells (filaments). In some the threads are branched, and in some they are anchored by means of a number of special cells forming a holdfast. The most advanced algae develop a characteristic body form, *e.g.* knotted wrack, bladderwrack and other familiar seaweeds.

Single-celled algae reproduce by simple division, and more complex species by a whole section developing into a new plant. The majority of the latter are also able to reproduce by means of spores. The so-called spore cases on some, *e.g.* bladderwrack, actually contain either male or female cells which, when ejected, unite to form spores.

Diatoms are single-celled algae. Primeval deposits of these are believed to be the origin of present-day deposits of petroleum oil.

Algae are grouped according to colour pigment, the four

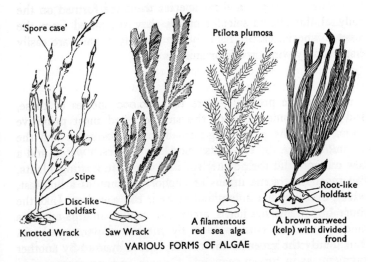

'Spore case'

Ptilota plumosa

Stipe

Disc-like holdfast

Root-like holdfast

Knotted Wrack   Saw Wrack   A filamentous red sea alga   A brown oarweed (kelp) with divided frond

VARIOUS FORMS OF ALGAE

main groups being blue-green, green, brown and red. It is not always easy to distinguish between red and brown, or between a real green and some of the greenish-browns which are classed as browns.

Blue-green algae (not represented in the Pupils' Book). In these, the green of the chlorophyll is masked by a blue pigment. They are mainly unicellular although in some species these cells form thread-like colonies.

Green algae. There are well over 5,000 species—mostly freshwater plants. Some kinds, *e.g.* the familiar spirogyra, are floating plants, and are especially found in stagnant water. Other kinds, *e.g.* oedogonium, are anchored by means of holdfasts. Marine species, *e.g.* ulva (sea lettuce), inhabit shallow water and are often exposed to the air. Vaucheria, sometimes found growing on the soil in plant pots, is terrestrial. So is the single-celled pleurococcus, masses of which form the familiar green 'powder' found on damp surfaces of concrete, brickwork, unpainted woodwork, or tree bark. (Pleurococcus does not feed on wood, of course, but merely lodges in moist cracks.)

Brown algae. There are some 900 species and almost all are marine. No single-celled species are known. Most have branching filaments, and most are anchored by strong multi-celled holdfasts. Typical examples are the wracks and the kelps. The latter produce the largest and most complex of plant bodies, lengths of 150 feet being authentically reported. Brown seaweeds grow in deep water, or in the zone between tide-marks where they are exposed at low tide. Sargassum or gulf weed is a floating brown alga. A huge accumulation of sargassum, at the centre of a vast eddy east of the West Indies in the North Atlantic, gives its name to the Sargasso Sea.

Red algae. There are some 2,500 species, most of which are marine, although some live in fresh water. They are the least common of the algae. The majority are multi-cellular but rarely exceed 3 feet in length. There is an assortment of forms, including many-branched filaments, rough stem-like bodies, and flat blades. Most grow in deep water down to 300 feet, but some exist between tide-marks, especially in rocky pools.

Mosses

With the liverworts, mosses form a class of simple plants

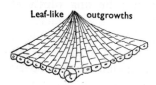

which are generally more compli-cated in structure than other simple plants. A moss has thin stem-like growths, with simple leaf-like growths which each con-sist of a single layer of cells. In addition, it has elongated cells called rhizoids which some-what resemble root hairs. Specialised though these growths are, they lack the structure of true roots, stems and leaves. Unlike true leaves, the leaf-like growths do not have pores, so that the whole plant surface is responsible for the exchange of gases and the absorption of water and dissolved mineral foods. Rhizoids serve to anchor the plant, and may also absorb oxygen and food. Some mosses, like some algae, attach themselves to dead or living things, but they do not feed on them.

Mosses reproduce from part of the parent, and clusters or 'cushions' of them are usually found together. They can also reproduce by means of spores, and these are formed in tiny cases or capsules which are raised on short stalks above the

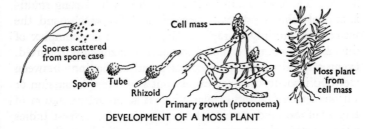

Spores scattered from spore case

Cell mass

Spore Tube

Rhizoid

Moss plant from cell mass

Primary growth (protonema)

DEVELOPMENT OF A MOSS PLANT

plants; these are sometimes misleadingly termed 'fruits'. The individual spores are very tiny.

Whereas the majority of algae are sea plants, the majority of mosses are land plants; some live in fresh water, but none in the sea. Distribution is worldwide—at the equator, on Antarctic islands and even 20,000 feet up Everest. Plenty of moisture is essential, so that the terrestrial species are commonly found along ditch sides and the banks of streams. They also occur in moist cracks on tree trunks, paths and walls. Some can resist drought, but they flourish only when damp conditions prevail. They are commonly the first plants to appear in the dust and wind-blown soil which accumulates in crevices.

There are over 600 British species, but many are rare, and many are tiny. The largest and most conspicuous are the hair mosses, some exceptional species of which may exceed a foot in height. Mosses occur in the greatest variety where the air is relatively unpolluted, but even so, quite a number are commonly found thriving in the unhealthiest of our industrial atmospheres.

Willow moss and sphagnum moss are the best-known freshwater mosses. Willow moss or great water moss (fontinalis) occurs in streams, rivers, ponds and lakes, usually submerged and anchored by a holdfast. Willow mosses are large, attaining heights of two feet. Reproduction is generally by means of a new plant growing from part of the parent, but spores may be produced during dry periods when the plant is stranded in wet mud.

The sphagnum or bog mosses occupy pools on moors and

heaths. There are about 30 British species whose general habit is to float submerged or on the surface. They soak up so much water and multiply so rapidly, that the pool is eventually reduced to a bog. The mosses, continually dying and sinking, eventually fill up the pool, subsequently changing an area of wet bog into dry peaty ground which provides habitation for various species of higher plants. Peat is, of course, composed largely of the dead remains of bog mosses. The water-retaining properties of sphagnum moss and peat are useful to nurserymen and gardeners. Nurserymen pack sphagnum moss round the roots of plants which have to be sent some distance, and gardeners use peat as humus.

Notes 1 Mosses should not be confused with clubmosses, which are spore-bearing herbs with true roots, stems and leaves.

2 The so-called carrageen moss or Irish moss is not a moss at all, but a red marine alga.

3 Reindeer moss is not a moss either, it is a lichen. (See the next lesson.)

Liverworts

Grouped with the mosses, are the liverworts, of which there are some 280 species in Great Britain. Liverworts are generally simpler in appearance than mosses, and their growth tends to be horizontal, while that of the mosses tends to be

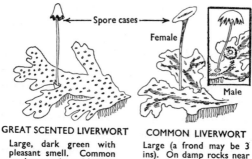

GREAT SCENTED LIVERWORT
Large, dark green with pleasant smell. Common on damp rocks and bridge-work beside streams

COMMON LIVERWORT
Large (a frond may be 3 ins). On damp rocks near streams and in gardens and heated greenhouses

FLOATING CRYSTALWORT
(Riccia fluitans)
A freshwater liver-wort. Grows in patches. No rhizoids. Reproduction mainly vegetative

upright. The main body of a liverwort consists of a flattened green frond (thallus) of cells, and this is often branched. On most species, the frond has pores like a true leaf. Most liverworts live on land, in moist places, but a few species live in fresh water. Like the mosses, those which live on land are normally held in position by means of rhizoids.

CODE

1 Observe any terrestrial algae on damp wood, old bricks or plant pots.
2 Observe any examples of freshwater algae:
   (*a*) Floating, *e.g.* pond scum (spirogyra, etc)
   (*b*) Anchored, *e.g.*
      (i) thread-like growths with a holdfast (oedogonium, etc)
      (ii) colonies of single-celled algae on the inner surface of a glass vessel containing 'mature' water left in sunlight. Such algae are often responsible for the green discoloration on the sides of an aquarium that receives too much sunlight.
3 Collect specimens of freshwater algae. These may be kept alive for observation by leaving them in a jar of water in sunlight.
4 Observe specimens of green, red and brown seaweeds. Small specimens may be preserved in 10% formaldehyde. (Rinse well before adding final preservative.) Large specimens may be mounted dry (as described on page 19). Dried seaweeds may regain their shape if placed in water. Observe any sucker-like or root-like holdfasts.
5 Mount suitable specimens of thread algae in notebooks. Wash them in running water. Squeeze out as much water as possible, and tease out on to a sheet of paper. Cover with second sheet of paper, and apply gentle pressure, *e.g.* with books. When dry, tease out separate threads and mount in notebooks, using cellulose tape.
6 Collect terrestrial mosses (preferably with spore cases) for observation purposes. Clumps gathered with a little of the soil on which they are found growing may be kept on a

layer of moist peat in a suitable container, *e.g.* a bowl or tin, and covered with a sheet of glass. A piece of rock or concrete on which moss is growing may be kept on a tin lid or tray and moistened by sprinkling with water.

7 Mount suitable specimens of moss in notebooks, using the same method as for thread algae above (No. 5).

8 Dried moss may be kept for long periods. Such plants, placed in lukewarm water, may absorb enough water to regain their shape.

9 Freshwater moss (fontinalis) may be kept floating submerged in a jar of water. Observe stem-like growths and simple leaf-like growths. Observe scab-like holdfast if this is present.

10 Preserve great water moss in 10% formaldehyde in the usual way.

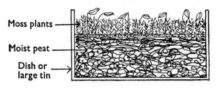

Moss plants —
Moist peat —
Dish or large tin →

KEEPING MOSS

NOTEBOOK WORK

Answers should be along the following lines.

1 Simple plants have no true roots, stems or leaves. They never have flowers, fruits or seeds.

2 Simple plants can have young by means of a new plant growing from part of the parent. Some can also have young by means of spores.

3 Most algae live in the sea.

4 Some algae and mosses have a holdfast to keep them anchored.

5 Most mosses live on land.

6 Rhizoids are tiny thread-like growths which hold a moss in place.

SIMPLE PLANTS—2

FUNGI AND BACTERIA

DEMONSTRATION MATERIAL

1 Any examples of fungi, *e.g.* moulds and mildews, bracket fungi on twigs and bark, toadstools

2 Any material to demonstrate the presence or action of bacteria, *e.g.* carrot with a mushy end, leaf skeleton, foul water in which flowers have been kept

SAMPLE LINK QUESTIONS

1 How do simple plants differ from herbs, trees and shrubs? (*They have no true roots, stems or leaves*)

2 What are the two main ways in which simple plants may have young? (*By means of a new plant growing from part of the parent; by means of spores*)

3 What do the spores of mosses and some algae develop in? (*In spore cases*)

4 What are the three main things which carry the spores of simple plants from place to place? (*Moving air (wind), moving water, moving animals*)

5 Spores are in the air about us all the time. Why do we not see them? (*They are too small*)

6 Where do most algae live? (*In the sea*)

7 What name do we give to algae that live in sea water? (*Seaweeds*)

8 Which are the most advanced of all the simple plants? (*Mosses*)

9 Where do most mosses live? (*On land*)

10 Certain kinds of simple plants and many animals use dead things. For what do they use them mainly? (*Food*)

Algae and mosses contain chlorophyll—the same green pigment found in plants with roots, stems and leaves. This means that algae and mosses are able to obtain their food by means of photosynthesis, just as herbs, trees and shrubs do. By photosynthesis, they utilise carbon from carbon dioxide in the air and convert dissolved mineral salts into organic compounds.

Fungi and bacteria, on the other hand, are simple plants which have no chlorophyll, and are therefore unable to convert inorganic materials into organic materials. This means that they—like animals—have to feed on organic substances, which have already been built up by other living things. Consequently—like animals—they attack living things and dead things, and also certain never-alive materials which have been extracted from living things, *e.g.* fat and milk. They also attack manufactured substances which contain any of these materials, *e.g.* cheese, bread, jam. As photosynthesis does not take place, they do not require sunlight, and so many fungi and bacteria develop best in darkness or subdued light.

Fungi and bacteria are widely distributed throughout the world. Bacteria are common on land, in fresh water and in the sea. Fungi are very common on land, not very common in fresh water and comparatively rare in salt water. When a substance is being utilised for food by these simple plants, it is said to be infected (as distinct from when it is being utilised by small living animals, when it is said to be infested). If the infected substance is alive, the fungi or bacteria responsible for the infection are termed parasites and the result is called a disease. Fungi or bacteria infecting a dead substance are called saprophytes and the resulting infection is generally termed decay. *Rot* is a general term applied to infected living or dead material.

Although some fungi and bacteria are a nuisance in that they cause diseases in humans, in crops and in cattle, and spoil food and products made from dead materials, the majority are beneficial. Saprophytes are particularly useful where they

272

decompose unwanted dead materials, breaking down organic substances into minerals which provide food for algae, mosses, herbs, trees and shrubs.

Fungi

Included amongst the fungi are moulds, mildews, rust fungi, smut fungi, blights, yeasts, truffles, puffballs, mushrooms and toadstools. They are chiefly many-celled, but a few, such as the yeasts, may be one-celled.

The main body of a typical many-celled fungus consists of tubular threads which penetrate the tissues of the host. These tubes (hyphae) continually branch, forming a network of threads (mycelium), through the walls of which food in solution is absorbed. When fully established, the mycelium produces special hyphae which grow away from the food. These hyphae, which are often the most conspicuous parts of the plant, are reproductive structures. They terminate in swellings that contain spores, and vary in size according to the species of fungus producing them. On the black pin mould found on bread, for example, they are comparatively small; on mushrooms and toadstools they are relatively large. A large mushroom may contain some 10,000 million spores and a giant puffball some 7,000,000,000,000. Fungal spores may be carried by air, water or animals to other suitable sources of food. Although too small to be visible to the naked eye, there are normally millions in the surrounding atmosphere, except following a heavy fall of rain or snow. In general, fungi develop best where the temperature is favourable, and where there is a sufficiency of oxygen, moisture and appropriate food. Sunlight tends to kill them, and their growth is most rapid in darkness or diffused light.

The spore cases of fungi are sometimes termed 'fruiting bodies'. They are not, of course, fruits, since a true fruit encloses one or more seeds.

Mushrooms and toadstools are amongst the best-known fungi, the saprophytic members feeding on leaf mould and animal manure. On these the umbrella-shaped spore case is the visible part, while the main body (mycelium) consists of very fine colourless branching hyphae. The terms *mushroom* and *toadstool* are somewhat loosely used—the former for those which are edible to humans, and the latter for the more poisonous varieties.

Yeasts consist of single cells or short chains of cells, whose reproduction is by division from a single cell. Yeasts ferment various sugars, dividing them into alcohols and carbon dioxide, and are thus of value in bread-making, brewing and distilling. When mixed into a dough, it is the bubbles of carbon dioxide released during the respiration of the yeast that cause the dough to rise.

Parasitic fungi cause many of the diseases of living animals and plants. Bluish, greenish and yellowish moulds on fruits, fluffy fungi on carrots and other vegetable foodstuffs, blotches on apples and pears, brown rot on peaches, plums, apricots and cherries, black rot on bananas, clubroot on cabbages, and blight on potatoes are examples of parasitic fungi attacking living plants. The bracket fungi which grow on trees are in most cases parasitic too. Saprolegnia—the fish fungus—is one of the water moulds attacking living fish, particularly goldfish. Diseases such as athlete's foot and ringworm are also caused by parasitic fungi attacking living animals.

Most fungi are saprophytic. Some are a nuisance, such as the mildews that feed on damp leather, paper and cloth, and the moulds on damp bread, jam and other mixtures containing organic materials. Dry rot (*Merulius lacrymans*) is an undesirable saprophyte which feeds on timber. Most saprophytes are useful to us in some way, however, as they feed on the remains of herbs, the trunks of fallen trees, the fallen leaves of deciduous trees, and the bodies of dead animals. Saprophytic moulds also include penicillium, from species of which are obtained such antibiotics as penicillin, streptomycin and aureomycin. *Penicillium camemberti* is a fungus inoculated into camembert cheese to assist ripening. Other saprophytes are responsible for the bluish-green patches in a number of cheeses.

Lichens

A lichen consists of a fungus which is mildly parasitic upon an alga, obtaining from it foods built up during photosynthesis by the alga. The alga is able to obtain water and mineral salts from the fungus, and thus continues to feed and grow, so that the two plants live in partnership. The partnership is rather one-sided, however, as the fungus could not exist without the alga, whereas the alga could exist without the fungus. Lichens are most familiar as flat patches on rocks, old walls, old roofs, tree trunks, and in particular on old gravestones. They vary in colour—mostly white, grey, orange, brown and yellowish-green. Lichens have various uses. The so-called Iceland moss and reindeer moss are lichens. Lichens were used for food even in the days of ancient Egypt, and various dyes, including litmus, are obtained from them.

Bacteria

A typical bacterium is a one-celled plant surrounded by a cell wall, through which its food is absorbed. The bodies of bacteria are much smaller than those of fungi. They are the smallest of all known living things, and are seen only under considerable magnification. A neat fullstop could cover over a thousand of average size, but developing colonies may be large enough to be seen by the naked eye, as may the decay resulting from their activities. They can also be detected by the obnoxious smell of gases released during the breaking down of tissue.

There are many kinds of bacteria. They exist in sea water, fresh water, in the soil on land, and are carried on specks of dust by moving air. Wherever water, soil or air is in contact with living or dead material, bacteria are also in contact with it. They have three common forms.

1 Spherical—generally the smallest and simplest

2 Rod-shaped—generally equipped with whip-like outgrowths (flagella) which enable them to swim in liquids such as blood and milk

3 Spiral—in this form the bacterium is twisted like a corkscrew.

Like other living things, bacteria respire. Most respire aerobically, *i.e.* obtaining free oxygen from the air or water where they live. Some, however, respire anaerobically, *i.e.*

obtaining oxygen by breaking down compounds containing it. Fermentation is often due to bacteria respiring in this way.

Like other simple plants, bacteria require considerable amounts of moisture. Like fungi, the majority are saprophytes, feeding on dead materials or organic products. Most of the others are parasites, feeding on living things.

The bacteria which inconvenience humans are in the minority, but include both parasitic and saprophytic species. The souring of milk and the rotting of meat are due to them, as are such plant diseases as common potato scab, bacterial spot on peaches and tomatoes, bean blight, tomato canker, black rot on cabbage and ring rot on potatoes. Soft rot in fruit, and the swollen crown galls of various herbs, trees and shrubs are due to bacteria entering through wounds. Once bacteria enter a tissue, they may be carried to other parts, *e.g.* by blood or sap.

Bacterial soft rot is one of the most destructive diseases on carrots, potatoes, radishes, parsnips, beetroots and turnips (all underground parts of herbs swollen for food storage). Where it occurs, the diseased part disintegrates into a wet, mushy and smelly mass of disorganised cells which eventually slough off, leaving the rest of the tissue quite firm. In warm damp weather, soft rot and fluffy fungus often flourish together.

Although bacteria are responsible for many diseases in animals (including humans), the majority are beneficial— particularly in breaking down dead materials. In this way the minerals from which living things are built are returned to the soil and to water. Bacteria reproduce by simple division, and given optimum conditions with reproduction once every hour, one bacterium could soon become something like 280,000 million. Normally such reproduction is inhibited by toxic waste and other factors. Some bacteria can contract into a spore state in order to withstand extremes of temperature or dryness.

CODE

1 Observe examples of moulds, mildews or other fungi feeding on various dead or living tissues, or on substances extracted or manufactured from dead or living things.

2 Observe examples of the action of bacteria, *e.g.* the patch of
   mushy soft rot on an infected carrot and the obnoxious
   smell of gases released during the decaying of foodstuffs
   by bacteria.
   Bacteria are responsible for the smell, and the black dis-
   coloration of aquarium gravel after the water has been
   polluted by bacteria feeding on excess food particles in the
   gravel.

3 Try to find bracket fungi on rotting branches or logs. See
   page 13 for method of mounting.

4 Living fungi and lichens, *e.g.* on twigs, may be kept on moist
   peat in a container which has a glass cover to retain the
   moisture.

5 A fish that has been killed by fungus may be preserved for
   demonstration purposes in 10%, or better still, 5% formaldehyde. (See pages 16-17 on Preserving.)

6 Terrestrial fungi, *e.g.* toadstools, may be preserved in 70%
   alcohol or 10% formaldehyde.

7 Skeletons of decayed leaves may be mounted in notebooks
   with cellulose tape, and should be preserved if the tape
   completely seals them from the air.

8 Spores from fungi, *e.g.* feeding on fruit, may be collected in a
   mass on a clean paintbrush, tapped or smeared on to the
   adhesive surface of a strip of cellulose tape, and thus
   mounted in notebooks or on glass or perspex.

9 Collect spores from a mature puffball fungus by placing the
   puffball in a polythene bag and shaking or hitting it.

NOTEBOOK WORK

Answers should be along the following lines.

1 (*a*) Algae and mosses feed on water and minerals dissolved
     in the water.
  (*b*) Fungi and bacteria feed on living or dead things, or on
     materials that have come from living or dead things.

2 The main body of a fungus grows buried in the food on
   which it feeds.

3 A toadstool is a big fungus spore case.

4 (*a*) Bacteria are carried about by moving animals, moving water, and on specks of dust in moving air.

(*b*) We may detect bacteria by the smell of something going bad.

5 When fungi or bacteria feed on living things, we call the result a disease. When they feed on dead things, we call the result decay.

(31) TAKE CARE OF LIVING THINGS

PROTECT YOURSELF FROM SIMPLE PLANTS

DEMONSTRATION MATERIAL

1 Sheet of white card or paper, and an object suitable for covering one half, *e.g.* a piece of glass or polythene, or a book

2 Any chart on oral hygiene

SAMPLE LINK QUESTIONS

1 Which two classes of simple plants feed on the same kinds of foods as the herbs, trees and shrubs? (*Mosses and algae*)

2 Which two feed on living and dead things, and materials made from living or dead things? (*Fungi and bacteria*)

3 When fungi and bacteria feed on living things what do we call the result? (*Disease*)

4 When they feed on dead things, what do we call the result? (*Decay*)

5 How are bacteria carried from place to place? (*By moving animals, moving water, and on specks of dust by moving air*)

6 What do we call the simple parts of which every living thing consists? (*Cells*)

7 How many cells has a single bacterium? (*One*)

8 In the many-celled animals and plants, different kinds of cells are grouped together into special parts. What do we call these parts? (*Tissues*)

9 How does a living cell multiply itself? (*By dividing*)
10 In what way are the outer protective cells of your skin
 similar to those making up the bark of a tree? (*They are
 dead cells*)

RELEVANT INFORMATION

The main points of this lesson are that many of the diseases from which we suffer are caused by simple plants—particularly bacteria, and that it is necessary to guard against bacteria—particularly those which cause dental disease.

Quite a number of small living animals and plants are prepared to feed on the internal tissues of human beings. Such parasites are loosely termed germs or microbes, and the results of their activities come under the general heading of disease. Some of these parasites are animals. Malaria, dysentery and African sleeping sickness, for example, are caused by simple one-celled animals (protozoans). A considerable number of human diseases are, however, caused by certain kinds of fungi and bacteria—particularly the latter. Fungi are responsible for such diseases as athlete's foot and ringworm. Bacteria are responsible for such diseases as tonsillitis, scarlet fever, tuberculosis, pneumonia, diphtheria, boils, whooping cough, pleurisy, leprosy, lockjaw, cholera and typhoid fever, together with bubonic and other plagues.

The minute animals and plants which cause diseases may enter the body in one of three main ways.

1 *Through the nose and throat during breathing.* Air-borne bacteria in particular may enter in this way. An individual so infected can pass on the acquired disease by exhaling. During coughing and sneezing, the offensive organisms are expelled with explosive force and, unless trapped by hand or handkerchief, may be carried close to another human, who may then inhale them.

2 *Through an open wound.* One of the main functions of the outer layer of dead cells in the skin is to protect the living tissue beneath, and in this respect it forms an efficient barrier against bacteria, fungal spores and other pests. These are normally present in the air and on the skin itself—particularly

where there are dirty hands, dirty nails, or sticky fingers to harbour them. Wounds and even small abrasions enable them to penetrate to the tissue beneath. The outward flow of blood tends to wash them out but may not remove them all, particularly when dirt enters the wound. The invading organisms may set up disease locally, or, if not counteracted, they may be transferred by the bloodstream to other parts of the body to set up disease there. For even the smallest puncture of the skin, washing and treating with an antiseptic is advisable.

Blood-sucking insects transmit various diseases from one individual to another by means of their piercing mouth parts. The mosquito transmits malaria and yellow fever in this way, and the tsetse fly transmits African sleeping sickness.

3 *When contaminated food—solid or liquid—is consumed.* Exposed foods are good settling places for germs—particularly soft and sticky foods. Cooking a food generally kills any living organisms on it, but foods such as cakes and unwrapped sweets are likely to be consumed together with a full quota of living germs. These germs may be deposited together with dust particles from the air, or by exhaled breath, or by insects—especially houseflies, which are known to carry the germs of various diseases, including typhoid fever and infant cholera. Nowadays there is fortunately an increasing tendency to display and supply foods which have been pre-wrapped, and at least to keep covered those which are not wrapped.

Careless handling of food by humans or insufficient attention to hygiene during its preparation can result in the food being contaminated—which in turn may lead to food poisoning.

Two of the main ways in which living germs may affect the body are

1 by attacking the living tissue;
2 by producing waste products which are poisonous to the system. These are known as toxins.

When thus attacked, human beings produce antibodies capable of destroying the invaders or neutralising the toxins. Antibodies are various substances produced in the blood to counteract diseases. It is thought that they are produced by white cells known as white corpuscles or leucocytes. These guardian cells are ever-present in the blood, and a single drop normally contains a few thousand of them. They envelop and feed on invading germs and, unless the invasion is too strong, localise it in one spot and prevent it from spreading. Antiseptics, disinfectants and antibiotics are all used to poison invading parasites—either by killing them or at least by providing conditions in which they are unable to feed and multiply.

A vaccine, which provides immunity from a particular bacterial disease, usually consists of dead or weakened bacteria, or a dilution of their toxin sufficient to promote the formation of antibodies which will thus prevent the disease from establishing itself.

A serum is a ready-made supply of antibodies, prepared from the blood of an animal which has had the disease and developed them.

Teeth

Probably the most wide-spread of all the diseases afflicting civilised communities in modern times is dental caries. In the western world over 95% of the population suffer or have suffered from it.

Dental caries is the result of bacterial activity. The mouth is normally swarming with bacteria, some of which attack residues of food—in particular, carbohydrates, *e.g.* sugary and starchy foods. The action of bacteria on particles of food produces acids (notably lactic acid). Where this acid is in contact with the surface of a tooth, it dissolves the calcium salts in the enamel, so that in time part of this enamel crumbles and exposes the dentine. The exposed dentine is then in turn subject to attack by acids and by other kinds of bacteria which enter the mouth.

If the cavity is detected in time, the progress of caries can be curtailed by filling. Filling involves removing the diseased dentine, cleaning the cavity, and stopping it with a suitable substance. Back teeth are usually filled with a metallic mixture (amalgam), and front teeth with an artificial porcelain which matches the colour of the tooth. Extraction is recommended only when the tooth is badly damaged or diseased.

If the progress of caries is not arrested in time, the pulp becomes infected and the result may be gumboils, abscesses round the tooth, infection of the jawbone or even certain forms

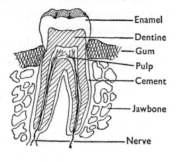

Enamel
Dentine
Gum
Pulp
Cement
Jawbone
Nerve

MAIN PARTS OF A TOOTH

ENAMEL. This covers only the exposed surface of the tooth. It consists chiefly of calcium salts, with practically no organic matter.
DENTINE. Main body of tooth. Hard bony substance consisting mainly of calcium salts, penetrated by fine threads of living protoplasm from the nerves.
PULP. Mass of blood vessels and nerves.

of mouth cancer. As the teeth are closely connected with the rest of the body by the blood stream, poison can be carried to other parts of the body and be responsible for other diseases there.

Safeguards for the Dental Health of Schoolchildren

1 A well-balanced diet
2 Fluoridation of water supplies. The addition of fluorides to drinking water (up to one part per million) has been shown to be of value to developing teeth during the first sixteen years of life.
3 NOT eating confectionery, *e.g.* sweets and biscuits, between meals
4 Eating cleansing foods at the end of meals, *e.g.* raw carrots, radishes, raw celery and raw fruits (particularly apples)
5 Regular brushing of teeth after meals—particularly the last meal of the day. The purposes of brushing are
   (*a*) to remove food particles from the biting surfaces and between the teeth. Brushing within ten minutes after a meal should remove almost all the carbohydrates in the mouth;

(*b*) to toughen the gums, by stimulating the blood circulation within them;

(*c*) to polish the teeth.

The back of the teeth as well as the front should be cleaned. The motion of the brush should be from the gum towards the biting surface of the teeth, and finally along the biting surfaces of the teeth. A toothpaste serves as a cleanser, but also provides some temporary alkalinity to offset the acidity caused by bacteria. After use, a brush should be thoroughly clean and dry before being used again, so two are useful.

6 Vigorous rinsing of the teeth with water, when brushing is not possible

7 Regular dental inspection to preserve both milk teeth and permanent teeth. Milk teeth should not be neglected. They play an important part in preventing the growing teeth from being displaced or crowded.

Development of Teeth

At the age of two, a child should have a complete set of 20 milk teeth. After the age of six most of these are gradually replaced by permanent teeth and extra teeth appear. By the age of twelve, with the eruption of the second molars, there will normally be 28 teeth—14 in each jaw. The four third molars— wisdom teeth—usually appear between the ages of eighteen and twenty, although some people never have any. Thus about twenty years are required for the development of the full complement of sixteen teeth in each jaw.

Notes

1 During childhood years, calcium, phosphorus and vitamins C and D are essentials in tooth formation. Vitamin C is important at all ages for healthy gums. Milk, cheese, eggs, lettuce and wheat are good providers of calcium. Milk, cheese, eggs, cereals and meats are good providers of phosphorus.

2 The term *decay* is normally used for dental caries. As caries seems to involve the dissolving of the never-alive parts of a tooth by acidic wastes, together with an attack on the living

tissue in a tooth both by acidic wastes and the bacteria responsible for them, the term *disease* is probably more appropriate.

3 Viruses, which are responsible for various diseases in plants and animals, *e.g.* common cold, foot-and-mouth disease, influenza, smallpox, rabies, warts and mumps, are not known to be living things. Although they are able to increase in amount, it is only when in the tissues of a suitable host, and they have not been shown to respire. Many are of molecular size, and they gain access to living tissues by the same means as other germs.

CODE

1 Experiment with a control to show how much dust settles on a given area in a given period. Place a piece of clean white card or paper in a 'safe' place, *e.g.* on top of a cupboard. Cover one half, and leave the other half exposed.

After, say, a week, observe the difference between the two halves.

2 Observe the need for washing hands before handling food, so as to avoid transferring germs; covering food so that it is not exposed to flies; washing cuts and scratches in order to remove dirt and dust, and treating with an antiseptic in order to kill or prevent the development of bacteria; buying foods already wrapped. This particularly applies to 'sticky' foods.

3 Collect any illustrations and charts on oral hygiene (*e.g.* from the Oral Hygiene service).

4 Observe the necessity for children to take care of their teeth in the following ways:

(*a*) By eating a hard cleansing food, *e.g.* raw apple, raw celery or raw carrot at the end of a meal.

(*b*) By brushing teeth after breakfast and after the last meal of the day, and whenever possible, after other meals.

(*c*) Rinsing teeth vigorously with water when brushing is not possible.

(*d*) Seeing the dentist for a check-up every six months.

5 An ejected milk tooth may be disinfected in an antiseptic, allowed to dry, and mounted in a small box with glue, or on cotton wool in a small specimen tube. (Most children are not squeamish about this.)

NOTEBOOK WORK

Answers should be along the following lines.

1 Germs may enter our bodies in the air we breathe, on the food we eat, or through an open wound.
2 White corpuscles are cells in the blood which feed on germs.
3 Antiseptics are chemicals which poison germs and stop them multiplying.

---

(32) TAKE CARE OF DEAD THINGS

PROTECTING DEAD PARTS FROM SIMPLE PLANTS

DEMONSTRATION MATERIAL

1 Small quantities of commercially dried foods, *e.g.* prunes, currants, raisins, sultanas, rice, oatmeal, cornflakes, Bemax, dried apple, dried apricot; a number of small jars with covers, or small tins with lids (*e.g.* tobacco tins)
2 Material for demonstrating the preservation of dead animal or plant parts in 10% formaldehyde or 70% alcohol. (See pages 15-17.)

SAMPLE LINK QUESTIONS

1 What are the four main needs of all living things? (*Oxygen, food, to grow, to have young*)
2 Which of the simple plants need plenty of moisture in order to feed, grow and multiply? (*All of them*)
3 What kinds of things do bacteria and fungi feed on? (*Living or dead things, or materials which have come from living or dead things*)

4 Which plants are the tiniest of all living things? (*Bacteria*)
5 Of how many cells does a single bacterium consist? (*One*)
6 How may we sometimes detect the presence of bacteria which are causing decay even though we may not see them? (*By means of smell*)
7 Which parts of a fungus are carried through the air to start new plants? (*The spores*)
8 What are antiseptics? (*Chemicals which poison germs and stop them multiplying*)
9 When the temperature of a living thing falls, does it become less active or more active? (*Less active*)
10 What happens to a living thing if its temperature becomes too low or too high for it? (*It dies*)

RELEVANT INFORMATION

In Pupils' Book 1 it was shown that dead things are of two kinds—dead plant and dead animal.

In Pupils' Book 2 it was shown that dead things are used by living things, (*a*) for food—by certain plants and by many animals, including human beings, (*b*) for protection against enemies or weather—by certain animals, including human beings.

In Pupils' Book 3 it was shown that (*a*) only human beings use dead parts in any other way, either as they are, or in the form of a manufactured material or fabric, (*b*) three of the most important uses of dead parts are for clothing, fuel and vehicles.

The main purpose of this lesson is to show that
1 if we wish to retain dead things for our own use, we may have to protect them from bacteria and fungi which cause decay;
2 four main ways of doing this are by (*a*) drying, (*b*) heating to high temperatures and then sealing from the air, (*c*) storing at low temperatures, (*d*) treating with chemicals.

Of all the living things that feed on dead things, the most difficult to control are the bacteria and fungi which are responsible for decay. Protecting dead parts is particularly important where food is concerned. Preservation of dead material from bacteria and fungi consists basically of providing it with an environment in which these simple plants cannot live, or at least in which they cannot feed and multiply. The chief methods of achieving this are outlined below.

Drying—Dehydration

Drying is the oldest method known. The principle is to reduce the moisture content of the material below the minimum required by bacteria and fungi. The material may be exposed to wind and sun, or dried in hot ovens, kilns or hot cupboards. In countries with ample sunshine, natural drying has much to commend it, but in damp temperate countries artificial drying is often necessary. Meat and fish are typical animal parts sometimes preserved by drying. Plant parts include peaches, apricots, grapes, plums, figs, and the stems or leaves of various herbs such as tea, parsley, sage and thyme. Foods with a high sugar content, *e.g.* grapes, plums and apricots need only partial drying, as the sugar acts as a preservative. Certain dead parts, *e.g.* bone, feathers and fur, are normally too dry to be attacked by bacteria or fungi.

The illustrations of drying in the Pupils' Book show:

1 Salmon being gutted and hung up to dry, a practice in northern latitudes in summer, especially Alaska, where dried fish forms a nutritious winter food for Eskimos.

2 Haymaking—one of the oldest practices of grassland farmers for securing winter fodder. Grass normally consists of about 80% water and this must be reduced to about 15% for hay to be stored in barns or ricks with little danger of bacterial action.

Sometimes dried parts are given different names, *e.g.* dried meat—biltong; dried plums—prunes; dried grapes—currants, raisins or sultanas according to variety.

Heating to High Temperatures and Sealing from the Air

The temperatures most suitable for the maximum growth and reproduction of most bacteria lie between 12°C and 40°C. Nevertheless many kinds can flourish outside this range, though few can withstand temperatures above 100°C.

Heating to a high temperature to kill bacteria or fungal spores is termed *sterilising*. Where food is involved, the sterilised material may then be sealed in sterilised jars, bottles or cans, so that when it cools, it is protected from outside bacteria. Imperfect sealing allows air to enter, together with air-borne bacteria which contaminate the food and result in obnoxious gases. Such gases may cause a can to swell or a glass jar to shatter. Food from a swollen can or any container giving off an obnoxious smell should never be eaten.

Some foods of low acidic content, *e.g.* peas, carrots, beans, are susceptible to certain bacteria which can withstand temperatures of 100°C. After such foods have been canned, these bacteria have to be killed by further heating to about 116°C, which is maintained for up to two hours.

The illustrations in the Pupils' Book show food being prepared for heating and canning, and also food being further sterilised after canning.

Storing at Low Temperatures

At low temperatures a bacterium or fungus becomes less active, and at 0°C it is forced into a dormant state which stops any development. Since 1877 this knowledge has allowed the transportation of chilled carcases of meat in special refrigeration ships from South America, Australia and New Zealand to Britain and Europe. More recently, freezing has been used commercially for an increasing number of foods. By maintaining temperatures below 0°C, frozen foods may be preserved for months or, in some cases, years.

The illustrations in the Pupils' Book show:

1 Fish being packed in ice for delivery from port to market. This chilling retards bacterial development long enough for the fish to reach the consumer.

2 A commercial container for frozen foods which maintains the contents at a lower temperature than that of the ordinary domestic refrigerator.

Treating with Chemicals

The object is to provide an environment sufficiently concentrated to be toxic to bacteria and fungi. The preservative used for foods must obviously not be toxic to humans, and salt, vinegar and sugar are the main chemicals used. A strong salt solution (brine) is a good preservative. Salt alone is comparatively poor, except when used in conjunction with drying, when its presence allows a greater percentage of water to be left in the tissue. Vinegar is used for pickling, and sugar for preserving fruits. Candied fruit is obtained by immersing the fruit in a syrup of sugar and glucose for several days, during which the water content of the fruit forms a chemical bond with the sugar, thus leaving insufficient for bacteria. Crystallised fruit is covered in sugar grains; glacé fruit is covered with a smooth sugar coating. Fruit may also be preserved by simply leaving it in a syrup.

Other chemicals in common use are sulphur, borax, salicylic acid and sodium silicate (waterglass). The last, dissolved in water, preserves eggs.

The illustrations in the Pupils' Book show:

1 *Tanning*—In the production of leather, animal skins (*e.g.* of cattle, goats and crocodiles) are treated and given protection by various chemicals (*e.g.* alum) or oils. Tanning does not provide absolute protection, as evidenced by mould on a shoe in damp surroundings.

2 *Spraying* timber with a preservative, *e.g.* creosote. Several types of fungi attack woodwork in buildings, the most destructive being dry rot, the spores of which germinate in damp unventilated places, particularly under floors and behind wooden panelling. Properly dried timber lacks sufficient moisture for fungi, but chemical impregnation preserves it against chance occasions when the timber may become damp. Telegraph posts do not decay although frequently exposed to damp conditions, as they are protected by preservatives forced in under pressure.

3 (*a*) Bacon (usually preserved by soaking the meat in sodium nitrate), (*b*) cockles preserved in brine, (*c*) pickles in vinegar, (*d*) candied peel in sugar.

CODE

1 Observe examples of dead parts which have been preserved by any of the four main methods.

2 Experiment with a control to show that dried dead foods are protected from bacteria and fungi. Obtain two small jars with covers, or two small tins with lids, *e.g.* tobacco tins. In each jar or tin place a dried prune. Soak one prune thoroughly in water. After a while, drain off any surplus, and replace the cover or lid. Leave the two containers side by side. Observe that the moist prune is subsequently attacked by fungus, while the dry prune is preserved.

Repeat this experiment, using small quantities of other commercially dried foods, *e.g.* currants, raisins, sultanas, rice, oatmeal, cornflakes, bemax, dried apple, dried apricot.

3 Demonstrate how to preserve dead plant and animal parts in liquid preservative for general school use. See *Method Using Liquid Preservative*, pages 15-17.

NOTEBOOK WORK

Answers should be along the following lines.

1 We preserve dead parts in order to prevent them decaying.

2 Drying dead things prevents bacteria and fungi from having enough moisture to feed, grow and multiply.

Heating to high temperatures kills bacteria and fungi. Sealing in an airtight container keeps out other bacteria and fungi carried by the air.

Many kinds of simple plants die at the temperature at which water freezes. Any kinds which can survive are too cold to do anything but rest.

Treating dead parts with poisonous chemicals kills bacteria and fungi, or at least provides conditions in which they cannot thrive.

ROCKS ARE WORN DOWN AND FORCED UP

THE CHANGING LAYERS OF THE EARTH'S SURFACE

DEMONSTRATION MATERIAL

1 Sand, gravel, iron filings, cement or plaster of paris, soil; jam jar of water
2 Smooth piece of cloth
3 Shallow tray; piece of polythene or old plastic mack; coloured water; ruler
4 Flat piece of wood or hardboard; materials for making strata models, *e.g.* plasticine, sandpaper, gravel
5 Sandstone, puddingstone (conglomerate rock), shale

SAMPLE LINK QUESTIONS

1 What are pebbles, stones and grains of sand small pieces of? (*Rock*)
2 What are the three main layers of rock which make up the earth? (*The core, the mantle, and the crust*)
3 What make up the surface layer of the crust? (*A number of layers of different kinds of rocks*)
4 What fraction of the earth's crust is covered by sea? (*About three-quarters*)
5 Rocks are made up of different never-alive substances. What are these substances called? (*Minerals*)
6 When do we call a rock an ore? (*When it contains minerals which are useful to us*)
7 Which rock is made of tiny grains of sand stuck together? (*Sandstone*)
8 What are the two things which, when moving, wear down rock? (*Moving air and moving water*)
9 What normally forms a layer at the bottom of a pond, lake or river? (*Mud*)
10 What is the difference between a volcano and an earthquake?

RELEVANT INFORMATION

A lesson in Pupils' Book 1 showed that boulders, stones, pebbles, grains of sand and clay are all rock. A lesson in Pupils' Book 2 showed that moving air and moving water are the main agents responsible for (*a*) wearing down rock into smaller pieces, (*b*) conveying the pieces from place to place.

A lesson in Pupils' Book 3 showed that (*a*) the earth is made of layers of rock; (*b*) most rocks are mixtures of two or more substances called minerals; (*c*) a rock which contains a sufficient quantity of a useful mineral is called an ore.

The main purpose of this lesson is to show that

1 most of the layers of rock that make up the surface of the land were formed from layers of sediment deposited under water;

2 these layers are in turn being worn down.

It is believed that the earth was once a rapidly spinning globe of hot gases which subsequently cooled and condensed into liquid. After many millions of years of further cooling, during which the denser heavier minerals were drawn towards the centre and the less dense minerals floated towards the surface, the outer parts of the earth began to solidify, sealing the remainder of the fiery molten mass within. There it still rages today.

As the solid surface cooled, it contracted, as did the seething liquid maelstrom within it. The resulting stresses and strains caused the surface to wrinkle as the skin of a drying apple wrinkles, forming the first mountains and valleys. Rain from the condensing water vapour in the atmosphere poured down these mountain sides, eroding them, carving new valleys, and carrying the fragments down to the lowest hollows where accumulating water formed the first seas.

As the thin solid shell of the already twisted surface continued to contract round its fiery interior, further shrinking and folding would slowly heave new continents and mountains above sea level, giant cracks (faults) would appear, and along them masses of rock would be forced to slide over one another, while here and there volcanic outbursts would spew molten rock over the ruptured earth.

The process continues. The earth is still young—probably no more than 4,000 million years old—but in our present age the effect of stresses and strains is generally gradual, although sudden movements of the crust still occur as earthquakes. The livid turbulence below the surface still forces hot gases and hot liquid rock to be erupted from volcanoes, and the presence of hot rocks near the surface is indicated in places by hot springs and geysers.

Today this thin outer crust of the earth, with its estimated maximum depth of about 40 miles, is still no thicker in relation to the rest of the earth than is the skin to the rest of an apple. Just over a quarter of this crust shows above the ocean, and each day some 8 million tons of this land is swept down into the sea.

The Wearing down of Rocks to Form Sediment

Factors contributing to the breaking down or denudation of the crust include

1 erosion of rock due to (*a*) disintegration and splitting, resulting from factors such as temperature changes, chemical action and pressure exerted by plant roots; (*b*) general wearing down by moving water and moving air.
2 the moving of particles of rock, owing to gravity, moving water and moving air.

Wind and rain play a large part in the weathering of inland rocks, odd formations resulting from the more rapid wearing down of softer layers. Water is largely responsible for transporting loose rock material. Rainwater washes it down slopes, and into brooks, streams and rivers which carry it in one of three ways.

1 In solution, *e.g.* salt and other minerals
2 In suspension, *e.g.* sand and larger particles
3 By dragging larger fragments along the bottom of the water-course

In the Arctic and the Antarctic, and in cold high mountains, water in the form of glaciers transports rock material towards the sea. Along the coasts, the sea itself wears away the land, undermining the cliffs, and carving out bays and gulfs.

Rocks Formed from Sediments Deposited under Water

As layers of sediment accumulate on the floor of a lake or sea, the lower layers become squeezed more and more by the weight of the layers accumulating on top of them. When a layer of sediment is subject to pressure in this way, water is forced out from it, and it becomes compacted into a firm mass. Mud becomes compacted to form clay. Further pressure forces out more water, and compacts the clay into a harder mass—shale.

Some sediments are converted into rock by various minerals cementing the particles together, the minerals themselves being deposited by percolating water. Sand is converted into sandstone, and pebbles into conglomerate (*e.g.* puddingstone) in this way.

Not all of the sediments which accumulate under water consist of particles carried down from pre-existing rocks of the land. For example, most of the several varieties of limestone consist of the accumulated debris from simple aquatic animals which had parts constructed of calcium carbonate. The shells of molluscs, crinoid fragments, coral colonies, and the shells of microscopic single-celled protozoans have all contributed to such debris. The limestones of Derbyshire are derived chiefly from the shells of molluscs and parts of crinoids (animals related to the starfish). Chalk, which is a soft white limestone, consists chiefly of the shells (tests) of single-celled marine protozoans (known as foraminifera). Coal—a sedimentary rock—consists of compressed plant parts—mainly clubmosses, horsetails and ferns which flourished and died in the vast swamps of 200 to 300 million years ago.

Some sedimentary rocks consist of minerals that were precipitated when the water in which they were dissolved evaporated. The great underground salt beds of Cheshire, which are up to 100 feet thick, were deposited when an ancient saltwater lake dried up long ago.

The Raising of Sediments to Form Land

The slow movement of the crust continues, so that in some parts land is rising above the sea, and in other parts land is sinking below it. For example, France appears to be tilting slowly northwards, sinking along the Channel coast, and rising in the south, so that some day the Atlantic Ocean may wash across great areas of what is at present Northern France, while layers of sedimentary rocks at present below the Mediterranean may eventually appear as land. Relative to the span of a human life, the rising and sinking of land is gradual, but a difference of one foot in a thousand years amounts to a thousand feet in a million years, and a million years is a very short length of time in the age of the world. Thus seas have changed and continents come and gone during the long procession of the ages.

All our high mountains—the Himalayas, Alps, Rockies and Andes—probably appeared during the last 60 million years, since the giant dinosaur reptiles became extinct. Most mountain ranges consist chiefly of sedimentary rocks; even Mount Everest consists mainly of sediments such as limestone and shale, with limestone forming the summit.

There are three main ways in which mountains may be formed.

1 *By folding*, *i.e.* gigantic pressure from below the sea-bed slowly forces it up into huge ridges. Most of the mountain ranges of today were formed in this way. The Pennine Range is an example of a simple upward fold, but there are many more complex examples where continued pressure has forced a simple fold over to form a double fold.

2 *By a fault*, *i.e.* rocks are forced to crack and break, one side being forced in a gigantic grinding movement to a higher level than the other. Mountains formed in this way are called block mountains, and cliffs formed in this way are called escarpments. Where cracks occurred, molten rocks from below the surface would often be forced up to fill them. There they would cool and solidify.

3 *By volcanic material*. Successive layers of volcanic lava

and ash build up a cone-shaped mountain. At present the earth has more than 500 active volcanoes in addition to the several thousands which are extinct or dormant.

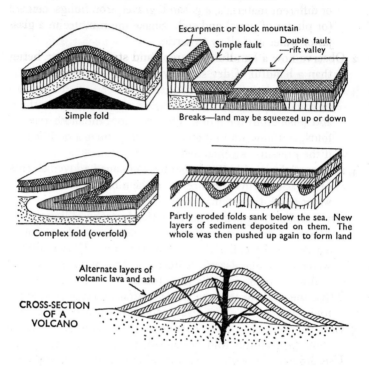

Simple fold

Escarpment or block mountain

Simple fault

Double fault —rift valley

Breaks—land may be squeezed up or down

Complex fold (overfold)

Partly eroded folds sank below the sea. New layers of sediment deposited on them. The whole was then pushed up again to form land

CROSS-SECTION OF A VOLCANO

Alternate layers of volcanic lava and ash

Obviously, some of the rocks at the surface of the land are not sedimentary. Basalt, granite and pumicestone result from the cooling and solidifying of a molten mass, and are termed igneous rocks. Subsequent heat and pressure on some igneous and sedimentary rocks can so change their nature that they are given a different name—metamorphic rocks. Gneiss is a metamorphosed granite; quartzite is a metamorphosed sandstone; marble is a metamorphosed limestone; and slate is a metamorphosed shale.

The commonest kinds of rocks found in the British Isles are sandstones, shales, limestones and clay, together with exposed outcrops of granite and basalt.

CODE

1 Demonstrate how particles settle in layers. Make a mixture of different materials, *e.g.* sand, gravel, iron filings, cement (or plaster of paris) and soil. Shake the mixture in a glass jar of water and allow to settle.

2 Observe how a handful of damp sand sticks together better than a handful of dry sand, when each is compressed.

3 Demonstrate how a flat layer of rock can be folded up into a mountain. Place a smooth piece of cloth on a flat surface, and push from the sides. Observe how the cloth rises in folds, and how a fold may bend over to form a double fold if the pressure is continued.

4 Demonstrate how upward folding can cause a layer of rock to be raised above water level, at the same time causing the water to be displaced.

On a shallow tray, arrange a piece of plastic material, *e.g.* polythene or a section from an old plastic raincoat. Insert a ruler between the plastic and the tray. Pour coloured water on to the plastic material so that it runs into any hollows and forms 'seas' and 'lakes'.

Twist the ruler so that the plastic surface changes, *i.e.* some folds sink below water level, and others rise above it.

5 On a flat piece of wood or hardboard, make simple models to show (*a*) a simple fold, (*b*) an overfold, (*c*) a break (fault).

Use different colours of plasticine and strips of sandpaper. Bits of gravel can be pushed into one of the layers of plasticine to represent puddingstone (conglomerate rock). Add surfaces of 'soil', 'grass' and 'trees'.

6 Observe specimens of sandstone, conglomerate or shale. Shale is sometimes supplied with poor quality coal and may split easily.

7 Where the locality permits, observe layers of sedimentary rocks—where a face of rock has been exposed by some means, *e.g.* in a quarry or on a cliff, and sometimes along the bank of a river, or where a road has been cut through a hill. These layers (strata) may be horizontal, tilted or folded. Some folds are only a few inches or a few feet

across, but others may be many miles across, and are not obvious to the casual observer. The thickness of a single stratum may be anything from less than an inch to many feet.

NOTEBOOK WORK

Answers should be along the following lines.

1 Layers of sediment are squeezed into rock by the weight of the upper layers.
2 (*a*) Sandstone is formed from sand; (*b*) shale is formed from mud.
3 Layers of rock are forced up to form land by the hot molten rocks below them.
4 As soon as rocks are forced up, wind and water begin to wear them down.

RECORDS IN THE ROCKS

FOSSILS

DEMONSTRATION MATERIAL

Any fossils; material for making a plaster cast of a fossil, *e.g.* plasticine, plaster of paris (or Keen's cement, or alabastine), a fossil with raised features, or a small shell, *e.g.* cockle

SAMPLE LINK QUESTIONS

1 What two things wear away the layers of rocks which form the surface of the land? (*Wind and water*)
2 What things carry rock fragments towards the sea? (*Streams and rivers*)
3 What do we call the deposited fragments? (*Sediment*)
4 What squeezes layers of sediment into firm masses of rock? (*The weight of the layers above them*)
5 What do we call the rocks which are formed from these sediments—pebbles, sand, mud? (*Puddingstone, sandstone, shale*)

6 What causes layers of rock from below the sea to be heaved up above sea level? (*Disturbances below the crust* or *hot molten rocks below the crust*)

7 What are crustaceans? (*Animals with crusty skins*)

8 What are molluscs? (*Animals which build limestone shells*)

9 To which class of animals did the dinosaurs belong? (*The reptiles*)

10 Of which three kinds of herbs is coal the remains? (*Club-mosses, horsetails and ferns*)

RELEVANT INFORMATION

The main points of this lesson are that

1 fossils show us what things were like ages ago;

2 most fossils are found in layers of rock that were formed under water;

3 most fossils are only impressions of things;

4 some are actual remains of things.

The term *fossil* is applied to something or to a trace of something which has been preserved naturally for a very long time. Fossils found in rock provide a record of events which happened before the rock was formed.

The most interesting fossils are those of animals and plants which died out long ago. Without them, we should have little or no record of living things which are now extinct.

Animal and Plant Fossils in Rocks

Fossil-bearing rocks are almost always sedimentary, and include limestone, chalk, chert, shale, sandstone, grit, marls and clays. The fossils of animals and plants which lived on dry land are seldom found in these rocks, as they would usually die on land and decompose long before there was any chance of sediment covering them. Such organisms occasionally become fossilised, however, when covered by wind-blown sand or dust which accumulated quickly and remained.

Most fossils of animals and plants are of those which died in water. The majority lived in water, although a terrestrial animal or plant falling into a swamp or river stood a chance of being fossilised as well. As fossils of aquatic animals and plants are found in rocks well above sea level, they indicate that the rocks themselves were originally laid down under water—on the beds of ancient seas, one-time estuaries, inland lakes and swamps.

The Main Types of Fossils

Some fossils consist of actual remains; the majority, however, are merely the impressions or mineralised reproductions of things which no longer remain, the original substance having disintegrated long ago.

Fossil Remains

Fossils consisting of the actual remains of things or parts of things are the least common. They have come into being in various ways.

1 Remains of animals and plants have sometimes been preserved for thousands of years where the earth has acted as a natural refrigerator. The bodies of mammoths and of a woolly rhinoceros have been found preserved in frozen mud in Northern Siberia. Preservation was complete from the fur covering the body down to the last meal still in the stomach. A baby mastodon, found frozen in Alaska, is still kept in refrigerated conditions in the New York Natural History Museum.

2 Small plant parts and small animals such as insects and spiders were sometimes trapped by the sticky resin exuding from the stems of gum-bearing trees—especially conifers. If they were completely covered, they were preserved against bacterial action. In time the resin dried and hardened into amber. As this looks something like yellow glass, the contents are not only preserved but are also visible. Amber itself is often termed fossilised resin.

3 The wood of some trees contains substances such as tannin which preserves it against bacterial action. Wood from trees such as giant redwoods has been preserved in this way for millions of years.

4 In certain parts of California large numbers of cones, wood fragments, leaves, seeds, and the bones of mammals and birds have been enclosed in asphalt which has seeped into the

sands and clays in which they were buried and thus preserved them against bacterial action.

Peat beds and oil pits have also served as preservatives. In general, it is hard parts such as bones, teeth and shells which have had the best chance of surviving the ravages of time.

Fossil Impressions

These are the most frequently found, and have also come into being in various ways.

1 The remains of plants and animals trapped in hardening sediments sometimes decomposed slowly, leaving impressions in the form of carbon deposits. Many fossils of fern leaves found in shale are of this type.

2 Imprints made on the land were sometimes preserved, as there was nothing to decompose. In the Permian period, for example, when Britain was under desert conditions, animals walked across drying muds or sands and left tracks which hardened in the sun. The footprints of dinosaurs, worm casts and worm trails, and even impressions made by drops of rain have been fossilised in this way.

3 The remains of animals and plants trapped in hardened sediments dissolved leaving only their surface impressions in the surrounding rock. The impression of an external surface formed in this way is known as an external mould, and the impression of an internal surface is known as an internal mould.

4 Often, an impression already made in hardened sediment was subsequently filled in by deposited mineral matter carried by water percolating through the rock. This deposit would take up the shape of the mould, and a cast would be formed. This is why, when some pieces of rock are split, two impressions are found. One of the two (sunk into the surface) is the original imprint. The other (raised from the surface) is a cast formed in the imprint which served as a mould. Minerals such as silica, calcium carbonate and quartz often make up these fossil casts. It is not easy to distinguish between an internal mould and a cast from an external mould.

5 Water containing dissolved minerals (*e.g.* calcite, pyrites, and haematite) penetrated the organic part of an animal or plant.

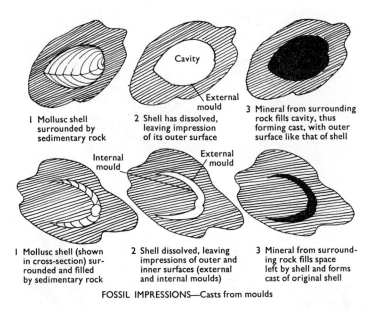

1 Mollusc shell surrounded by sedimentary rock

2 Shell has dissolved, leaving impression of its outer surface

3 Mineral from surrounding rock fills cavity, thus forming cast, with outer surface like that of shell

1 Mollusc shell (shown in cross-section) surrounded and filled by sedimentary rock

2 Shell dissolved, leaving impressions of outer and inner surfaces (external and internal moulds)

3 Mineral from surrounding rock fills space left by shell and forms cast of original shell

FOSSIL IMPRESSIONS—Casts from moulds

The mineral matter precipitated out of the solution replaced the organic substance molecule by molecule. The whole tissues of plant parts (as in petrified forests), and the skeletons of dinosaurs and other animals have been gradually rebuilt in rock in this way. This process—petrifaction—has enabled the cellular structure of the original substance to be observed.

The Main Uses of Fossils

Fossils—the hallmarks of time—are of considerable value to biologists and geologists in several ways.

1 The record they provide is of utmost value in the study of evolution. From it we learn how animals and plants changed with the passing of the ages and how new species gradually evolved. We can read in it the different chapters in the story of evolution.

2 The species of fossils in a layer of rock give an indication of the conditions and climate in that area at the time that the rock was laid down. Thus plant fossils in coal indicate the one-

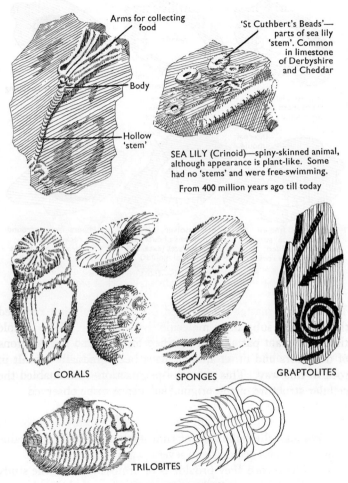

Arms for collecting
food

Body

Hollow
'stem'

'St Cuthbert's Beads'—
parts of sea lily
'stem'. Common
in limestone
of Derbyshire
and Cheddar

SEA LILY (Crinoid)—spiny-skinned animal,
although appearance is plant-like. Some
had no 'stems' and were free-swimming.

From 400 million years ago till today

CORALS

SPONGES

GRAPTOLITES

TRILOBITES

SOME TYPICAL FOSSILS

CORAL—Various forms. Limy skeletons formed structures for fossils. Known to have
lived 420 million years ago as well as today

SPONGES—Limy skeletons formed structures for fossils. Known to have lived 500
million years ago as well as today

GRAPTOLITES—Many forms. Floated on surface of sea in colony sheaths, which sank on
death of colony. Usually in shale. Like pencil marks. 300-500 million years ago

TRILOBITES—Crustaceans, from $\frac{1}{16}$" to 18". 260-500 million years ago

time existence of swampy forests; coral and sea lilies and the shells of marine molluscs show that the area was covered at that time by the sea; shells of freshwater molluscs indicate the one-time presence of lakes and rivers; crocodiles and tropical plants indicate the kind of climate, and so on. Plant fossils are more useful in determining climatic conditions, as plants were fixed in their places of growth and could not migrate from latitude to latitude as animals could.

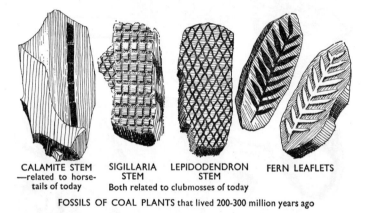

| CALAMITE STEM —related to horse-tails of today | SIGILLARIA STEM | LEPIDODENDRON STEM | FERN LEAFLETS |

Both related to clubmosses of today

FOSSILS OF COAL PLANTS that lived 200-300 million years ago

3 The variety of fossils present in the same layer of rock normally enables its age to be estimated. During each geological period, new forms of life evolved, some underwent changes, and others became extinct, so that the actual variety differed from period to period. Even though rocks in different parts of a country may consist of different materials, the presence of the same variety of fossils indicates that they are the same age.

Where to Look for Fossils

In Great Britain today there are rocks representing every geological period of time. As soil and superficial deposits cover most of these, fossils are best sought where layers of rock are exposed, *e.g.* road cuttings, cliffs and quarries. Usually those in rock at the bottom of a deep quarry or cliff will be millions of years older than those near the top.

Fossils occur in most sedimentary rocks including lime-

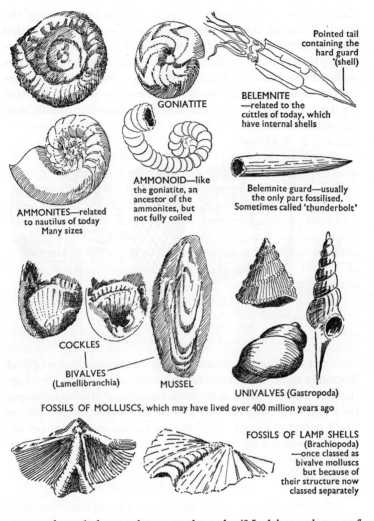

GONIATITE

BELEMNITE
—related to the
cuttles of today, which
have internal shells

Pointed tail
containing the
hard guard
(shell)

AMMONOID—like
the goniatite, an
ancestor of the
ammonites, but
not fully coiled

Belemnite guard—usually
the only part fossilised.
Sometimes called 'thunderbolt'

AMMONITES—related
to nautilus of today
Many sizes

COCKLES

BIVALVES
(Lamellibranchia)

MUSSEL

UNIVALVES (Gastropoda)

FOSSILS OF MOLLUSCS, which may have lived over 400 million years ago

FOSSILS OF LAMP SHELLS
(Brachiopoda)
—once classed as
bivalve molluscs
but because of
their structure now
classed separately

stone, clay, shale, sandstone and marl. (Marl is a mixture of limestone and clay.) Exposed rocks in limestone regions, *e.g.* Derbyshire, Cheddar Gorge, and the chalk cliffs near Dover, are often rewarding. Piles of flints in chalk quarries are worth examining for the small fossils frequently attached to them. Shale on coal tips and broken rock at a cliff base may also provide specimens. Fossils found in clay are usually flattened, but the nodules and concretions which occur in clay may contain good specimens. (A concretion is mineral matter, originally in solution, which tended to accumulate round various remains; flints found in chalk or clay are concretions.) Fossils are not common in sandstone as its porosity not only allowed the easy infiltration of water carrying chemicals which dissolved the remains, but also allowed the water to dissipate the remains as it filtered on.

Lyme Regis on the Dorset coast is famous for fossil ammonites. Here twelve-year-old Mary Anning was the first to find the fossil of an ichthyosaur, a prehistoric marine reptile.

Whitby is also famous for fossils. Black Whitby jet, used for beads and other ornaments, is the fossilised wood from ancient conifers. Ammonites are also plentiful. They were once believed to be snakes turned into stone by St Hilda, the abbess of Whitby Abbey, in the seventh century—hence the three snakes in the Whitby arms.

Fossils are not always found in the area where they originated. During the Great Ice Age, for example, fossils were carried away and deposited in other areas, together with the rocks and soil that were moved by the ice. This material is known as boulder clay. Some of it forms sea cliffs on part of the Yorkshire coast. Seas and rivers have also played their part during the ages of wearing away rocks containing fossils and laying them down in new deposits. Fossils which have been removed to other areas in ways like these are known as derived fossils.

For a determined search with the purpose of extracting fossils, a good hammer, small and large cold chisels and a pick are necessities.

CODE

1 Collect fossils and number them. Pass round for identification in terms of what they are, *e.g.* leaf, mollusc shell, tooth.
2 Demonstrate how an imprint may occur as a fossil.
Press a suitable specimen showing prominent outlines into a block of plasticine. If no suitable fossil is available, a cockle shell or a leaf will do.

Remove the specimen and observe the impression. (This is the equivalent of an external mould.)

Note. Smear the surface of the specimen with a thin film of some greasy substance such as vaseline or thin oil and wipe off; this will reduce the possibility of plasticine adhering to the specimen as it is removed, and should make for a more detailed impression. Rolling a jam jar over the specimen may help to press it evenly into the plasticine.

3 Demonstrate how the imprint may serve as a mould, and a cast be taken from it.

Surround the block of plasticine containing the impression (made in 2 above) with a small raised wall, *e.g.* with strips of wood or hardboard.

Make a liquid mixture of plaster of paris (or Keen's cement or alabastine) and pour into the mould to a depth of about one inch. Leave until set hard.

Remove the walls, and peel off the plasticine impression, leaving a cast similar to the original specimen. Paint or crayon this to distinguish it from the rest of the plaster.

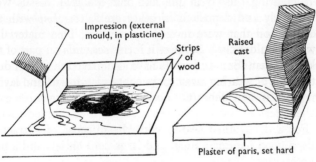

Impression (external mould, in plasticine) — Strips of wood — Raised cast — Plaster of paris, set hard

TAKING A CAST FROM A MOULD

NOTEBOOK WORK

Answers should be along the following lines.

No. 1 is a starfish.   No. 4 is a dinosaur footprint.

No. 2 is a shark's tooth.   No. 5 is a spider in amber.

No. 3 is a fern leaf.   No. 6 is a mollusc shell.

(The mollusc shell appears among the coloured illustrations.)

35 THE BRITISH REPTILES

LIZARDS AND SNAKES

DEMONSTRATION MATERIAL

1 Living or preserved specimen of a British lizard or snake
2 Moulted skin, *e.g.* of grass snake; section of lizard skin

SAMPLE LINK QUESTIONS

1 What are the two main kinds of living things? (*Animals and plants*)
2 What are the three main ways in which animals have young? (*By part of the parent growing into a new animal*; *by means of eggs*: *by means of tiny babies*)
3 Which animals have hair on their bodies and have young that drink milk? (*Mammals*)
4 Which are the only animals with feathers? (*Birds*)
5 Which animal has both gills and fins? (*A fish*)
6 Which class of animals developed from fish? (*Amphibians*)
7 Which class of animals developed from amphibians? (*Reptiles*)
8 What kind of skin has a reptile? (*A scaly skin*)
9 What do reptiles have for taking oxygen from the air? (*Lungs*)
10 When a reptile has young by means of eggs, where are the eggs always laid? (*On land*)

RELEVANT INFORMATION

The main points of a lesson in Pupils' Book 2 were that
1 reptiles are a class of animals which evolved from primitive amphibians, and as a class they are adapted from birth to withstand conditions on land, *i.e.* they have scaly skins and lungs;
2 the prehistoric monsters were reptiles;
3 the eggs of modern reptiles are always laid on land;
4 modern reptiles include the crocodiles, turtles, snakes and lizards.

The main aim of this lesson is to show
1 the characteristics common to the British reptiles,
2 the main differences between them.

Reptiles in General

Of the back-boned animals, reptiles were the first true dwellers on land. They evolved from primitive amphibians— probably during the later stages of the coal age. They have more efficient lungs than adult amphibians and are more capable of resisting excessive loss of moisture when in dry surroundings. This resistance is due to (a) a thicker body skin, and (b) eggs protected by a tough shell. The skin is covered with small horny plates (scales). These scales differ in structure from those of a fish. They may be flat, fitting together like a mosaic, or they may overlap like the tiles on a roof. Some modern reptiles, e.g. the crocodiles and the turtles, may hunt for their food in water, but they still take their oxygen from the air and return to land to lay their eggs.

Lizards and snakes are closely related. They are the most successfully established of the modern reptiles, and are most common in tropical regions. On both, the tongue is sensitive, serving as an organ of touch; but whereas on a lizard it is only slightly notched at the tip, on a snake it is distinctly forked. A lizard has eyelids, but a snake has none, so that its eyes cannot be closed when sleeping. A lizard can shed its tail readily as a means of defence and then grow a new one. This is not the case with a snake. On some lizards an external ear patch is visible, a feature which snakes lack. Both lizards and snakes slough their skins periodically as they grow, exposing new clean layers underneath.

More precise information on reptiles, including the pre-historic dinosaurs and the different kinds of modern reptiles, will be found on pages 182-8 of Teacher's Book 2.

British Lizards and Snakes

Three species of lizards and three species of snake live wild in the British Isles. They all feed on other living animals; they all hibernate during winter, and none of them cares for its young. Two additional species—the wall lizard and the green lizard—are found in the Channel Islands, but these are not strictly classed as British. The abhorrence with which these reptiles are sometimes regarded is out of all proportion to their characteristics, as, in general, they are harmless to man, and in fact very useful in that they consume many of the smaller and less desirable animals. Only one—the viper—is poisonous, and even this only bites in self-defence when disturbed or alarmed.

Lizards

The common lizard is widely distributed throughout the British Isles, particularly on heaths and amongst heather. Each of its four legs has five toes with a claw on each toe. It can run swiftly, climb rough surfaces and jump. Adult length is 5-7 inches, half of which is tail. Two ear patches are visible on this lizard. It makes no vocal sound. Food consists of insects, spiders and small worms. Eggs are usually retained until after hatching so that the young are born free of the egg membrane. At birth, the 6-12 young are about an inch long and almost black. Hibernation begins about October, usually in holes dug with the head and forelegs.

The sand lizard is the least common of our lizards and is confined almost entirely to Dorset and Surrey and to sandhills along the Lancashire coast. The head is broader and the snout blunter than on the common lizard. The body is stouter, and the animal less active than the common lizard. Adult length is about 8 inches, more than half of which is tail. The female looks purple-brown, but the male is greenish. A clutch of 5-12 eggs is laid in June or July. These are covered by sandy soil or leaves, and left to incubate. The eggs have a parchment-like covering, and the young hatch in 6-12 weeks. Hibernation is below ground.

The slow-worm is a legless lizard. It is also known as the blind-worm and the deaf adder, but is not slow, blind or deaf and is neither a worm nor an adder. It is common throughout the British Isles with the exception of Ireland, and may be distinguished from British snakes by the small round scales covering the whole of its body and by the thin dark line down the centre of its back. The tail often has a rounded instead of a pointed tip, indicating that a new length is growing to replace one which has been lost. Adult length is about 12 inches, but 18 inches is possible. Heaths and the fringes of woodlands are customary haunts, where daylight hours are spent under stones or in burrows. Food consists mainly of small grey slugs, although insects, spiders and small worms are also taken. Occasionally soft transparent-shelled eggs are laid, but these are usually retained until they have hatched, so that the young are born free of the egg and quite active. This occurs in August or September. The 6-16 young are thin and silvery and about 2 inches long. Slow-worms hibernate in autumn, under stones or in loose dry earth, and are the first reptiles to emerge the following spring. Chief enemies are hedgehogs, vipers, and those humans who fail to appreciate their usefulness.

Snakes

The grass snake is widely distributed throughout England, Wales and S.E. Scotland but is not found in Ireland. It is easily identified by the bright collar behind the head. This is usually yellow or orange, but may be white, and behind it are two black patches. The adult length of this, our largest, reptile is 3-4 feet, one-fifth of which is tail. As is customary with snakes, growth continues throughout life. Food consists mainly of frogs, but other amphibians and fish may be taken, and the grass snake is a good swimmer. Like other snakes it can swallow food three times the size of its own head owing to the elastic muscle joining the lower jawbones. (In this respect snakes differ from lizards.) Up to 50 oval eggs, with cream-coloured parchment-like shells, and joined end to end in a string, are laid from June to August in the warmth of manure or rotting vegetation. The 6-8 inch baby snakes hatch after 6-10 weeks and feed at first on insects and worms. The skin is moulted four or five times a year. This is shed intact, the snake catching the skin at the edges of the jaws against a stone or stem, and then gliding out of its own mouth so that the skin is turned inside out. So complete is the process that even the transparent covering of the eyes is removed. The grass snake is harmless to humans and quite easily tamed, but hisses when frightened and emits an evil-smelling secretion—its only defence. Hibernation, often in numbers, begins in autumn, usually under brushwood or tree roots.

The smooth snake, the least common of British snakes, is confined to a few southern counties, particularly where the sand lizard occurs. Slim, graceful, and generally brownish in colour, it is easily mistaken for a viper. The scales on its head differ from those of a viper, and the pupil of its eye is circular, while that of a viper is slit-like. Adult length is about 2 feet, sometimes up to 3 feet, and the tail is less than a quarter of this. This snake is rarely seen, as it hunts in the evening, feeding on sand lizards, slow-worms and small rodents. The eggs are retained until hatched, and up to 15 young are born about August to September, each measuring 5-7 inches. The smooth snake, like the grass snake, emits an objectionable smell when captured, but is easily tamed.

The viper (*or adder*), our only poisonous snake, is widespread through England, Wales and Scotland, usually on commons, sandy heaths and dense hedgebanks. It is distinguished by a black zigzag line running centrally down the back, but this is not always observable. Eyes are a bright coppery red with vertical slit-like pupils. Total length of the thick short body seldom exceeds two feet, one-eighth of which is tail. Food—hunted both night and day—consists of rodents, although other reptiles, amphibians, slugs and insect larvae add to the diet. Large prey is paralysed by the poisoned bite before being swallowed whole. Eggs are retained until hatched, and 5-12 active young are born in August or September, each measuring 4-8 inches. Hibernation begins in autumn, under heather, moss or grass, where several vipers may sleep together.

The viper is not aggressive to humans, and will escape rather than attack. It bites in self-defence, especially when trodden on, but the poison is seldom fatal to humans, especially when there is prompt medical attention.

Children sometimes confuse newts with lizards. Newts, of course, are amphibians, do not have scaly skins, and are more frequently found than lizards. The most easily observed differences are:

1. A lizard has a scaly skin. A newt has a skin which is either smooth and moist, or rough and dry, but never scaly.

2. A lizard's tail is long and rounded. A newt's tail is flattened.

3. A lizard has claws on its fingers and toes. A newt has no claws on its fingers or toes.

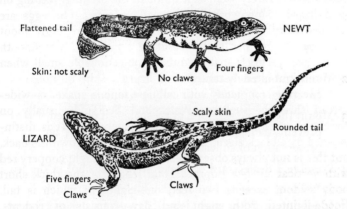

On land, of course, a newt's movements are slow and ungainly, whereas those of a lizard can be very swift. Thus, although children could catch a newt quite easily on land, they would probably have extreme difficulty in catching a lizard.

CODE

1 Examine a whole lizard or snake, and observe
   (a) on a lizard with four legs

       (i) the appearance of the scales on the back and the belly,
       (ii) the five fingers or toes on each of the four feet,
       (iii) colour and markings;

(*b*) on a slow-worm

   (i) the appearance of the scales—particularly the many small round ones on the belly which distinguish it from a snake,

   (ii) the dark line down the centre of the back,

   (iii) the tail (which will be rounded and blunt if it is a regenerated section),

   (iv) general colour;

(*c*) on a snake

   (i) the appearance of the scales—particularly those on the belly, which overlap, and stretch from side to side of the body,

   (ii) colour and markings—particularly the coloured collar and black marks on the neck of a grass snake.

2 Mount moulted sections of a lizard's skin in notebooks, covering completely with cellulose tape.

3 Mount the whole skin of a grass snake—if obtained—so as to prevent damage through handling. (See page 14 on preservation of collected material.)

4 Preserve a dead lizard or snake in 70% alcohol in the usual way.

5 If a living lizard or snake is kept as a pet for observation purposes, a suitable environment should be provided. Being cold-blooded animals, their activities are influenced by temperature, and therefore a suitable temperature should be ensured. Lizards are the easier to keep in school. Of these, the legless slow-worm is one of the most amenable. Common lizards and sand lizards are often sold in pet shops. Green lizards and wall lizards—as found in the Channel Islands—are also available. Grass snakes too are available in pet shops. Dealers will sometimes sell more cheaply a lizard that has lost its tail. It is worth buying in order to observe the regeneration of the tail. Spring and early summer are the best times for purchasing, and for both lizards and snakes the accommodation is similar.

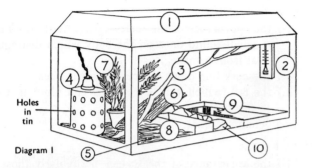

Diagram I

HOME-MADE VIVARIUM FOR LIZARDS OR SNAKES

1 Electric light shade on glass tank. Make sure there is sufficient ventilation between the two, and yet insufficient space to allow the animal to escape

2 Thermometer

3 Branch of tree or shrub (for climbing)

4 Heating equipment – pierced dried-milk tin containing 40-watt electric light bulb. Tin should not touch glass

5 Compost or peat covering floor of tank. Moisten occasionally

6 Piece of bark – for shade

7 Potted fern for ornamentation

8 Food receptacle   9 Pool (water in tin)   10 Rocks

(a) *Accommodation.* Where this is indoors, either the home-made vivarium (Diagram 1) or the commercially-produced vivarium (Diagram 2, overleaf) is suitable.

A 2′ × 1′ × 1′ aquarium with an all-over electric light shade can be made into a suitable container for lizards and snakes. It is advisable to provide artificial heat, as lizards and snakes feed better at temperatures above 15°C. Precautions should obviously be taken with any electrical fittings.

(b) *Food* consists of other living animals.

Lizards. Insects are the staple diet. Maggots, which may be bought from suppliers of fishing-tackle, are particularly useful. Lizards will feed on the maggots themselves, on the pupae, and also on the adult bluebottles which emerge from the pupal skins. It is better, if the

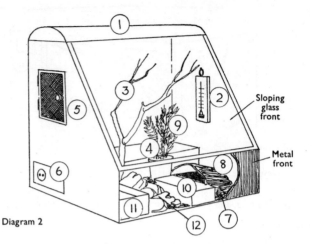

Diagram 2

COMMERCIALLY-MADE VIVARIUM

1 Lights (above a glass cover)

2 Thermometer

3 Branch

4 Shelf covering light bulbs used for heating

5 Small door for feeding (Mesh allows ventilation)

6 Access to light bulbs used for heating

7 Peat on floor	8 Bark for shade	9 Potted fern
10 Food receptacle	11 Pool	12 Rocks

maggots are imprisoned in some container, *e.g.* a small tin standing in a saucer of water, so that they cannot escape into the surrounding compost. Slow-worms in particular will also feed on the small grey and white slugs found in the garden, and on spiders and small earthworms.

Some lizards are inclined to be vicious towards their smaller relatives. This applies in particular to green lizards and sand lizards. If more than one lizard is kept, it may pay, therefore, to have them approximately the same size.

316

Snakes. Grass snakes' main diet consists of living amphibians and fish. This makes them unpopular with children.

(c) *Hibernation.* Out of doors, reptiles would hibernate during winter. In an indoor vivarium, it is advisable to keep them awake, provided food and temperature can be maintained. This is fairly easy with lizards in a school. Snakes, quite obviously, are difficult to cater for.

NOTEBOOK WORK

Answers should be along the following lines.

1 (a) Lizards have eyelids; snakes do not.
  (b) The common lizard, slow-worm, smooth snake and viper do not usually lay eggs.
2 (a) The common lizard and the sand lizard are four-legged.
  (b) Sand lizards and smooth snakes are rare.
  (c) The viper is poisonous.
3 (a) British lizards eat insects, spiders and small worms.
  (b) Grass snakes feed on amphibians and fish.
4 (a) A grass snake has a colourful collar and two black patches on its head.
  (b) A British viper has a wide zigzag line down its back, and golden-red eyes with slit-like pupils.

QUESTIONS ON LESSONS 25 TO 35

1 What are the stages in the life of a dragonfly? *Egg, larva, adult*

2 What are the stages in the life of a caddis fly? *Egg, larva, pupa, adult*

3 Which has a special lip for catching small animals—the dragonfly larva or the caddis fly larva? *Dragonfly larva*

4 Which larva builds a case to protect itself from enemies? *Caddis fly larva*

317

5 What do the larvae of dragonflies and caddis flies have, to help them take oxygen from the water? *Gills*

6 How many wings does each of these insects have in the adult stage? *Four*

7 How many wings has a true fly, such as a housefly, bluebottle or midge, in the adult stage? *Two*

8 What do we call the very tiny living things of which every animal and plant consists? *Cells*

9 Are the outer protective cells of your skin and nails alive or dead? *Dead*

10 How does a living cell multiply itself? *By dividing*

11 What are the four main flower parts? *Sepals, petals, stamens, pistils*

12 Which of these parts protect the flower before it opens? *Sepals*

13 Which of these parts are usually the most attractive? *Petals*

14 Which two flower parts are the most important? *Stamens and pistils*

15 Which two flower parts are not found on grass flowers? *Sepals and petals*

16 On some flowers such as bluebells and tulips, the sepals and petals are not separate. What do we call the coloured outer leaf-shaped parts on one of these flowers? *Perianth*

17 What is developed in the anther of a flower? *Pollen*

18 On a plant, what does an ovary develop into after fertilisation? *A fruit*

19 What does an ovule develop into after fertilisation? *A seed*

20 Where do most algae live—on land, in fresh water or in the sea? *In the sea*

21 Where do most mosses live—on land, in fresh water or in the sea? *On land*

22 What is a common name for sea algae? *Seaweeds*

23 Some algae and mosses grow anchored in water by a sucker-like part or a root-like part. What do we call this part?   *A holdfast*

24 What do we get from the remains of dead bog mosses?   *Peat*

25 What is the general name for moulds, mildews, toadstools, mushrooms and dry rot?   *Fungi (fungus)*

26 Which simple plants can be detected by means of smell, when they cause something to go bad?   *Bacteria*

27 How many cells make a single bacterium?   *One*

28 Simple plants can have young by part of the parent growing into a new plant. By what other means may many kinds of simple plants have young?   *Spores*

29 When fungi or bacteria feed on living things, what is the result?   *Disease*

30 When fungi or bacteria feed on dead things, what is the result?   *Decay*

31 What is a common name for any simple plants or simple animals which can live and feed on us?   *Germs*

32 Which simple plants attack teeth?   *Bacteria*

33 What should you do to your teeth after a meal, to remove these simple plants?   *Brush them*

34 Which are better for your teeth and gums— raw apples, sticky sweets or sweet cakes?   *Raw apples*

35 On which parts of its body may a housefly carry germs to our food?   *Feet and mouth parts*

36 When we preserve dead parts, which two kinds of simple plants are we protecting them from?   *Fungi and bacteria*

37 Three methods of preserving dead parts are to heat to a high temperature and seal from the air, to store at a low temperature and to treat with chemicals. What is a fourth method?   *Drying*

38 Which two things are gradually wearing away the rocks which form the surface of the land? *Wind and water*

39 What do we call a layer of worn-down rock particles deposited on the bed of a lake, sea or river? *Layer of sediment*

40 Which kind of sediment, when compressed, forms shale? *Mud*

41 Disturbances below the earth's crust cause the surface layers to be heaved up. Some layers may be broken. What may happen to others? *They may be folded*

42 Where were most of the layers of rocks in which fossils are found, formed? *Under water*

43 Do most fossils consist of actual remains or just impressions of remains? *Impressions of remains*

44 What name do we give to the hardened resin in which the actual remains of insects and spiders are sometimes found preserved? *Amber*

45 Do British reptiles feed on other living animals or on living plants? *Living animals*

46 Which British snake has a colourful collar and two black patches on its neck? *Grass snake*

47 What is the name of the only poisonous British snake? *Viper (adder)*

48 What is the common name for the British lizard which has no legs? *Slow-worm*

49 What does a grass snake feed on? *Fish and amphibians*

50 What kind of a line has a British viper down the centre of its back? *A zigzag line*

MOUTH AND STOMACH ANIMALS
AND ANIMALS WITH SPINY SKINS

DEMONSTRATION MATERIAL

Living or preserved specimens of sea anemones, starfish, or sea urchin; living specimens of hydra; starfish with one or more arms in process of being regenerated

SAMPLE LINK QUESTIONS

1 How many legs has an adult insect? (*Six*)

2 How many legs has a spider or harvestman? (*Eight*)

3 What name do we give to animals with crusty skins? (*Crustaceans*)

4 Name some crustaceans. (*Lobster, crab, prawn, shrimp, etc (in the sea); crayfish, freshwater louse, freshwater shrimp, pond fleas, etc (in fresh water); woodlouse (on land)*)

5 What are two kinds of animals with many legs? (*Centipedes and millepedes*)

6 What is the difference between a centipede and a millepede? (*A centipede has one pair of legs on most of its segments. A millepede has two pairs of legs on most of its segments*)

7 What kind of body has a worm? (*A long soft body*)

8 What is a mollusc shell made of? (*Limestone*)

9 Name some molluscs. (*Whelk, top shell, periwinkle, cowrie, limpet, snail, etc (single shells); cockle, mussel, oyster, razor shell, scallop, etc (double shells); cuttle and squid (internal shells); the octopus, which no longer builds a shell*)

10 Why is *shellfish* a bad name for molluscs? (*A mollusc is not a fish; it has no fins*)

RELEVANT INFORMATION

Animals in General

Probably the principal distinction between animals and plants is that no animal is capable of converting inorganic material into organic during feeding, and must therefore rely on food partly made up by plants. Directly or indirectly, therefore, the animal kingdom is dependent upon the plant kingdom. Other general differences can be noted, however. For example, most animals move from place to place to find their food. (Species such as the acorn barnacle, sponge and sea anemone which settle down to a sedentary life are exceptional.) Most plants on the other hand remain in the same place, with only exceptional species such as the one-celled microscopic chlamydomonas capable of self-propulsion. Again, animals tend to be compact and restricted to a definite shape, while plants spread out and have a less definite shape. Most animals reach a state of full growth, but most plants continue to grow throughout their lives.

The animal classes of mammals, birds, fish and insects were the subjects of lessons in Pupils' Book 1. Amphibians, reptiles, spiders, crustaceans, and the many-legged centipedes and millepedes were the subjects of lessons in Pupils' Book 2. British amphibians, worms, univalve and bivalve molluscs were the subjects of lessons in Pupils' Book 3.

Mammals—the class of animals to which human beings belong—are the only animals whose young need to be fed on milk, and they all have hair. Where there is a lot of hair, it is termed fur. Whales are mammals which have returned to feed in the sea, and bats are the only mammals which can fly.

Birds are the only living things with feathers. Their legs still bear scales like the reptiles from which they are descended, and their front limbs are developed as wings.

Fish are animals with gills and paired fins. They were the first animals to have backbones. Most kinds, but not all, have scales.

Amphibians, the first of the back-boned animals to walk on land, in general live part of their lives in water and part on land.

Reptiles are animals with scaly skins and lungs.

Insects are animals which have six legs in the adult stage. Most adults have four wings, some have two, and certain species have none.

Spiders and harvestmen are animals with eight legs. They belong to the arachnid class, which also includes scorpions and mites.

Crustaceans are animals with crusty skins. They are represented in the sea by the crab, lobster, prawn and shrimp, in fresh water by the crayfish, freshwater shrimp, water louse and pond fleas; and on land by the woodlouse.

Centipedes and millepedes are land animals with many pairs of legs all the way along the body. Centipedes have one pair per segment, and millepedes have two pairs to nearly every segment.

Fish, amphibians, reptiles, mammals and birds are all vertebrates, *i.e.* animals with an internal skeleton. Mammals and birds evolved from primitive reptiles; reptiles evolved from primitive amphibians; amphibians evolved from primitive fish. The ancestors of fish are presumed to have been related to the ancestors of worms.

Insects, arachnids, crustaceans, centipedes and millepedes have jointed limbs but no internal skeleton. Instead they have a tough outer skin (the exoskeleton) made of a horny substance called chitin, which protects the soft inner parts. These four major classes of animals (*arthropods*) have bodies divided into segments, and are believed to have evolved from the ringed worms.

The main groups of animals which appeared earlier in the evolutionary story than those mentioned above were relatively simple animals. As well as lacking other advanced features, none had jointed limbs. Four of these groups of simple animals have prominent representatives in modern times. These are the worms, the molluscs, the mouth and stomach animals, and the spiny-skinned animals.

Worms include a vast assembly of elongated, crawling, simple animals with representatives in the sea, in fresh water and on land. A considerable range of species are parasites.

Many animals which are not worms are confusingly termed worms, *e.g.* slow-worm, glow-worm, mealworm, silkworm.

Molluscs are soft-bodied simple animals with representatives in the sea, in fresh water and on land. They include the slugs, snails, limpets, cockles, mussels, oysters, squids and octopuses, and presumably they evolved from the worms. The most outstanding feature common to most of them is the hard limestone shell.

The mouth and stomach animals (coelenterates) and the animals with spiny skins (echinoderms) differ from all the forementioned in having bodies with a radial symmetry. That is to say there is no definite left-hand or right-hand side, so that no matter which way an individual is cut through the centre, the two halves will be identical. They all live in water, absorbing oxygen from the water, and some of them are wrongly termed *fish*. The coelenterates are chiefly marine with a few freshwater representatives, but the echinoderms are exclusively marine.

Mouth and Stomach Animals (*Coelenterata*)

These include the jellyfishes, the sea anemones and corals, freshwater hydra, Portuguese man-o'-war, sea-fir and various small animals known as sea-gooseberries or comb-bearers. The 'body' of such animals is basically a simple sac with a single opening at one end through which food is taken in and waste expelled.

Surrounding a coelenterate's mouth are one or more rings of tentacles which are armed with stinging cells (except in the case of the comb-bearers). Embedded in a stinging cell is a capsule filled with poisonous fluid and containing a long hollow thread which is usually coiled. When something touches a stinging cell, the thread is shot out to pierce it. Poison then flows down the thread, and if the victim is a small animal, it may be paralysed or killed. The prey is then carried by the tentacles to the mouth and pushed into the sac which serves as a digestive cavity or stomach. Larger victims, being comparatively unharmed, can tear themselves loose.

Sea anemones are very common on rocky coasts. They are,

of course, animal, although in a rocky pool they may look like flowers. The 'petals' ringing the mouth are hollow tentacles, each armed with stinging cells. A tubular gullet leads from the mouth to the stomach whose digestive capabilities are increased by thin sheets of tissue hanging curtain-like in the cavity.

Oxygen is absorbed from the water, but between tides these animals can remain exposed to the air by filling the sac with water which supplies the oxygen. When thus exposed, the tentacles are folded inwards. Sometimes children, knowing no better, squeeze a sea anemone to see this reservoir of water ejected.

Food consists of marine animals, *e.g.* worms, crustaceans and fish. The sea anemone may reproduce by the parent dividing into two and each section growing into a new animal, or by means of eggs. The young, hatching out in the sea or in the parent's body, are able to swim, but subsequently settle down, attaching themselves to a suitable surface.

Jellyfish. When swimming, a jellyfish has its mouth underneath. The gelatinous mass is called an umbrella, and from this dangles a fringe of tentacles. Also, from the corners of the mouth extend four fleshy tentacles, each studded with stinging cells. Food consists of any small animals which become ensnared within the umbrella.

Reproduction is by means of eggs hatched within the parent. The larva which develops from each egg is hollow and equipped with cilia (thread-like outgrowths) which enable it to

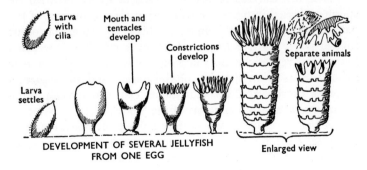

Larva with cilia

Mouth and tentacles develop

Constrictions develop

Separate animals

Larva settles

DEVELOPMENT OF SEVERAL JELLYFISH FROM ONE EGG

Enlarged view

325

swim. Subsequently it settles down on the sea bed, and a mouth surrounded by tentacles appears at the upper end. Beneath these tentacles a number of constrictions appear. These gradually deepen, until the body looks like a stack of saucers on a short stalk. Beginning at the top, these saucer-like forms become detached one by one, invert themselves, and swim away, growing eventually into new jellyfish.

A jellyfish swims by a rhythmic expansion and contraction of the umbrella. It consists of about 99% water, so that when one dies on the shore and the water evaporates, all that remains is a stain to show where it lay.

Hydras. Freshwater hydras bear a superficial resemblance to sea anemones. There are three accepted British species, usually distinguished by colour—green, brownish or grey. The 'body' is a hollow sac with the mouth at the upper end surrounded by tentacles whose surfaces are studded with stinging cells. Food consists chiefly of small crustacea and tiny aquatic worms which are trapped in the sticky threads from the cells, poisoned, and then pushed into the mouth.

Oxygen is obtained by absorption, and a certain amount of this comes from the photosynthetic activities of a number of minute one-celled algae (zoochlorellae) which live in the hydra's inner layer of cells. These plants are not parasitic, but live in partnership (symbiosis) with the hydra, obtaining nitrogen from the hydra's food and supplying oxygen in return. They are also responsible for the animal's colour, as each species of hydra has its own species of zoochlorellae.

A hydra can reproduce by means of eggs (fertilised by sperms released into the surrounding water), or by part of the parent growing into a new animal. This new growth may occur in two ways. Where the temperature is suitable, a well-fed hydra can reproduce by budding, by which means a new animal grows from the side of the parent and subsequently becomes detached. New individuals can also develop from fragments taken from any part of the 'body'.

A hydra is normally a solitary animal. It may remain in one place for long periods, but can move from place to place by turning somersaults or by looping like a caterpillar.

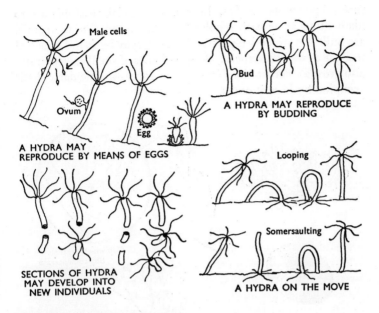

A HYDRA MAY REPRODUCE BY MEANS OF EGGS

A HYDRA MAY REPRODUCE BY BUDDING

SECTIONS OF HYDRA MAY DEVELOP INTO NEW INDIVIDUALS

A HYDRA ON THE MOVE

Other Species of Coelenterates

Although no coelenterates live on land, and very few in fresh water, they are among the commonest marine animals, and a number of different kinds form conspicuous colonies there. Corals are limestone structures built by colonies of such animals. They are responsible for tropical atolls and the Great Barrier Reef of Australia. A few species of stony corals are found off the south-west coast of the British Isles.

The Portuguese man-o'-war is a complicated colony consisting of a number of coelenterates of different kinds; each kind has a different task, such as feeding, movement, reproduction, and attack or defence. The stinging cells of the attack/defence kind are particularly powerful, which is why bathers should avoid them. A Portuguese man-o'-war is rare on British coasts, but specimens do appear occasionally on south-west coasts after persistent south-west winds.

More commonly found on British coasts are the horny plant-like structures built by various colonies. These structures, known as sea-firs, bear a superficial resemblance to filamentous algae with regular branching, and, like the corals, are built for protective purposes. They may be found attached to algae as well as to rocks. Some colonies of small coelenterates also grow as incrustations on shells or rocks—particularly shells occupied by hermit crabs.

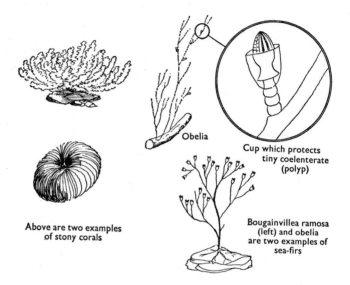

Obelia

Cup which protects
tiny coelenterate
(polyp)

Above are two examples
of stony corals

Bougainvillea ramosa
(left) and obelia
are two examples of
sea-firs

Animals with Spiny Skins (*Echinoderma*)

More advanced than the coelenterates, these animals include the starfishes, brittle-stars, sea urchins, sea cucumbers and feather-stars (also known as sea-lilies or crinoids). The skin is strengthened by small rods and plates of calcium carbonate (limestone) with an additional protection of spines, which give rise to the terms 'spiny-skinned' and 'hedgehog-skinned'.

The Common Starfish (also known as the spiny crossfish) has a body consisting of a central disc from which radiate five arms (rays). The mouth is on the underside of the disc and gives access to a sac-like stomach. Along the underside of each ray are pairs of soft white tubular bodies which can be withdrawn or protruded at will and, when required, used as suckers.

These tiny tube-feet are used to assist movement and to grip things.

Starfish are general scavengers, and also prey on any living animals they can overcome, mussels and oysters being regular victims. These bivalve molluscs are attacked by the starfish humping itself over its prey, gripping the two shells with its tube-feet and forcing them apart by a prolonged pull. The starfish then turns part of its stomach inside out through its own mouth, and digests the exposed mollusc. Small prey may be taken in through the mouth and digested internally; unwanted parts are disgorged later.

A starfish can reproduce in one of two ways.

(a) By means of eggs, fertilised in the sea, from which appear tiny free-swimming animals that subsequently settle to develop into starfish

(b) By part of the parent growing into a new starfish

Like so many of the lower animals, starfish are capable of regeneration, *i.e.* growing new parts to replace any which are lost, and a common starfish often has one or more rays either missing or just developing. Oyster beds suffer considerably from the attacks of starfish, and before their regenerative powers were appreciated, keepers of oyster beds would, in temper, tear apart any starfish they caught, and toss the pieces back into the sea—thus ensuring a steady increase in the number of starfish raiding the beds.

The tiny flat spot on the upper surface of the disc of a starfish is a sieve plate, pierced with fine holes through which sea-water can filter. This gives access to a complicated series of canals which traverse each of the rays and connect with the tube-feet.

Other Species of Echinoderms

The other species of spiny-skinned animals differ in the details of their appearance and habits from the common starfish. A *bird's-foot starfish* has its five rays joined by a membrane; a *brittle-star* has its central disc and five rays clearly defined. When attacked, a brittle-star readily shatters itself, leaving the rays separated from the disc. A *sunstar* has its rays separate, and has more than the customary five. A *sea urchin* is five-rayed, but the rays are not free, although their outline can be discerned. When alive, sea urchins are equipped with long spines and tube-feet. Remains washed up on the shore usually lack these parts; they also lack the soft inside tissues, as these decompose rapidly after death.

CODE

1 Observe, on a sea anemone, the tentacles surrounding the mouth when open, and its appearance when closed.

2 Observe, on a freshwater hydra, the tentacles and any budding young.

3 Observe, on a starfish, the spines, mouth, number of rays and the tube-feet.

4 Observe, on the remains of a dead sea urchin, the mouth, the marks where the spines used to be, and the outline of the rays that this species used to have.

5 Marine animals can be kept satisfactorily only in a salt-water aquarium—rarely a practical proposition for inland schools. Where a marine aquarium is installed, sea anemones are very suitable occupants and may be induced to feed on small pieces of raw meat or fish. A small starfish may also feed on similar food, but is more likely to attack any univalve or bivalve molluscs present. Small green and red algae may be put in such an aquarium, but brown algae should be excluded. In general, the best temperature for a British marine aquarium is 13-15°C, which means keeping it in a cool place in summer. It is also advisable to aerate the water. This breaks up the surface 'skin', and permits a more rapid interchange of gases at the surface. A simple method of aerating water is illustrated on page 203 of Teacher's Book 3.

6 If hydras are kept in a freshwater aquarium, they need to be supplied with pond water containing freshwater fleas. As a hydra can contract into a small rounded blob many times smaller than its normal expanded length, it is not easily observed on plants which have just been removed from water. One way of obtaining a number of specimens is to

remove a quantity of duckweed from a pond, ditch or fen, and place it in a jar of water for future examination when the expanded hydras may eventually be seen. They are particularly common in the Norfolk Broads in July and August, when they may also be found attached to the underside of water-lily leaves.

7 Specimens of sea anemones may be preserved in 5% formaldehyde in the usual way. A sea anemone can be removed from a rock by gently inserting a penknife blade between its foot and the rock, and gradually working it round until the animal's grip is loosened.

8 A starfish may also be preserved in 5% or 10% formaldehyde.

9 The dry spiny skin of a starfish or sea urchin may be retained as it is but should be secured from careless handling.

NOTEBOOK WORK

Answers should be along the following lines.

1 (a) A jellyfish is a mouth-and-stomach animal. It swims. Its mouth and tentacles are underneath.

(b) A sea anemone is a mouth-and-stomach animal. It remains in one place. Its mouth and tentacles are on top.

(c) A common starfish is a spiny-skinned animal. It has short blunt spines.

(d) A bird's-foot starfish is a spiny-skinned animal. It has five joined rays.

(e) A brittle-star is a spiny-skinned animal. It has five brittle rays.

(f) A sunstar is a spiny-skinned animal. It has more than five rays.

(g) A sea urchin is a round spiny-skinned animal.

(h) A freshwater hydra is a mouth-and-stomach animal and lives in fresh water.

2 (a) Jellyfish and starfish are poor names because these animals are not fish.

(b) Sea anemone is a poor name because it makes you think this animal is a flower.

INDEX

Accumulator, 204
Adder, 312
Air, 148
  compressed, 91, 156-8, 194
  pressure of, 148-50, 183
Aircraft, 177, 179, 192
  propulsion of, 176-7, 186, 191-2,
    193-5
Alcohol, 137, 274
Algae, 264-6
  and lichens, 274-5
  single-celled, 235, 264, 326
'Alive', 24-5
Alpha particles, 41
Amber, 199, 300
Amoeba, 235, 236, 237
Ampere, 220
Amphibians, 308, 309, 312, 322, 323
Angiosperms, 242, 246
Animals, 322
  cellular structure of, 235-6
  classes of, 322-3
  evolution of, 323
  fossils of, 299-306
  mouth and stomach, 323, 324-8
  simple, 323
  spiny-skinned, 323
  vertebrate, 323
Anthers, 252, 253, 255, 256
Antibiotics, 274, 281
Antibodies, 280-1
Antiseptics, 281
Arachnids, 323
Arthropods, 323
Asteroids, 45-7
Atmosphere, 124-5
Atomic—energy, 42-3, 186, 220
  numbers, 37-8, 40
  reactors, 43
Atoms, 31-2, 35
  of hydrogen, 31, 32, 35, 36
  of oxygen, 31, 32

Bacteria, 235, 236, 263, 272-3, 275-6
  causing decay, 286, 287, 288
  causing disease, 279-80, 284
  forms of, 275
  optimum temperatures for, 287,
    288

Bacteria (*cont.*)
  parasitic, 276
  protection against, 279-80, 286-9
    300
  reproduction of, 276
  respiration of, 275-6
  saprophytic, 276
Basalt, 296
Battery, 199, 202-3, 211
  charging a, 204
Beta particles, 41
Bioluminescence, 74
Birds, 322, 323
Blight, 273, 274
Bracts, 247
Brittle-star, 329
Budding, 326
Bulbs, 69
  indoor cultivation, 70-1
Burning, 75, 135, 196

Cacti, 65, 70, 243
Caddis flies, 231-2
Caisson, 97, 157
Calyx, 244, 245, 248
Carbon, 32
  and photosynthesis, 272
  atom of, 37
  conducting electricity, 209
  dioxide, 32, 148, 274
  in living things, 239
  in sugar, 32, 239
Carpels, 247, 253-4
Catkins, 259, 260, 261
Cells, 235-9
  and fertilisation, 257
  chain of, 264
  functions of specialist, 236, 280-1
  fusion of, 257
  multiplication of, 238, 257
  parts of, 237-8
    composition of, 239
  reproduction of, 238-9
  shape and size of, 236-7
Centipedes, 323
Cereals, 248
Chalk, 294
Chlorophyll, 272